An Organic Chemistry Monograph

Consultant Editor: M. F. Grundon, The Queen's University of Belfast

Oldbourne Chemistry Series

Carbanions in Synthesis

D. C. AYRES, B.Sc., Ph.D., A.R.C.S.

Lecturer in Organic Chemistry
Westfield College, University of London

AMERICAN ELSEVIER PUBLISHING
COMPANY, INC.
52 Vanderbilt Ave., New York, N.Y. 10017

OLDBOURNE BOOK CO. LTD.
1–5 Portpool Lane, London, E.C.1

Printed in Great Britain
by Spottiswoode, Ballantyne & Co. Ltd.
London and Colchester

PREFACE

The degree of condensation which this small volume represents will be apparent to anyone who scans the sources acknowledged in the bibliographies. In making a selection the aim has been to extend the treatment of topics which cannot be dealt with in any detail in the time available in the first year of a University course. It is hoped that the text will be of use to senior undergraduates and research students in Universities and Technical Colleges; also that cross referencing between chapters and discussion of some of the theoretical background will make it possible for them to speculate profitably *in extensio*.

The examples in the text have all been taken from the literature and practical details given in many instances as a guide to the design of experiments; many of these references are given in the quoted sources. Relevant information can also be extracted from the references given as a guide to the problems. These are mostly of moderate difficulty, selected both to test comprehension of the text and to extend it by introducing closely related topics.

The author gratefully acknowledges the many helpful comments made by Dr M. F. Grundon and the valuable criticisms of Mr H. Williams who also read the entire manuscript. Sincere thanks are due to my wife who helped in the preparation of the book and, with the rest of the family, tolerated the author while it was being written.

Hampstead, 1966   *D. C. Ayres*

v

CONTENTS

Contents

CHAPTER 1

INTRODUCTION

A carbanion is the conjugate base formed by the abstraction of a proton from a C—H bond:

$$-\overset{|}{\underset{|}{C}}-H + :B \rightleftharpoons -\overset{|}{\underset{|}{C}}:^{\ominus} + BH^{\oplus}$$
(A)

and although acid dissociation is familiar when the negative charge then resides on a very electronegative element, as for the dissociation of an alcohol:

$$R-O-H \rightleftharpoons RO^{\ominus} + BH^{\oplus}$$

it is evident from the position of carbon on the electronegativity scale that special structural features which stabilize negatively charged carbon must be present if the dissociation (A) is to proceed to the right.

Stabilization of Carbanions. The metal derivatives of alkanes cannot be prepared directly because of the strength of the C—H bond and the absence of any stabilizing feature, but when obtained by indirect methods (Chapter 2) it is apparent that a carbon atom acquires increasing carbanion character on sharing bonding electrons with metals of decreasing electronegativity (see table, p. 14). The simple alkyls of the most electropositive metals dissociate into metal cation and a carbanion where the negative charge is located at one intensely reactive centre.

Conjugative Effects. Carbanion formation will be encouraged and its reactivity will be reduced if the charge can be delocalized, that is shared between one or more other atoms in the molecule. The enhanced acidity of phenols as compared with alcohols is a case in point:

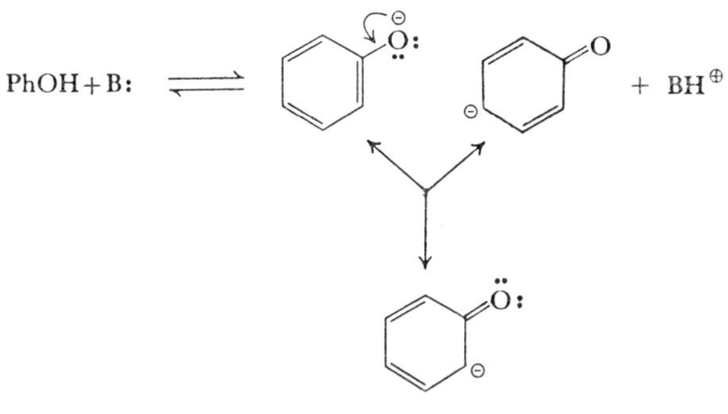

PhOH + B: $\rightleftharpoons$ ... $+ BH^{\oplus}$

1

If a sodium alkyl is added to toluene exchange occurs because the phenylmethide anion (C) is stabilized in this way.

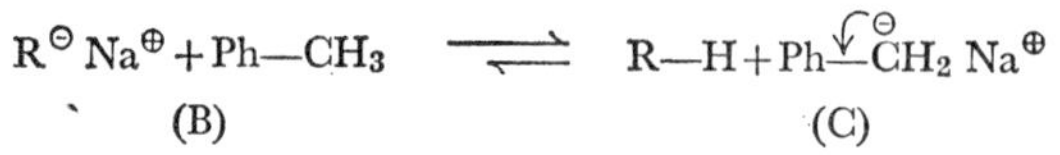

$$R^{\ominus} Na^{\oplus} + Ph{-}CH_3 \rightleftharpoons R{-}H + Ph{-}\overset{\ominus}{CH_2} Na^{\oplus}$$
$$\text{(B)} \qquad\qquad\qquad \text{(C)}$$

This can be proved by streaming carbon dioxide into the system (p. 30) when sodium phenylacetate is formed from (C) with no detectable amount of alkanoate from (B). A rough acidity scale for hydrocarbons was constructed by comparing them in pairs by this technique (cf. colorimetric scale, p. 3).

Stabilization by an aromatic nucleus will be more effective if it carries an electronegative substituent such as $-C{\equiv}N$, $-CO-$, $-NO_2$, or $-CO_2R$. These groups also stabilize negative charge on an adjacent carbon atom:

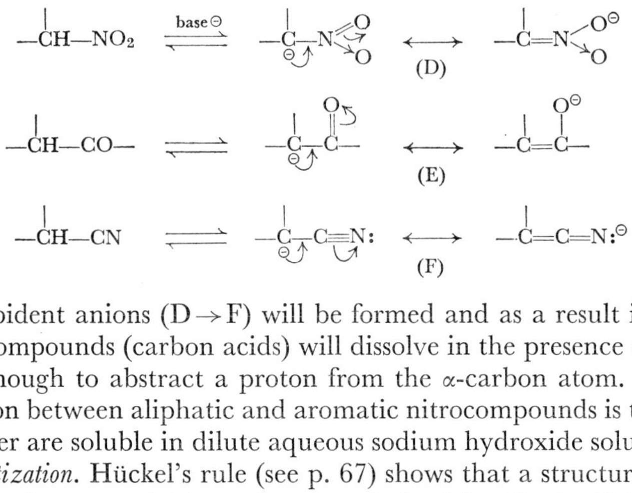

The ambident anions $(D \rightarrow F)$ will be formed and as a result insoluble parent compounds (carbon acids) will dissolve in the presence of a base strong enough to abstract a proton from the α-carbon atom. A useful distinction between aliphatic and aromatic nitrocompounds is that only the former are soluble in dilute aqueous sodium hydroxide solution.

Aromatization. Hückel's rule (see p. 67) shows that a structure having $(2 + 4n)$ π-electrons which can be extensively delocalized will be resonance stabilized; that is, it will have aromatic character. The cyclopentadienyl anion (G) has six electrons $(n = 1)$ in π-orbitals and complete delocalization of charge is possible in the planar molecule:

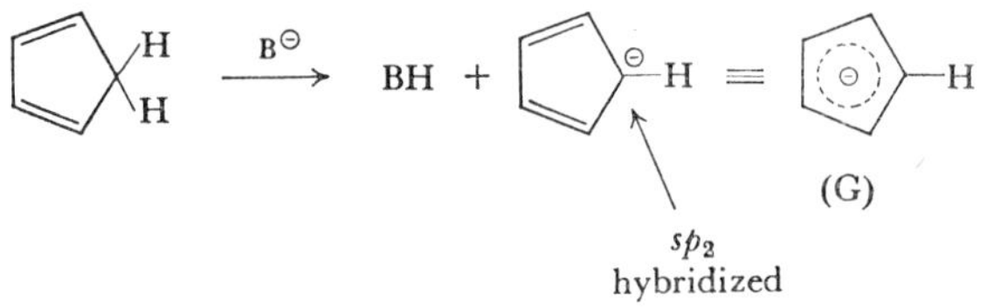

this aromaticity in its conjugate base makes cyclopentadiene a strong acid on the hydrocarbon scale. The common stabilizing requirements of

2

carbanions, carbonium ions, and radicals will be mentioned from time to time; note here that exceptional stability is found in the cyclohept-atrienyl cation (H)

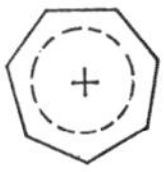

(H)

and that azulene (I), the non-benzenoid analogue of naphthalene, can be represented as a fusion of the ions (G) and (H):

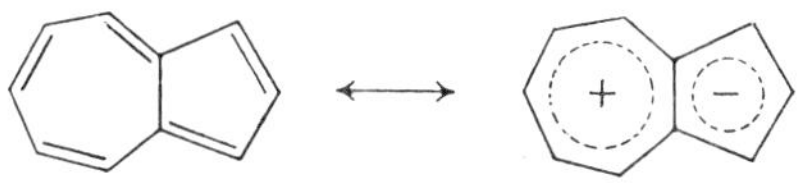

(I)

Relative Strengths of Carbon Acids. When charge is delocalized absorption of visible light commonly occurs and Conant and Wheeler used a colorimetric method to construct the first hydrocarbon acidity scale in 1932. Provided the hydrocarbons differ in their acidities by at least two pK_a units the equilibrium (J),

$$R\text{—}H + R_1^{\ominus}Na^{\oplus} \rightleftharpoons R^{\ominus}Na^{\oplus} + R_1\text{—}H$$

(J)

will lie almost entirely to one side and the colour of the carbanion derived from the stronger acid will predominate. The scale includes:

$$RH < PhH < PhCH_3 < Ph_2CH < Ph_3CH <$$

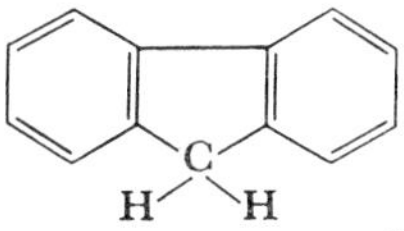

(25)

red (35·5)   orange (35)   orange– red (32·5)   yellow

Compare NH_3 (36), $PhNH_2$ (27), $HC{\equiv}CH$ (25), $PhCOCH_3$ (19), $EtOH$ (18)

(pK_a values in parenthesis)

where the colours must be those of ion pairs because the solutions have low conductivity; only when dissociation is complete will the colour of a carbanion be independent of the metal ion in the dissolved salt. The five acids in the lower section of the table were placed by McEwen (1936), who extended the scale to include acids other than hydrocarbons, his method depended on the difference in the optical rotation of menthol and its sodio-derivative which are both soluble in benzene. Addition of

3

alcohol, amine, or a hydrocarbon appreciably more acidic than benzene, will establish an equilibrium:

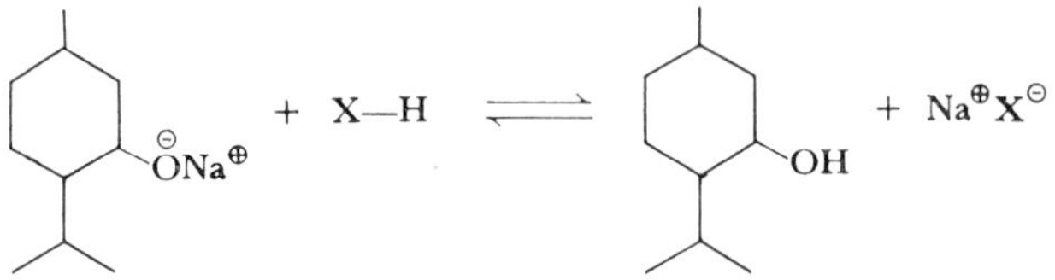

Menthol

where the concentrations of menthol and sodium menthoxide follow from the measured rotation and hence the dissociation of X—H was determined.

Kuhn has given an account of the chemistry of hydrocarbons where great delocalization of charge is possible in the carbanion. One example (K) is shown where conjugation takes place between fluorenyl and diphenylmethyl residues on abstraction of proton by base:

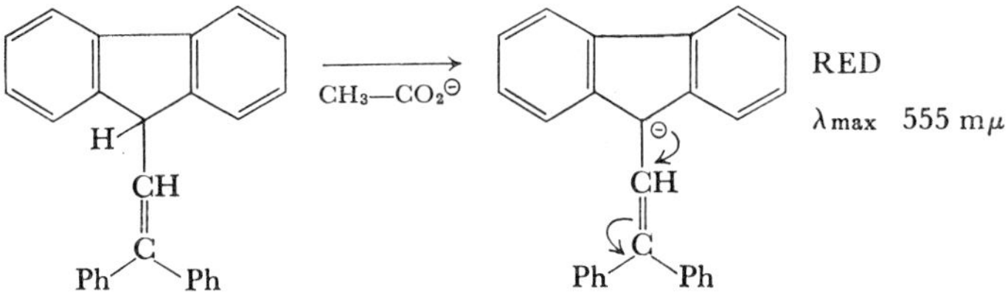

RED

λ max 555 mμ

(K)   (L)

This hydrocarbon (K) lies between water and acetic acid (pK_a 4·76) on the acidity scale and the colour of the carbanion appears on addition of acetate to a partly aqueous solution. In fact the pK_a of this compound is about 10·0, which is comparable with that of phenol (9·89).

The acidities of acetylene and benzene (see table above) cannot be the result of charge delocalization, but must accrue from the increasing electronegativity of a carbon atom as its hybridization changes from sp^3 through sp^2 to sp. Accumulation of negative charge on a carbon atom occurs as the s-character of the orbitals increases because of the greater attraction between the electrons in them and the nucleus. In the same way one can relate progressive changes in the hybridization of C—N bonds to electron availability and the decreasing base strengths of the nitrogen atoms in the sequence:

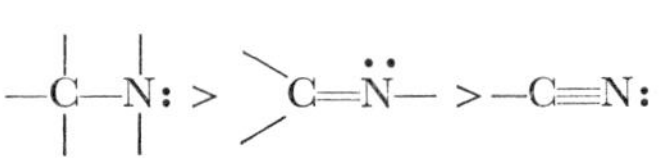

sp_3 sp^2 sp

4

Kinetically Controlled Acid Dissociation. The relative acid strengths so far discussed were obtained when equilibrium had been established between each acid and its conjugate base, that is when the acidity was thermodynamically controlled. In some synthetic applications, for example bromination of ketones (p. 99), the initial acid dissociation (M, k_1) is rate determining and irreversible because the subsequent reaction of the carbanion (k_2) is faster:

(M) $\qquad$ X—H + Base $\underset{k_{-1}}{\overset{k_1}{\rightleftharpoons}}$ B.H$^\oplus$ + X$^\ominus$ $\xrightarrow[k_2]{}$ products

Therefore it must be stressed that the position of an acid on the thermodynamic scale may not coincide with its position as determined by the relative ease of proton abstraction (kinetically controlled scale). Pearson and Dillon have correlated the strengths of many acids on the two scales. Diethyl malonate ionizes (k_1) at about one thousand times the speed of nitroethane (k_1) in water yet it is a far weaker acid on the thermodynamic scale (K_a):

$$\text{EtO}_2\text{C—CH}_2\text{—CO}_2\text{Et} \underset{k_{-1}}{\overset{k_1}{\rightleftharpoons}} \underset{\ominus}{(\text{EtO}_2\text{C})_2\text{CH}} + \text{H}_3\text{O}^\oplus$$

$$\text{CH}_3\text{—CH}_2\text{—NO}_2 \underset{k_{-1}}{\overset{k_1}{\rightleftharpoons}} \underset{\ominus}{\text{CH}_3\text{—CH—NO}_2} + \text{H}_3\text{O}^\oplus$$

	k_1	k_{-1}	$K_a = k_1/k_{-1}$
Diethyl malonate	$2\cdot5 \times 10^{-5}$	5×10^8	$5\cdot0 \times 10^{-14}$
Nitroethane	$3\cdot7 \times 10^{-8}$	$1\cdot5 \times 10$	$2\cdot5 \times 10^{-9}$

The rates of ionization tend to be higher than indicated by the position of the acid on the thermodynamic scale when the anionic charge is chiefly located on the carbon atom as in diethyl malonate.

Acid dissociation is detected and its rate (k_1) determined by study of the exchange between hydrogen isotopes. Shatenshtein's group showed that three hydrogen atoms of n-heptane were exchanged in deuterated liquid ammonia in the presence of potassium amide at 120° after 500 hr. Half the hydrogens of benzene were exchanged at 25° in 2 hr. Hydrogen is directly displaced from the more acidic hydrocarbons by metals:

$$\text{Ph}_3\text{CH} \xrightarrow{\text{Na}} \text{Ph}_3\text{C}^\ominus\text{Na}^+$$
$$\text{(N)}$$

5

Radicals, Carbonium Ions, and Carbanions. Oxygen slowly converts triphenylmethyl sodium (N) into the radical which reverts to the sodium salt on shaking with sodium amalgam:

$$Ph_3C^{\ominus}Na^{\oplus} \xrightleftharpoons[\text{Na}^{\bullet} \text{ reduction}]{O_2} Ph_3C^{\bullet} + Na\!-\!O\!-\!O^{\ominus}$$

This redox relationship was strikingly demonstrated by Kuhn, who showed that a yellow radical was obtained by oxidation of a solution of the anion (L) with aqueous ferricyanide; the red colour of the anion reappeared on addition of a reducing agent.

Radicals and carbonium ions being electron deficient are predictably stabilized by alkylation at a carbon centre. Thus, isobutane is readily autoxidized by homolysis of the tertiary C—H bond and the unimolecular mechanism involving a tertiary carbonium ion predominates in the reactions of t-butyl halides. Carbanions, on the other hand, are destabilized by alkyl groups as is shown by the reduced rate of base-catalysed hydrogen–deuterium exchange, which is minimal at the methine hydrogen of isobutane.

Geometry. The appearance of colour in the three species $(O \rightarrow Q)$ is due to the extension of conjugation which can arise when one bond of an sp^3-hybrid undergoes heterolysis or homolysis and will be most marked for resonance-stabilized planar carbonium ions; carbanions almost certainly retain some pyramidal character and radicals may do so.

Reactions involving stabilized planar intermediates occur with racemization at the reactive centre because in the second step an entering group can approach from above or below the plane of the intermediate complex (R, for example). Solvolysis of α-phenylethyl chloride in ethanol is an S_n1 reaction:

and attack on the carbonium ion (R) gives a largely racemic product. A small amount of the ether is produced with the inverted configuration

6

(S) since the ion (R) was not sufficiently long-lived to become solvated entirely by solvent molecules and attack of the residual ion-pairs occurs from the side remote from the bulky chloride ion with invertion of configuration.

The spectra of the methyl radical show that it has high symmetry and is therefore planar, but larger radicals may not have this configuration since they would have higher energy than pyramidal forms owing to non-bonded interactions:

(T) (U)

Unstabilized free radicals are very short-lived and react with racemization at ambient temperature either because of their planarity or through rapid invertion of the pyramidal forms (T → U).

A pyramidal configuration is assumed for carbanions as the methide ion (V) is isoelectronic with ammonia, which is known to have a pyramidal form and to undergo rapid invertion:

(V)

Although a planar sp^2-hybridized configuration is reasonable for the six bonding electrons of a carbonium ion it is not acceptable for a carbanion; one expects the additional electron pair to be accommodated in an orbital having s-character (cf. above discussion of the acidities of benzene and acetylene) and not in a pure p-orbital. Many of the reactions of carbanions mentioned in the sequel are conducted in solvents of low polarity, where the configuration is maintained through association with the metal cation. The formation of a free carbanion, its inversion, and reaction with racemization are expected when polar solvents such as dimethylformamide (p. 53) are added to the system. As seen for the carbonium ion reaction (of R) the degree of retention will depend on the lifetime of the carbanion. A planar intermediate cannot be formed at a bridgehead carbon atom and non-planar carbonium ions are evidently highly strained since the hydrolysis rate of bridgehead halides, for example apocamphyl chloride (W, $x = Cl$), is very slow compared to that

7

of the S_nI reaction of acyclic tertiary chlorides. The bridgehead geometry does not constrain radical reactions and the peroxide of apocamphane-carboxylic acid (W, $x = CO_2H$) decomposes in carbon tetrachloride and apocamphyl chloride is formed by radical capture. These halides can be used to prepare metal camphyls of normal reactivity. Evidence of carbanion character at a bridgehead is found in triptycene (X) for hydrogen-isotope exchange shows that the acidity of the bridgehead atoms of this compound approaches that of the benzene ring hydrogens.

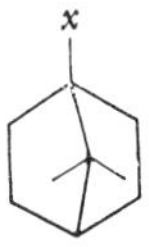

(W) 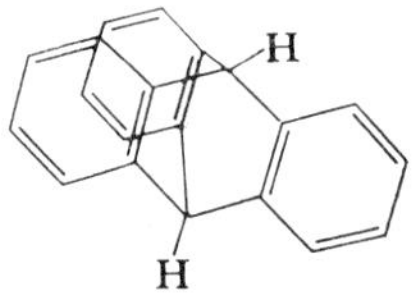   (X)

In the triptycide ion the charge at the bridgehead cannot be stabilized by delocalization on to the benzene rings and its acidity must be due to the inductive effect of the more electronegative ring carbon atoms. Pure inductive stabilization is effected by α-substituted fluorine atoms and by quaternary nitrogen.

Doering and Hoffmann showed that the rate of hydrogen-isotope exchange in tetramethylphosphonium and trimethylsulphonium ions was at least 10^6 times as fast as that found in tetramethylammonium salts. This large difference results from enhancement of inductive stabilization by overlap of the orbital containing the electron pair and d-orbitals of the phosphorus and sulphur atoms. Sulphonates and sulphones, for example

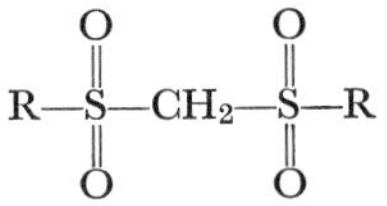

$$R-\overset{\overset{O}{\|}}{\underset{\underset{O}{\|}}{S}}-CH_2-\overset{\overset{O}{\|}}{\underset{\underset{O}{\|}}{S}}-R$$

provide further illustrations of carbon acids in which inductive and d-orbital effects are jointly effective.

The stability and lifetime of ions are increased by hyperconjugation; one can compare the structures (Y) and (Z):

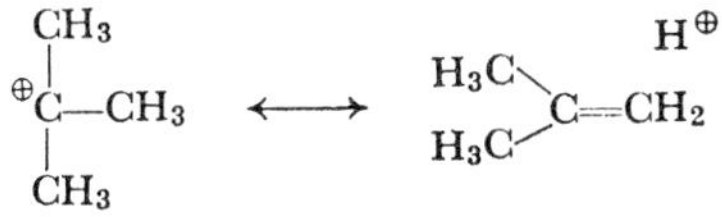

(Y) 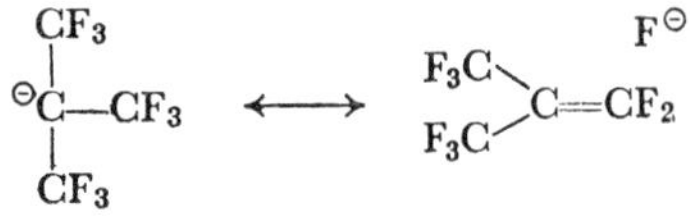   (Z)

Forms which invoke hybridization of fluoride ions will be minor contributors to the hybrid if the model is non-planar.

Further Reading

GENERAL

D. J. CRAM, *Fundamentals of Carbanion Chemistry*. Academic Press, New York and London, 1965.

J. E. LEFFLER, *The Reactive Intermediates of Organic Chemistry*. Interscience, New York, 1956.

PROBLEMS

1. Place the following compounds on the acidity scale (p. 3):

Ph$_2$N—H, 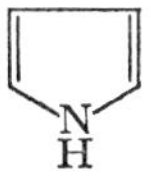 , *p*-MeOC$_6$H$_4$NH$_2$, MeOH

t-BuOH   PhCOEt

2. (*a*) What relative rates of hydrogen-isotope exchange in KNH$_2$/NH$_3$ are expected for the *o*-, *m*- and *p*-positions in toluene? How does this rate compare with that found for benzene?

(*b*) The rate of isotopic exchange in alicyclic hydrocarbons is similar to their acyclic counterparts save for cyclopropane which is much more acidic than propane: account for this.

3. What rate order would you expect for the recapture of proton (k_{-1}) by the conjugate bases of the following ketones in water:

CH$_3$—COCH$_3$ CH$_3$—CO—CH$_2$Cl   CH$_3$—COCHCl$_2$ CH$_3$—COCH$_2$—NO$_2$

CHAPTER 2

METAL ALKYLS

The title includes all compounds with a direct bond between metal and a carbon atom in an alkyl or aryl group. Since metallic character is such a wide-ranging concept attention has been paid to derivatives of established synthetic value.

PREPARATIVE METHODS

Direct Displacement. This requires a leaving group which is not itself subject to nucleophilic attack and potential oxyanions are excluded. Only the halides are satisfactory and even they may cause side-reactions by halogen–metal exchange (see pp.12,17). The method is suitable for the more electropositive metals of groups I and II of the Periodic Table and was used by Frankland in his original preparation of zinc diethyl in 1849.

$$2Zn + 2EtI \longrightarrow 2ZnEtI \longrightarrow ZnEt_2 + ZnI_2$$
80% yield by distillation in $CO_2(N_2)$

The zinc–copper couple or intimate mixture of zinc and copper (5%) dissolves in hot alkyl iodides in about 2 hr. Bromides are very much less reactive and the reaction fails with chlorides and aryl halides. The disproportionation of the first-formed zinc ethyl iodide occurs at the reflux temperature, zinc derivatives being particularly facile in this way.

The more electropositive the metal the more reactive it will be towards alkyl halides, thus reactivity falls as one goes from left to right in the series:

K   Na   Li   Ba   Sr   Ca   Mg   Zn   Cd   Hg

and sodium reacts readily when it is dispersed in a solvent boiling above its melting point (97°) and a solution of an alkyl halide is added at about 30°. Sodium phenyl can be obtained in nearly quantitative yield in this way from a halide of low reactivity, namely chlorobenzene.†

Lithium derivatives are most conveniently obtained by displacement of bromine:

$$n\text{-BuBr} + Li \xrightarrow[-10°/Et_2O]{\text{in } N_2} n\text{-BuLi} + LiBr$$
90%

† *Sodium Dispersions*, U.S. Industrial Chemicals Co., p. 36.

The metal must be beaten into foil with a mallet before addition in small amounts to ensure a large surface of contact; hydrocarbon solvents are acceptable.

Calcium, strontium, and barium dimethyl have been prepared by interaction of the metals and methyl iodide in pyridine.

Direct displacement was the method originally used by Grignard (1900), the discoverer of the alkylmagnesium halide reagents which are named after him, and which supplanted the zinc dialkyls in synthesis. Noller has listed four difficulties in the application of zinc alkyls:

(*a*) They are spontaneously inflammable in air.
(*b*) Preparation of the necessary Zn/Cu couple is troublesome on a large scale.
(*c*) Expensive alkyl iodides are needed as precursors.
(*d*) Yields are low save for zinc diethyl and zinc dimethyl.

The Grignard reagents do not suffer from these disadvantages and are conveniently prepared by stirring magnesium of better than 99% purity with an alkyl halide in diethyl ether as solvent; dry apparatus and reagents are essential. Owing to the vigour of the reaction, once started, the halide is added in portions affording a solution of the alkylmagnesium halide in ether:

$$R—Hal + Mg \longrightarrow R—Mg—Hal \quad \text{(see p. 21 on structure)}$$

The rate of reaction for halides follows the sequence $I > Br > Cl$ and the low reactivity of fluorine is illustrated by the low-temperature preparation of heptafluoro-n-propyl magnesium iodide in 65% yield:

$$CF_3—CF_2—CF_2—I \xrightarrow[Et_2O]{Mg} CF_3—CF_2—CF_2—Mg—I$$

Aryl halides are less reactive than the corresponding alkyl derivatives, and the chlorides do not react under normal conditions.

A Grignard reaction may be difficult to start, particularly if a chloride is being used, and a great deal of chemical folklore derives from methods of initiating the reaction: two effective techniques are the addition of an iodine crystal or the use of a little ethylene dibromide. Iodine reacts to form magnesium iodide which will remove last traces of water as its hydrate and leave a clean metal site. The reaction between ethylene dibromide and magnesium is an elimination similar to that brought about by zinc (p. 39) and also leads to surface cleansing and dehydration:

$$BrCH_2CH_2Br \xrightarrow{Mg} MgBr_2 + CH_2{=}CH_2$$

11

Aluminium alkyls are obtainable from the reaction between the metal and alkyl halides in a diluent (methylcyclohexane):

$$2Al + 3R\text{—}Hal \longrightarrow R_3Al.AlHal_3 \quad (A)$$

The aluminium halide formed is an electron-deficient molecule and the complex (A) is formed by the anions forming a bridge between the metal atoms (cf. p. 44). The aluminium alkyl is liberated by reduction with, for example, sodium metal:

$$R_3Al_2Hal_3 + 3Na \longrightarrow R_3Al + Al + 3NaCl$$

Halogen–Metal Exchange. When direct displacement fails with an unreactive halide, exchange with a readily preformed alkyl is often effective, for example:

As an alternative, tetrahydrofuran may be used to induce reaction by virtue of its greater solvating power (cf. vinylmagnesium halides, p. 40). Thus 2-bromoquinoline affords the lithio-derivative at $-50°$ in this solvent and phenyl lithium is obtained from chlorobenzene in a yield of 54%.

Exchange with Metal Salts. The general equation is:

$$MHal + M'R \rightleftharpoons MR + M'Hal$$

and a new metal alkyl, MR, can be made when the equilibrium lies to the right, that is when M' is considerably more electropositive than M. Grignard reagents are now obtained commercially by the addition of anhydrous magnesium halides to suspensions of sodium alkyls in hydrocarbons; this avoids using the expensive magnesium metal. Grignard reagents in their turn afford zinc and cadmium alkyls by exchange with salts of these metals:

$$2R\text{—}Mg\text{—}Hal + CdCl_2 \rightleftharpoons R\text{—}Cd\text{—}R + 2MgHal_2$$

Cadmium chloride is not hygroscopic and can be added directly to a solution of Grignard reagent in ether; zinc chloride is more difficult to handle hence the cadmium compounds are usually used in the important ketone synthesis (p. 35) although the former may well give comparable yields.

Aluminium alkyls (p. 42) are now commercially available in large quantities and can be used in exchanges of this type, particularly in the synthesis of tin alkyls.

Exchange between Metals. This is valuable when a derivative of one of the less reactive metals is required. Mercury dialkyls are obtained from a halide and sodium amalgam using a solvent such as xylene as a diluent:

$$\text{Ph—Br} + 2\text{Na} \longrightarrow \text{Ph—Na} + \text{NaBr}$$

whence in the presence of excess mercury:

$$2\text{Ph—Na} + \text{Hg} \xrightleftharpoons{} \text{Ph—Hg—Ph} + \text{Na/Hg}$$

Mercury diphenyl is the only soluble component and is isolated by filtration and evaporation of the solvent. Mercury compounds have always been of importance in industry because of their potential in medicine and agriculture; the more volatile substances are very toxic but their stability makes them useful precursors for other metal derivatives. Equilibrium in the above reaction lies to the left and is further displaced in the presence of an excess of a 'higher' metal:

$$\text{HgEt}_2 + 2\text{Li}\binom{\text{metal}}{\text{chips}} \longrightarrow 2\text{LiEt} + \text{Li/Hg}$$

Three days at 65° are needed for completion and lithium ethyl crystallizes after filtration. Trialkyl aluminium compounds react in a comparable time only at 100° in a sealed tube.

Methods for the detection and determination of metal alkyls are referred to when their reactions are discussed (see pp. 26, 33).

PROPERTIES AND REACTIONS

A comparison of the physical properties and stabilities of the metal alkyls most used in organic chemistry is made in the table on p. 14. Ethyl derivatives were chosen because the methyl compounds are atypical.

The properties of monoalkyl compounds, R—metal—X, will tend to be ionic if X is very electronegative, as for chloride, but to have more covalent character otherwise, as for bromide or iodide.

Ionic character is most marked for the more electropositive metals and sodium alkyls are considered to be crystalline compounds $R^{\ominus}Na^{\oplus}$ with a high lattice energy. A number of colligative properties could be used to demonstrate dissociation into ions but the experimental difficulties are often very great, thus the conductivity of sodium alkyls cannot be measured because they react with all the usual solvents. Once solutions of metal alkyls have been obtained their electrolysis is often complicated

13

Metal and negativity value†	Ethyl derivative		Other characteristics
	b.p. °C	m.p. °C	
Sodium 0·9	—	dec.	Stable only in N_2; insoluble in all solvents and reacts with all save alkanes
Lithium 1·0	—	95	Stable only in N_2; soluble in ether, slightly soluble in alkanes‡
Magnesium 1·2	—	176	Soluble in ether; slow reaction with O_2
Cadmium 1·4	64/19 mm	−21	Slow reaction with O_2; soluble in ether and hydrocarbons
Aluminium 1·5	194	−52	Decomposes in air; soluble in organic solvents
Zinc 1·5	118	−28	Decomposes in air but stable in CO_2; soluble in ether and hydrocarbons
Mercury 1·9	159	—	Insoluble but stable in H_2O, stable in air; soluble in ethers
Boron 2·0	95	−93	Decomposed by air and slowly by H_2O; soluble in organic solvents

† From Sanderson, *Chemical Periodicity*, Reinhold, 1960, p. 35.
‡ Higher alkyls are appreciably soluble.

by interactions between ions and solvent, which for Grignard compounds (p. 21) leads to deposition of metal and of products characteristic of the organic residue at both electrodes. Interesting results may be obtained by solution of one metal alkyl in another, for example dissociation of sodium ethyl occurs in zinc diethyl:

$$\text{NaEt} + \text{ZnEt}_2 \rightleftharpoons \text{Na}^{\oplus} + [\text{ZnEt}_3]^{\ominus}$$

The resulting solution has a low conductivity suggesting that the ions have not been independently solvated by the low polarity solvent but remain associated as ion pairs.

The Mechanism of the Formation of some Metal Alkyls and their Reactions with Alkyl Halides. Sodium alkyls are probably formed by homolysis of the C—Hal bond and pairing with single electrons at the metal surface:

$$\text{R}\overset{\curvearrowright}{\cdot}\text{Hal} \longrightarrow \text{Na:R} + \text{Na:Hal}$$

Na metal

Radicals do not become detached during sodium alkyl formation; there is no evidence of their interaction with the solvent (cf. pp. 18–19).

Alkyls of the more electropositive metals react with the parent alkyl halides according to the simplified equation:

$$R—Metal + R—Hal \longrightarrow R—R + Metal—Hal$$

This coupling reaction excludes the use of all iodides but methyl iodide for the preparation of Grignard and lithium derivatives and methyl lithium is prepared by addition of the halide to the metal in ether to limit competitive coupling. When C—Hal bond fission generates a resonance stabilized ion (or radical) then only the coupled product may be isolated:

$$2CH_2{=}CH—CH_2Br \xrightarrow[Et_2O]{2Mg} CH_2{=}CH—CH_2—CH_2—CH{=}CH_2$$
$$\text{Diallyl}$$

$$Ph—CH_2—Cl \xrightarrow[Me_2O]{2Na} Ph—CH_2—CH_2—Ph$$
$$\text{Dibenzyl } 90\%$$

Sodium benzyl can be obtained in high yield by the metalation of toluene with sodium phenyl (p. 3). The coupling reaction is favoured by basic solvents such as ethers which can co-ordinate with the metal cation.

The coupling reaction was first used synthetically by Wurtz (1855) for sodium alkyls and alkyl halides. Formation of sodium amyl was demonstrated by Morton, who showed that caproic acid could be obtained in 90% yield by carbonation (p. 30) of amyl chloride in contact with excess sodium. Very little decane was obtained at this stage but addition of more of the halide led to its isolation in 40% yield with substantial recovery of unreacted chloride. It has been suggested that the sodio-derivative attacks the halide as nucleophilic carbon:

$$Na^{\oplus}R^{\ominus} + R_1—Hal \longrightarrow R—R_1 + Na^{\oplus}Cl^{\ominus}$$

This mechanism is acceptable for reactions of lithium alkyls and of less electropositive metals in solution, although a number of examples are given in this text where the reaction course varies with the metal ion when other factors are constant; the cation must therefore feature in the transition state. Morton has pointed out that sodium alkyls are solid ionic aggregates and proposes that here the halide first co-ordinates with the cation

$$R—X + Na^{\oplus}R_1^{\ominus} \longrightarrow [R—X{\rightarrow}Na]^{\oplus}R_1^{\ominus}$$

15

and since an unsolvated carbanion is very unstable it will prefer to lose an electron and form a radical:

$$R_1^{\ominus} \text{ donates } e \text{ to } [R\!-\!X\!\rightarrow\!Na]^{\oplus}$$

$$\downarrow$$

$$R_1\cdot + R\!-\!X\!\rightarrow\!Na\cdot \quad (B)$$

(B) affords $R\cdot + Na^{\oplus}X^{\ominus}$ owing to the tendency for sodium to acquire positive charge and also to the stability of halide ions. The radicals $R\cdot$ and $R_1\cdot$ can combine to give the hydrocarbons $R\!-\!R$, $R_1\!-\!R_1$, and $R\!-\!R_1$ or disproportionate to give $R\!-\!H$, $R_1\!-\!H$ and the corresponding olefines. This multiplicity of products restricts the use of the Wurtz reaction in synthesis, but acceptable yields are obtained when an aryl halide is used (Fittig, 1863) or when an alkyl and an aryl residue are coupled in the Wurtz–Fittig reaction; bromides are generally preferred for this reaction. n-Alkylbenzenes may usually be prepared in higher overall yield by acylation followed by Clemmensen reduction:

	Wurtz–Fittig (%)	Clemmensen (%)
Propylbenzene	55	82
Butylbenzene	70	88
Amylbenzene	55	90

Similar results are obtained when Grignard reagents react with alkyl halides. The latter must enter the cage of solvent molecules (see p. 22) when association with the metal ion assists in breaking the C—Hal bond; at the same time the alkyl group of the Grignard acquires more carbanion character and probably attacks via a second molecule of reagent in a six-centre transition state:

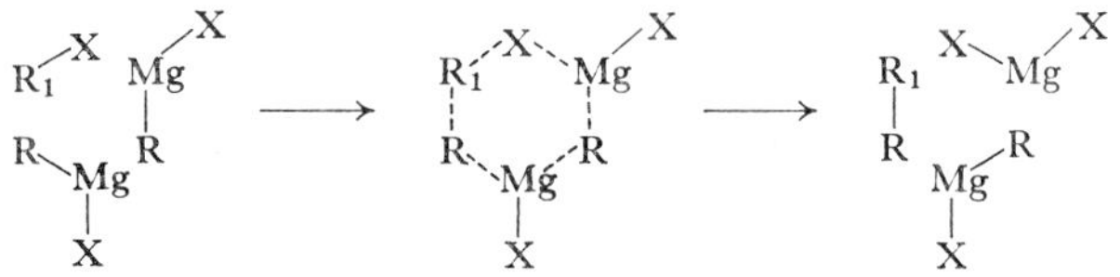

The side-products formed are analogous to those of the Wurtz reaction:

$$CH_3—CH_2—Br + CH_3—CH_2—MgBr \longrightarrow CH_2{=}CH_2 + CH_3—CH_3 + MgBr_2$$

$$(CH_3)_3C—Br + CH_3—Mg—I \longrightarrow$$

$$\begin{array}{c} H_3C \\ {\displaystyle \diagdown} \\ H_3C \end{array} C{=}CH_2 + (CH_3)_4C + (CH_3)_3C—C(CH_3)_3 + CH_4$$

$$\underset{\substack{39\% \quad \text{'Normal'} \\ \text{product}}}{}$$

Halogen–metal exchange leads to the formation of 2,2,3,3-tetramethyl-butane. An ionic elimination is more likely for the Grignard reaction:

$$\longrightarrow \begin{array}{c} R—CH_2—CH_3 \\ R—CH{=}CH_2 \end{array} + MgHal_2$$

The predominantly ionic character of Grignard reactions can be verified by deliberately inducing a radical mechanism, and when this is done quite different product analyses are obtained. Radicals may be generated as intermediates in a Grignard reaction by the addition of a salt such as cobaltous chloride, when we have the exchange:

$$R—MgHal + CoCl_2 \rightleftharpoons R—Co—Cl + Cl—Mg—Hal$$

This is followed by a homolysis:

$$R—Co—Cl \rightleftharpoons R{\cdot} + {\cdot}Co—Cl$$

which is favoured because the cobaltous subchloride radical is stabilized, the unpaired electron being accommodated in the available *d*-orbitals.

The normal course of the reaction between cinnamyl chloride and methyl magnesium halide

$$Ph—CH{=}CH—CH_2Cl + MeMgHal \longrightarrow \underset{\text{1-Phenyl-1-butene}}{Ph—CH{=}CH—CH_2—CH_3} \quad 89\%$$

$$+ \underset{\text{1,6-Diphenylhexa-1,5-diene}}{(Ph—CH{=}CH—CH_2)_2} \quad 6\%$$

is changed by the addition of cobaltous chloride and yields 12% of 1-phenylbut-1-ene and 70% of 1,6-diphenylhexa-1,5-diene, the dominant mechanism then being:

$$Ph—CH{=}CH—CH_2Cl + {\cdot}CoCl \rightleftharpoons Ph—CH{=}CH—\overset{\cdot}{C}H_2 + CoCl_2$$

$$2Ph—CH{=}CH—\overset{\cdot}{C}H_2 \longrightarrow \text{1,6-diphenylhexa-1,5-diene}$$

17

Methyl radicals formed in the process have much greater reactivity than the resonance stabilized radical and they would react extensively with the solvent. This induction of radical coupling is of general synthetic value.

The Stereochemistry of Metal Alkyls. Optically active halides may retain their activity during reactions with metal alkyls:

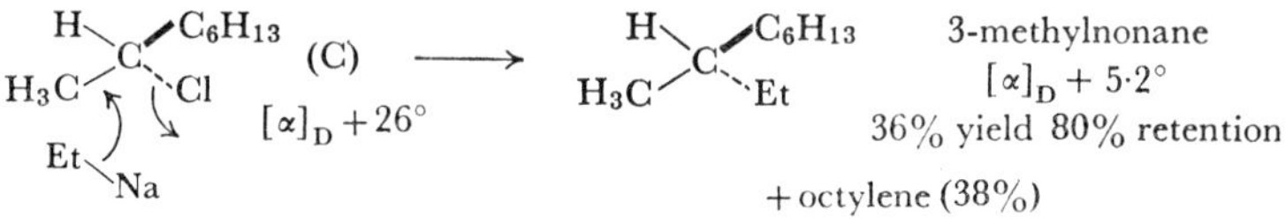

3-methylnonane

$[\alpha]_D + 5\cdot2°$

36% yield 80% retention

+ octylene (38%)

in contrast is:

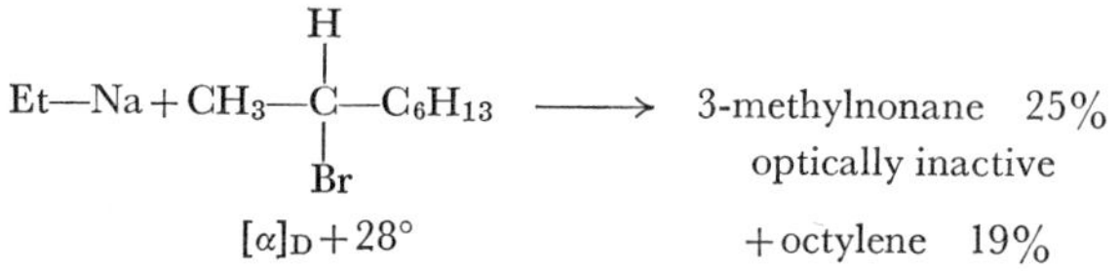

$$Et-Na + CH_3-\overset{\overset{\displaystyle H}{|}}{\underset{\underset{\displaystyle Br}{|}}{C}}-C_6H_{13} \longrightarrow$$

$[\alpha]_D + 28°$

3-methylnonane   25%
optically inactive
+ octylene   19%

Young and Walborsky showed that the cyclopropyl bromide (D) afforded an optically active Grignard reagent which was trapped

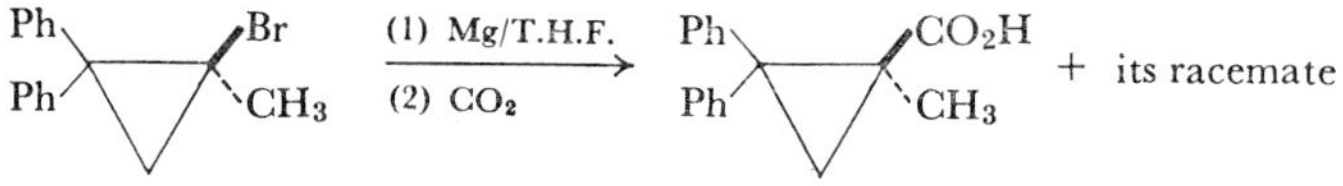

(D)   (E)

by carbonation (see p. 30) and although largely racemized the acid retained 12% of optical purity. The lithium derivative of (D) afforded the acid (E) with complete retention of activity and configuration and it was then shown that racemization occurred during the Grignard formation and not during its carbonation. Thus following the exchange:

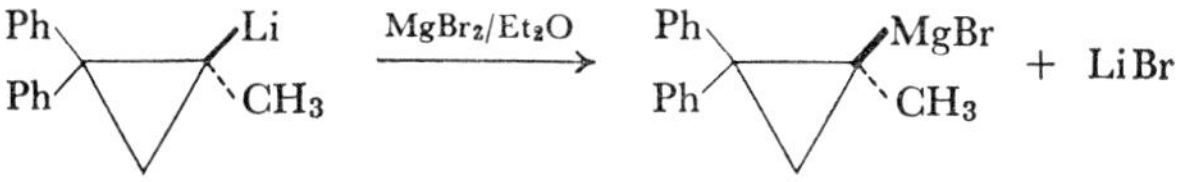

(F)

carbonation of (F) yielded (E) with complete retention. Racemization during Grignard formation can occur if the complexed halide (G)

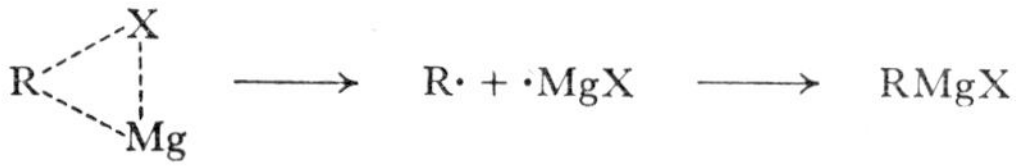

(G)

18

separates into radicals where R· is free to invert; capture of hydrogen from the solvent by radicals with this degree of freedom has been observed during some Grignard syntheses. The degree of retention of activity of halides falls in the order Cl→Br→I which is the order of decreasing bond energy, which in turn would govern the amount of bond breaking during Grignard formation. The contrasting results obtained above with sodium ethyl are explicable in that the C—Br bond will break before the new bond to the ethyl residue is formed with consequent racemization, whilst for the chloride a concerted process (C) is more probable, where the entering and leaving groups are on the same side of the molecule and retention results.

Interactions with Solvents. Lithium alkyls are sufficiently covalent to dissolve as aggregates in hydrocarbons. Ethyl lithium is hexameric and t-butyl lithium is tetrameric in benzene; addition of t-butyl lithium increases the solubility of ethyl lithium in this solvent owing to an exchange of alkyl groups between the two components.

All alkyls of metals above mercury in the table (p. 14) abstract protons from protic solvents:

$$\text{(H)} \quad \begin{array}{c} \text{R--MgHal} \\ \text{H--O--R} \end{array} \longrightarrow \begin{array}{c} \text{R} \quad \text{Mg--Hal} \\ | \; + \; | \\ \text{H} \quad \text{OR} \end{array}$$

This evolution of alkane, equivalent to one 'active' hydrogen in O—H, N—H, S—H groups and in the more acidic hydrocarbons, affords a means of determining the number of active hydrogens in a structure of known molecular weight. The method is named after Zerewitinoff who was largely responsible for its development. A useful alternative procedure is to substitute a solution of lithium aluminium hydride in ether or tetrahydrofuran and measure hydrogen evolved:

$$4\text{R--X--H} + \text{LiAlH}_4 \longrightarrow \text{LiAl(XR)}_4 + 4\text{H}_2$$

The alkyls of the most electropositive metals react immediately with nucleophilic solvents including ethers:

$$\begin{array}{c} \text{R} \diagdown \quad \diagup \text{R} \\ \text{O} \\ \text{Na}^{\oplus} \; \text{R}_1^{\ominus} \end{array} \longrightarrow \text{R--O}^{\ominus} \, \text{Na}^{\oplus} + \text{R--R}_1$$

Temperature control is important when working with lithium alkyls because in ethereal solvents a similar but slower fission occurs. The order of stability of three of the more important reagents in ether is: MeLi > PhLi > n-BuLi. Methyl lithium is stable for several weeks in diethyl ether at room temperature, whilst n-butyl lithium has a half-life of 140 hr

19

in this solvent at 25°. Tetrahydrofuran is more reactive and a lower range of working temperatures is recommended: MeLi at 0°; PhLi between 0° and −30°; n-BuLi below −35°.

Butyl lithium reacts with diethyl ether to form lithium ethoxide and hydrocarbons; the mechanism is probably an elimination within a six-centred transition state:

$$\begin{array}{c} H_2C\!\!-\!\!CH_2 \\ H \quad O\!-\!Et \\ Bu\!-\!Li \end{array} \longrightarrow \quad products$$

Ethers may be subject to metalation at the α-position: thus butyl lithium reacts readily with dimethyl ether to form lithium methoxide, butane, and higher hydrocarbons:

$$Bu\!-\!Li + CH_3\!-\!O\!-\!CH_3 \longrightarrow \underset{Bu\!-\!Li}{LiCH_2\!-\!O\!-\!CH_3} + BuH$$

$$\downarrow$$

$$BuCH_2\!-\!Li + LiO\!-\!CH_3$$

$$\downarrow$$

$$Bu\!-\!CH_3 \quad etc.$$

An alternative formulation is that carbene is produced and homologous hydrocarbons are formed by the insertion reaction (p. 188):

$$\begin{array}{c} CH_2\!-\!O\!-\!CH_3 \\ | \\ H \\ Li\!-\!Bu \end{array} \longrightarrow \begin{array}{c} BuH \\ \\ + \; CH_2\!-\!O\!-\!CH_3 \\ Li^{\oplus} \end{array} \longrightarrow \begin{array}{c} :CH_2 \\ + \\ LiOCH_3 \end{array}$$

Nuclear magnetic resonance spectroscopy provides valuable information about the structure of metal alkyls in solution and the work of Eastham's group on n-butyl lithium provides an example. It was shown that this compound exists in ether as a solvated dimer $(BuLi)_2.Et_2O$.

The 1;3;3;1 signal of the methylene protons of diethyl ether in hexane is at +204 c/s (downfield from tetramethylsilane) at 60 Mc, but on addition of >0·5 mol. of butyl lithium this peak shifts downfield to +218·5 c/s because co-ordination with the metal causes deshielding; with less than this amount of butyl lithium an average value is obtained due to exchange between complexed and free solvent molecules. The

20

α-methylene signal (1;2;1) of the metal alkyl in hexane solution is at −50 c/s (upfield from TMS) but the peak shifts upfield to −59 c/s when sufficient ether is added to form the complex. No change in this signal results on addition of more ether which can therefore be only loosely co-ordinated with the complex.

Derivatives of metals less electropositive than lithium are stable in ether, but it is evident that co-ordination of ether molecules is essential for the preparation of Grignard reagents at ambient temperature, since forcing conditions are required for their formation in hydrocarbons. Phenylmagnesium chloride is only obtained at 160° in absence of ether, and Bryce-Smith has carried out the reaction:

$$\text{n-BuI} + \text{Mg} \xrightarrow[\text{isopropylbenzene}]{130°} \text{n-Bu—MgI}$$

The 85% yield obtained is above average for this type of preparation when much loss is normally occasioned by reactions of the Wurtz type. The product has a complex structure and analyses for Bu_3Mg_2I or $Bu_2Mg.Bu$—Mg—I. Owing to its appreciable solubility even the latter formulation is not adequate, a macromolecular structure being more probable, for example:

(J) is one possibility

Metal alkoxides catalyse the formation of Grignards in non-ethereal solvents, aluminium and magnesium derivatives being most effective. The salt $Mg[(AlOiPr)_4]_2$ complexes with MeMgI in xylene affording an interesting product which is much more stable than normal Grignards in protic solvents (p. 19), surviving for an hour on mixing with ethanol at 20°.

The structure of Grignard reagents solvated by ethers has long been the subject of controversy. In 1929 the Schlenks proposed that RMgHal was predominant in the equilibrium (K).

$$2\text{RMgHal} \rightleftharpoons \text{R}_2\text{Mg} + \text{MgHal}_2 \rightleftharpoons \text{R}_2\text{Mg}.\text{MgHal}_2$$

$$\text{(K)}$$

A number of workers observed that on electrolysis of Grignard solutions magnesium and alkyl radicals were discharged at both electrodes consistent with the existence of ions of the type: $RMg^{\oplus}$, $RMgHal_2^{\ominus}$, derived from the species in (K). The concentration of ions in the solutions can only be small however because of their low conductance. Anions would

21

be weakly solvated and neutral molecules and cations strongly solvated by ether molecules, for example:

$$\begin{array}{c} \text{Et—O—Et} \\ \downarrow \\ \text{R—Mg—X} \\ \uparrow \\ \text{Et}^{\diagup}\text{O}^{\diagdown}\text{Et} \end{array}$$

Ashby's group showed that ethylmagnesium halides were essentially monomeric in tetrahydrofuran solution and by addition of benzene they were able to isolate the complex $EtMg_2Cl_3$ (L) which had an association factor of 0·5 in tetrahydrofuran due to complete dissociation into two species:

$$EtMg_2Cl_3 \longrightarrow EtMgCl + MgCl_2$$
$$\text{(L)} \qquad\qquad \text{(M)}$$

The existence of the species RMgHal in diethyl ether cannot be demonstrated in this way because the complex (L) is insoluble, but boiling point elevation showed that chlorides had a molecular weight nearly twice (M) whereas bromides and iodides were monomeric at low concentrations $\left(\dfrac{M}{20}\right)$ and were more nearly dimeric at molar concentrations. Grignard solutions are usually of intermediate concentration when used synthetically and will contain both species in equilibrium.

Dessy recently showed that isotopically labelled magnesium bromide combined with diethylmagnesium to give a solution identical to ethylmagnesium bromide in which the labelled metal was redistributed:

$$Mg^{25}Br_2 + Et_2Mg \;\rightleftharpoons\; EtMg^{25}Br + EtMgBr$$

this was demonstrated by precipitation of magnesium bromide carrying half the original label as the insoluble dioxan complex. In another similar experiment Dessy was unable to demonstrate exchange which may be sensitive to inclusions of trace metals. Exchange probably occurs by dissociation of dimer molecules (N, cf. J):

$$R\text{—Mg}\underset{\diagdown X\diagup}{\overset{\diagup R\diagdown}{\rightleftarrows}}\text{Mg—X} \;\rightleftharpoons\; 2RMgX$$
$$\text{(N)}$$

Six-centred transitions, as written on p. 25 and p. 28, are expected for reactions of monomeric alkylmagnesium halides although a four-centre transition as (N), cf. (H), cannot be excluded and will often be written here for brevity.

22

Reactions with Oxygen. The more electropositive metal alkyls react rapidly, sodium alkyls are spontaneously inflammable and the aluminium alkyls having unoccupied low energy orbitals behave similarly at ambient temperature. Electron-donating groups such as RO— and R_2N— decrease the reaction rate as also do vinyl and aryl residues. A typical reaction is that of the lithium compounds:

$$R—Li \xrightarrow{O_2} R—O—O—Li \xrightarrow{(O)} 2LiOR \quad (P)$$
$$Li—R$$

where a concerted reaction between the peroxide (O) and excess of the alkyl yields the alkoxide (P). Higher alcohols are obtained commercially by working up the products of aluminium alkyl growth reactions (p. 43) by oxygenation followed by hydrolysis in water:

$$—Al—R + nC_2H_4 \longrightarrow —Al—(CH_2—CH_2)_n—R$$

$$—Al—O—(CH_2—CH_2)_n—R \xrightarrow{H_2O} R—(CH_2—CH_2)_n—OH + Al_2O_3$$

Some reaction between the reagent and oxygen may occur during a Grignard preparation in dry air, but it is usually necessary to stream the gas into the system when oxygenation probably follows the course:

$$R—Mg—X \xrightarrow{O_2} R—O—O—MgX \xrightarrow{R—MgX} 2RO—Mg—X$$

Acidification of the alkoxide formed affords the alcohol but the reaction is of little preparative importance since only rarely does one need to convert a halide into an alcohol. The formation of peroxides in ethereal solvents is a hazard.

Following the hydroboration of olefines in diglyme (p. 45) the boron alkyl can be oxidized by the addition of alkali and hydrogen peroxide. One suggested mechanism for this reaction involves successive shifts of carbanion to oxygen in the anion and ejection of hydroxide ion; movement of the alkyl group with two electrons is consistent with the observed retention of configuration in these reactions.

$$H_2O_2 + OH^{\ominus} \rightleftharpoons H—O—O^{\ominus} + H_2O$$

$$R_3B + HO_2^{\ominus} \longrightarrow \left[\begin{matrix} R \\ R—B^{\ominus}—O—OH \\ R \end{matrix} \right] \longrightarrow \begin{matrix} R \\ R—B + OH^{\ominus} \\ OR \end{matrix}$$

23

The final step is hydrolysis of B—O—R bonds in the alkaline medium to borate and the alcohol. The synthetic value of this conversion is that overall hydration of the starting olefin has occurred contrary to the Markownikoff rule.

Asymmetric synthesis of alcohols can be achieved by hydroboration of a hindered optically active alkene, for example (+)-α-pinene, which proceeds to the dialkylborane stage (1):

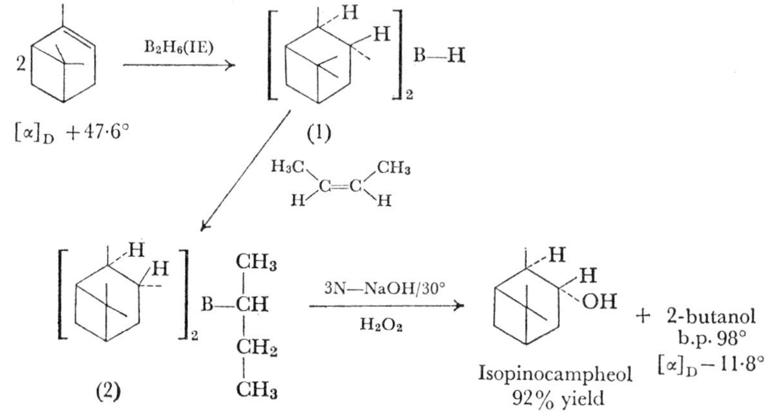

whence addition of *cis*-2-butene affords the unsymmetrical trialkylborane (2) stereoselectively, since subsequent oxidation and hydrolysis gave a high yield of 2-butanol, $[\alpha]_D$ − 11·8° (87% optical purity). *trans*-Alkenes are less reactive than the *cis*-isomers.

Alkylboranes have on occasion been oxidized directly to carbonyl compounds with aqueous chromic acid.

Reactions with Aldehydes and Ketones. The normal reaction yields an alcohol as a result of nucleophilic attack by the potential carbanion on the carbonyl carbon atom. By appropriate choice of starting material this leads to a preparative method for primary, secondary, and tertiary alcohols:

$$R—MgHal + \begin{cases} H—CHO & \longrightarrow R—CH_2OH \\ R_1—CHO & \longrightarrow R—CH(OH)—R_1 \\ R_1—CO—R_2 & \longrightarrow R_1R_2—C(OH)R \end{cases}$$

There is evidence that 2 moles of Grignard reagent are needed to initiate addition to a carbonyl group which must displace one of the solvating ether molecules:

24

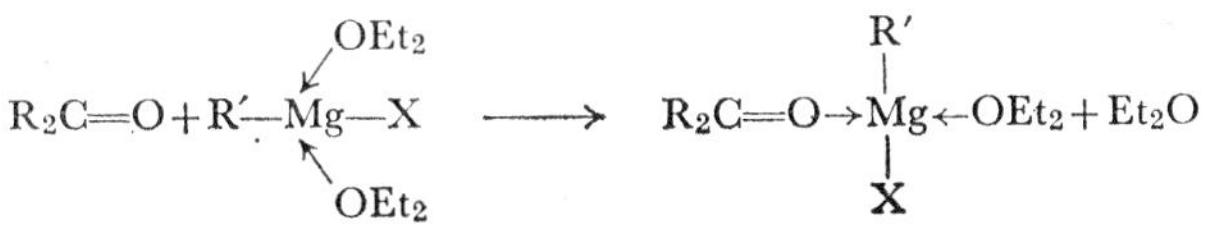

$$R_2C{=}O + R'{-}\underset{\underset{\textstyle OEt_2}{|}}{\overset{\overset{\textstyle OEt_2}{|}}{Mg}}{-}X \longrightarrow R_2C{=}O{\rightarrow}\underset{\underset{\textstyle X}{|}}{\overset{\overset{\textstyle R'}{|}}{Mg}}{\leftarrow}OEt_2 + Et_2O$$

and then enter a six-centred transition state including a second molecule of Grignard:

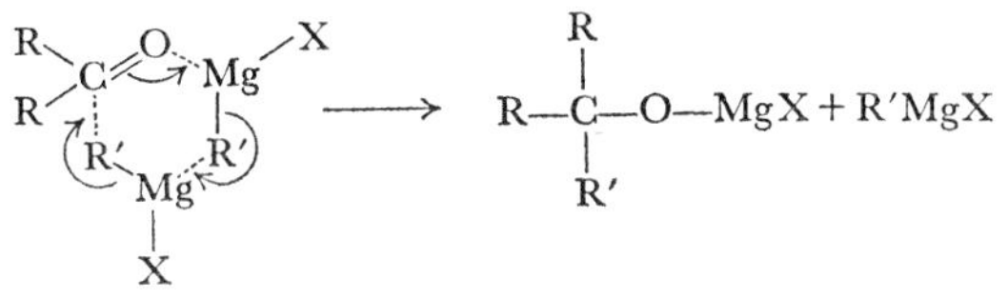

$$\longrightarrow \quad R{-}\underset{\underset{\textstyle R'}{|}}{\overset{\overset{\textstyle R}{|}}{C}}{-}O{-}MgX + R'MgX$$

Formaldehyde required for primary alcohol synthesis is conveniently prepared by heating one of its solid polymers and streaming the evolved gas into the Grignard solution under nitrogen. A simpler method which may lead to lower yields is the direct addition of the polymer.

$$H{-}CHO \text{ gas}/N_2 + s{-}C_4H_9MgBr \longrightarrow s{-}C_4H_9{-}CH_2OH$$

38 g absorbed in 5 min worked up in water. Yield 67%.

$$H{-}CHO \text{ as solid} + n{-}C_{18}H_{37}MgCl \longrightarrow n{-}C_{19}H_{39}{-}OH$$
Trioxymethylene

6 hr reflux worked up in 30% H_2SO_4. Yield 59%.

Other products were octadecane and octadecene, probably by a dis-proportionation (pp. 16–17) and also the formal $(C_{19}H_{39}O)_2CH_2$ perhaps derived as follows:

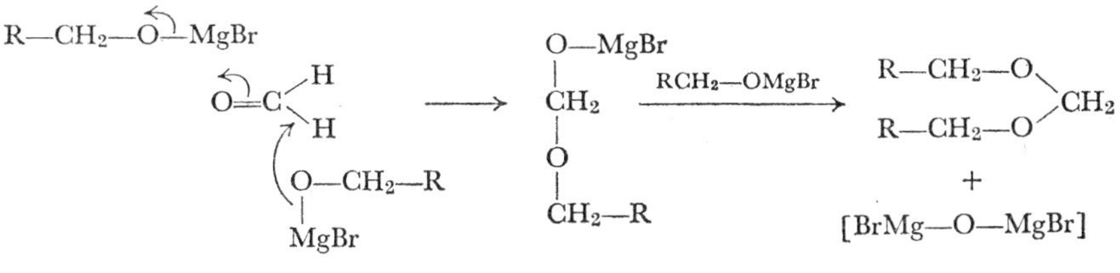

With aldehydes as precursors secondary alcohols are formed.

$$CH_3{-}CHO + EtMgBr \longrightarrow CH_3{-}CH(OH){-}Et$$
as paraldehyde $\qquad\qquad$ 67%

Acetaldehyde and n-octylmagnesium bromide give 2-decanol in 80% yield, but very little of the alcohol is formed when n-octylmagnesium iodide is used. Another synthesis of 2-decanol would be from an ethyl-magnesium halide and octanal; but the availability of starting material usually determines the choice. In any case, reduction of carbonyl

3   25

compounds by metal hydrides is often preferable to a Grignard reaction. A typical preparation of a tertiary alcohol is:

$$CH_3—CO—CH_3 + n\text{-}C_4H_9MgCl \longrightarrow (CH_3)_2—C(OH)—C_4H_9$$
$$70\%$$

Yields of 50–70 % are normal, but care may be needed in working up the *t*-alkoxymagnesium halide because of the ease with which the products form olefins by an acid-catalysed elimination:

$$\overset{HO}{\underset{|}{-C}}\overset{H^{\oplus}}{\underset{|}{-C}}- \longrightarrow -C\!=\!C- + H_3O^{\oplus}$$

Elimination may usually be avoided by decomposition of the Grignard complex in an acetate/HCl buffer or in potassium hydrogen tartrate solution with pH control.

The formation of tertiary alcohols from Michler's ketone (Q1) was shown by Gilman to provide a useful colour test for lithium, magnesium and zinc derivatives since all react with the test reagent, a 1 % solution of the ketone in benzene:

$$Me_2N-\!\!\left\langle\;\right\rangle\!\!-CO-\!\!\left\langle\;\right\rangle\!\!-NMe_2 \;\xrightarrow{\text{R-metal}}\; Ar_2—C(OH)R$$

(Q1).

Hydrolysis with water and treatment with a little iodine in acetic acid affords the blue–green colour of the corresponding carbonium ion:

$$Ar_2C(OH)R \;\xrightarrow[\text{AcOH}]{I_2}\; [Ar_2CR]^{\oplus}I^{\ominus}$$

When R = Ph the product is Malachite Green.

Abnormal Reaction Products. There are three principle side-reactions which occur to a greater or less extent during syntheses with carbonyl compounds.

(1) *Enolization.* In simple aldehydes and ketones the proportion of enol in equilibrium is small

$$R-\overset{\overset{\displaystyle\overset{\oplus}{H}}{||}}{\underset{|}{C}}-\overset{}{\underset{|}{C}}-H \;\rightleftharpoons\; R-\overset{\overset{\displaystyle OH}{|}}{C}\!=\!C\!\!\left\langle\begin{array}{c}H\\H\end{array}\right. \; + \; H.\,Base^{\oplus}$$

The strong co-ordination between Grignard reagents and ethers shows that they are in effect Lewis acids and one possible course for enolization is therefore:

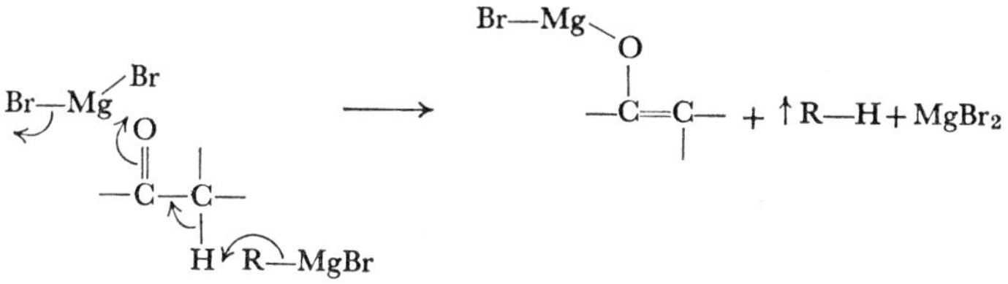

It will be noted that alkane equivalent to substantial amounts of enol may be evolved irreversibly by displacement of the original equilibrium and that the original carbonyl compound is regenerated from the enolate on acidification of products. Methyl triethylmethyl ketone is an extreme example and is recovered in 94% yield following reaction with methylmagnesium bromide. β-Diketones are normally appreciably enolized and hence the enol-magnesium derivative will be formed extensively; one example is that of cyclohexane-1,3-dione:

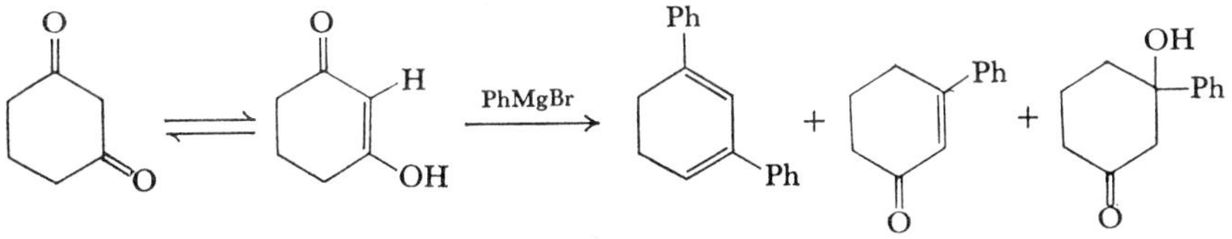

(Q2)   (R) 10%   (S) 53%   (T) 19%

1,3-diphenylcyclohexa-1,3-diene (R) is formed by reaction of 2 moles of Grignard and with the elimination of the tertiary —OH groups on working up. 3-Hydroxy-3-phenylcyclohexanone (T) corresponds to reaction of the enolate (cf. Q2) with 1 mole of reagent. 3-Phenylcyclohex-2-en-1-one (S) is formed from (T) by the elimination of water. Conjugated systems of this kind may undergo 1,4 addition of Grignard reagents (see p. 153).

Moderate yields of ditertiary alcohols or of keto-alcohols may be obtained from α-diketones. The method may be useful for compounds which are difficult to make by other routes:

i-Pr—CO—CO—i-Pr + EtMgI ⟶ i-Pr.Et.C(OH)—CO—i-Pr

30%

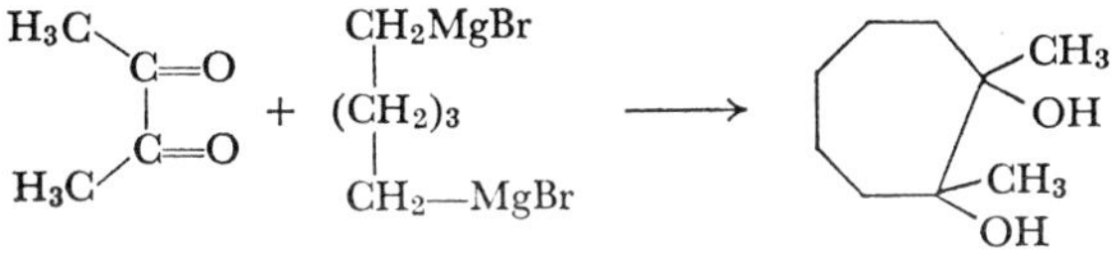

27

(2) *Aldol Condensation.* This occurs widely albeit as a small proportion of the overall reaction in most examples, aldehydes being more prone to the side-reaction than ketones and it may be recalled that extensive aldolization occurs if one attempts the reduction of aldehydes with aluminium alkoxides. Exceptional behaviour is found in the reaction between cyclopentanone and isopropylmagnesium halides:

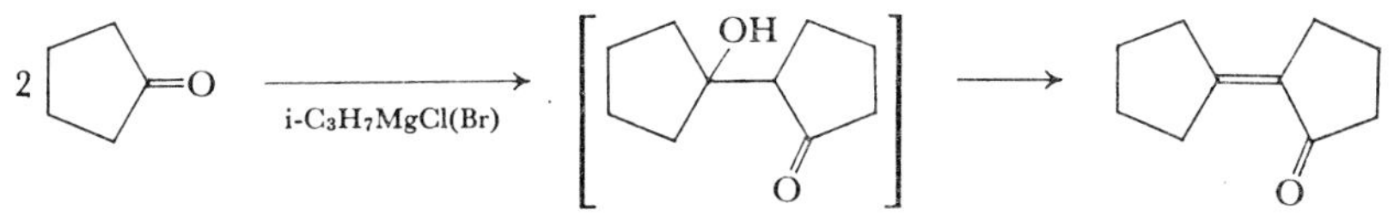

Cyclopentylene-
cyclopentanone as
sole product

This is an example where dehydration during working-up affords a conjugated product and is therefore particularly facile.

(3) *Reduction of the Carbonyl Compound.* This tends to take place when C—C bond formation is hindered by bulky alkyl groups in the reagents, for example di-isopropyl ketone and methylmagnesium bromide afford the normal product 2,3,4-trimethylpentan-3-ol in 78% yield, but when isobutylmagnesium bromide is used a quite different course is followed:

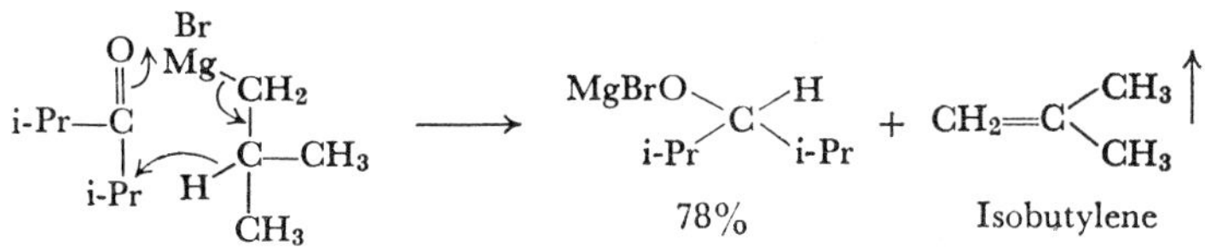

together with only 8% of the normal product tri-isopropyl carbinol and 10% of recovered ketone. The mechanism written for the reduction involves magnesium acting as a Lewis acid and the setting up of a six-membered transition state, with transfer of a hydride ion to the carbonyl carbon in a manner closely related to the Meerwein–Ponndorff–Verley reduction of ketones by aluminium alkoxides:

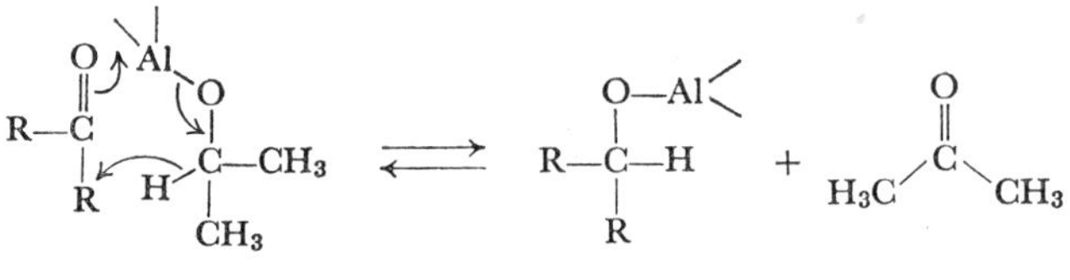

Tertiary alcohols are better derived from hindered ketones by their reaction with lithium alkyls when reduction does not generally occur:

$$\text{i-Pr—CO—i-Pr} \xrightarrow{\text{i-PrLi}} (\text{i-Pr})_3\text{C—OH}$$

28

Only one alkyl residue of an aluminium alkyl can be donated to a carbonyl compound:

$$Ph—CO—Ph + AlPh_3 \longrightarrow Ph_3C—O—AlPh_2$$

and this makes alcohol synthesis inefficient: on the other hand the competing reduction is a valuable alternative to lithium aluminium hydride and is cheaper on an industrial scale.

Reduction predominated in the reaction of chloral with aluminium triethyl

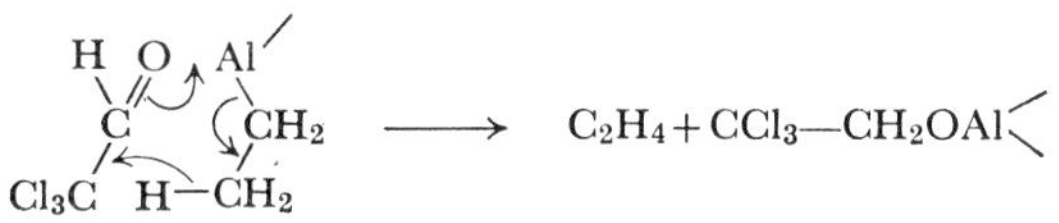

$$\underset{\substack{Cl_3C \quad H^{\frown}CH_2}}{\overset{\substack{H \; O \; \nearrow Al^{\diagup} \\ \diagdown \; /\!\!\!\diagup \quad \diagup \\ C \quad \; CH_2}}{}} \longrightarrow C_2H_4 + CCl_3—CH_2OAl\!\!<$$

where the carbonyl group is very liable to nucleophilic attack, the probable mechanism of reaction, cf. (28), is hydride transfer following complex formation.

As shown above, bulky groups hinder alkyl donation and hence isobutyl and higher alkyls are preferred as reducing agents. Reduction of aldehydes, ketones, esters, lactones, amides, nitriles, oximes and Schiff's bases has been effected and typical reactions are illustrated:

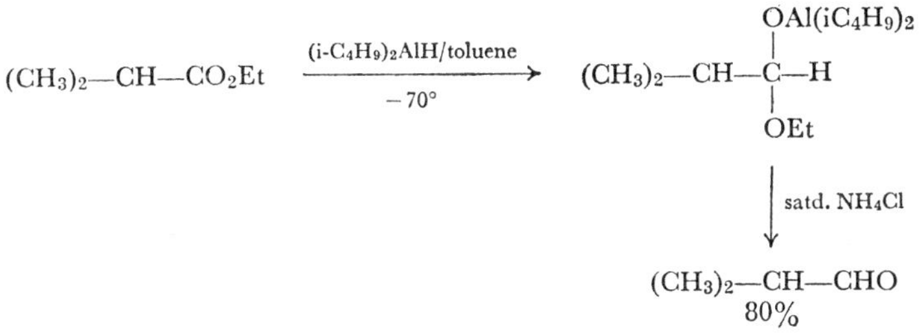

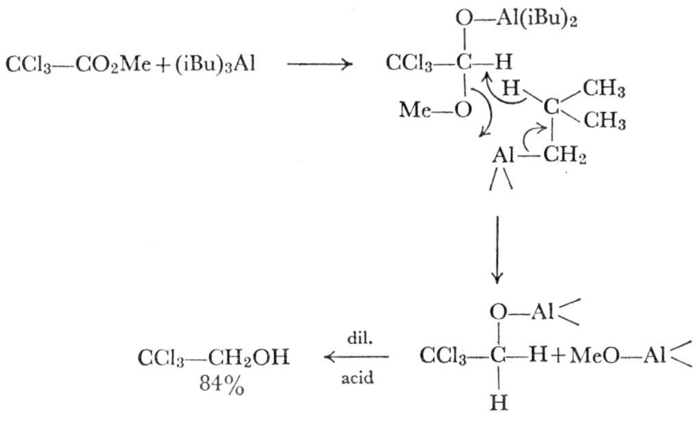

$$(CH_3)_2—CH—CO_2Et \xrightarrow[-70°]{(i\text{-}C_4H_9)_2AlH/toluene} (CH_3)_2—CH—\underset{\substack{| \\ OEt}}{\overset{\substack{OAl(iC_4H_9)_2 \\ |}}{C}}—H$$

$$\Big\downarrow \text{ satd. NH}_4\text{Cl}$$

$$\underset{80\%}{(CH_3)_2—CH—CHO}$$

$$CCl_3—CO_2Me + (iBu)_3Al \longrightarrow CCl_3—\overset{\substack{O—Al(iBu)_2 \\ |}}{C}—H$$

$$\Big\downarrow$$

$$\underset{84\%}{CCl_3—CH_2OH} \xleftarrow[\text{acid}]{\text{dil.}} CCl_3—\overset{\substack{O—Al< \\ |}}{\underset{\substack{| \\ H}}{C}}—H + MeO—Al<$$

When an excess of the alkyl was used reaction was complete after 15 min at 60°.

$$H_2C \underset{H_2C}{\overset{C}{\diagdown}} \underset{CH_2}{\overset{O}{\diagup}} \quad + \quad 2\,HAl(iBu)_2 \quad \longrightarrow \quad 2 \text{ isobutene} + \text{alkoxide}$$

with these proportions
reaction was very fast

$$\downarrow$$

$$HO—(CH_2)_4—OH$$
67% by distillation

$$N{\equiv}C—(CH_2)_{10}—C{\equiv}N + HAl(iBu)_2 \quad \longrightarrow \quad \text{isobutene} + R—CH_2—N \overset{Al}{\underset{Al}{\diagdown}}$$

4 hr heating at 80°
with four equivalents of the alkyl

$$\downarrow \begin{array}{l} \text{(1) dil. acid} \\ \text{(2) basify} \end{array}$$

$$H_2N—(CH_2)_{12}—NH_2$$
m.p. 66°, 78%

The Carbonation Reaction. Aluminium alkyls, Grignard reagents, and derivatives of metals more electropositive than magnesium react with carbon dioxide. It is not essential to exclude atmospheric carbon dioxide during the preparation of a Grignard reagent as protection is afforded by the solvent vapour: however, a reaction analogous to the carbonation of sodium alkyls will proceed if carbon dioxide is introduced. The most convenient form is the powdered solid, dry ice, and on working-up in dilute mineral acid the carboxylic acid corresponding to the magnesium salt is liberated.

$$\begin{array}{c} R—Mg—Hal \\ O{=}C{=}O \end{array} \quad \longrightarrow \quad R—\underset{\underset{O}{\|}}{C}—OMgHal \quad \xrightarrow[\text{acid}]{\text{dil.}} \quad R—CO_2H + HOMgHal$$

This reaction illustrates the power of metal alkyls as nucleophilic reagents, for carbon dioxide rarely acts as an electrophile. One other example is the Kolbe-Schmitt synthesis (p. 168). Some typical examples of carbonation follow:

$$CH_3—(CH_2)_3—MgCl \quad \xrightarrow[-2°]{CO_2} \quad CH_3—(CH_2)_3—CO_2H$$
80%

86%

In an experiment with cyclohexyl magnesium bromide none of the normal acid product was isolated, but the reaction afforded:

cyclohexene, possibly through an elimination reaction during the preparation of the Grignard solution;

cyclohexylmethanol, $C_6H_{11}-CH_2-OH$, by reduction of the normal product;

bicyclohexylmethanol, $C_6H_{11}-CH(OH)-C_6H_{11}$, by reduction of the corresponding ketone (for mechanism see p. 28) which may sometimes be isolated for example:

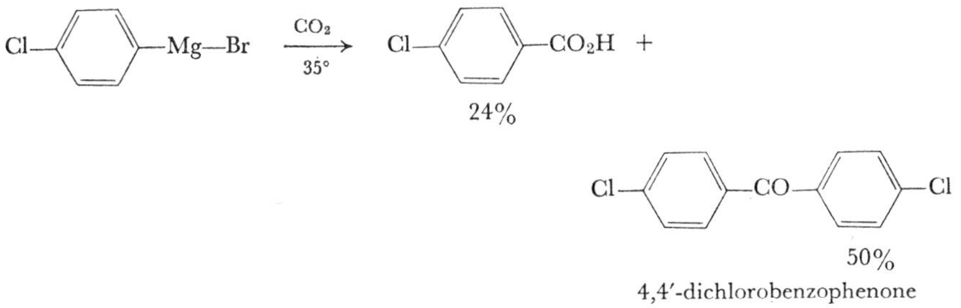

24%

50%
4,4'-dichlorobenzophenone

Here also note the preferred formation of the magnesium bromide. The ketones are derived from a further reaction of the Grignard with magnesium carboxylate

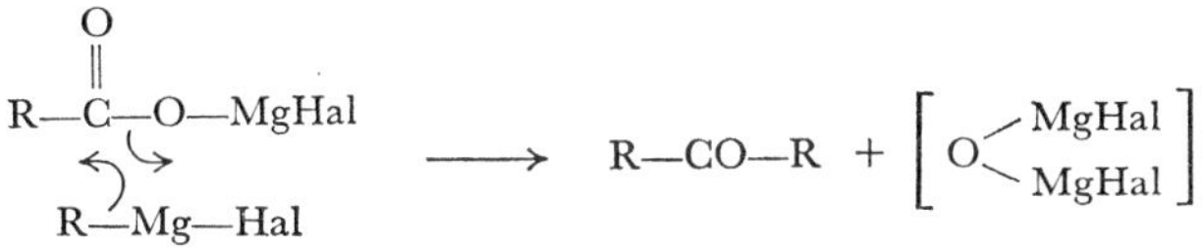

and the sequence will continue in most instances either by addition to the $C=O$ group (p. 24) or by reduction: in the example above 4,4'-dichlorobenzophenone is unchanged, in keeping with the low reactivity of diaryl ketones towards nucleophiles. In order to reduce the extent of side-reactions it is worth while to take the following precautions:

(1) Employ inverse conditions and add the Grignard solution to a large excess of solid carbon dioxide.

(2) Keep the temperature down to encourage the separation of the normal product $R-CO_2MgHal$ from solution.

By these means *p*-chlorobenzoic acid may be obtained from *p*-chlorophenyl magnesium bromide in 80% yield at $-40°$, accompanied by only 4% of ketone.

31

During carbonation of lithium alkyls substantial amounts of ketone may be formed by a route comparable to that followed by the Grignard reagents; here also temperature control is necessary if good yields of the lithium carboxylate are to be obtained. At $-50°$ lithium phenyl affords the benzoate as the major product, whereas passage of carbon dioxide into a boiling ethereal solution gives benzophenone in 76% yield and after acidification only 1·6% of benzoic acid is isolable.

The ready formation of ketones from the lithium salts of carboxylic acids is ascribed to the activity of lithium alkyls as carbanion donors. Some examples of synthesis follow:

0·008(8) mol   0·018 mol   77%

10–30 min reflux for reactions
   of acids of this type

$$CH_3-CH_2-CH_2-C{\overset{O}{\underset{OLi}{\diagdown}}} + PhLi \longrightarrow Ph-CO-C_3H_8$$
                                                    62%

The methylketone (AC) required for vitamin A synthesis (p. 39) was prepared in over 90% yield from the polyunsaturated acid and methyl lithium which was superior to the zinc and cadmium dimethyls.

The further reaction of ketones to form tertiary alcohols, normal for Grignard reagents, is not experienced with the lithium derivatives under the above conditions and adds to the value of the method. The failure of lithium alkyls to react is ascribed to the irreversible formation of the species (U) which resists attack by carbanion. In some instances, e.g. the reaction of lithium benzoate and phenyl lithium, such an intermediate was precipitated when analysis confirmed the composition $(Ph)_2C(OLi)_2$ and treatment with water afforded benzophenone and lithium hydroxide; the mechanism of formation would be:

Free ketones do of course react with lithium alkyls in the normal way (see p. 28).

32

Carbonation of one aluminium–carbon bond, by simultaneous passage of carbon dioxide and a trialkyl into a hydrocarbon solvent, follows the course

$$AlR_3 + CO_2 \longrightarrow \underset{(V)}{R_2Al{-}O{-}CO{-}R}$$

and a good yield of acid may be obtained by hydrolysis of this product (V); alternatively its reaction with two more molecules of the alkyl leads to synthesis of tertiary alcohols:

$$R_2AlO{-}CO{-}R + 2AlR_3 \longrightarrow R_2Al{-}O{-}AlR_2 + R_2Al{-}O{-}CR_3 \xrightarrow{H_2O/H^{\oplus}} R_3C{-}OH$$

Determination of acid formed in a carbonation reaction is a useful way of estimating the yield in a metal alkyl synthesis, but clearly this can only give an approximate figure. A better method is the reaction between the alkyl and trimethylsilyl chloride:

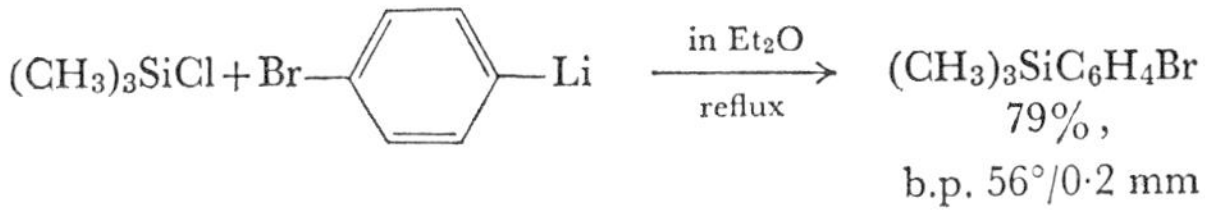

(CH3)3SiCl+Br—
—Li
in Et2O
reflux
(CH3)3SiC6H4Br
79%,
b.p. 56°/0·2 mm

Reactions of Carboxylic Acids and their Derivatives. *Esters* provide an alternative route to tertiary alcohols:

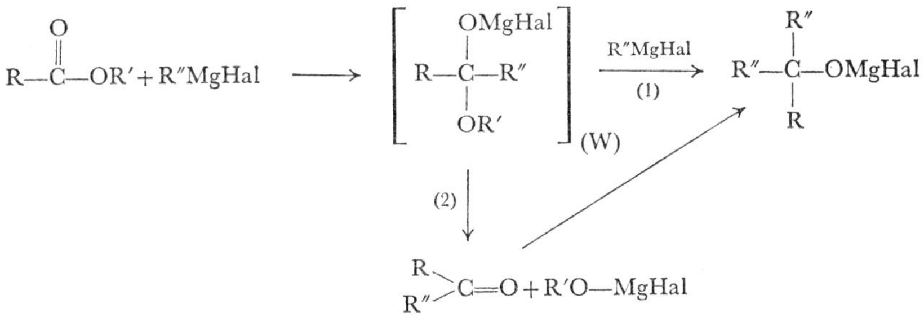

R—C—OR′+R″MgHal
OMgHal
R—C—R″
OR′
(W)
R″MgHal
(1)
R″—C—OMgHal
(2)
C=O+R′O—MgHal

It is not possible to distinguish clearly between the two possible mechanisms shown above but reaction (1) of the ketal type (W) with a second molecule of Grignard is preferred to that requiring the formation of a molecule of ketone (2). A number of records exist where choice of the ketone as starting material lead to inferior yields of t-alcohol as compared to the reaction of the corresponding ester; for the simpler alcohols there is little to choose between these two routes.

The reaction can rarely be limited in practice to that between an ester and 1 mole of Grignard, for if this is attempted the usual product is a mixture of alcohol and the equivalent of unreacted ester, the consequence of more rapid uptake of reagent by the ketal (W). Therefore if an alcohol having three different alkyl groups is required the starting point must be an unsymmetrical ketone and this may be made by a Grignard synthesis:

$$R—CHO + R'—MgBr \longrightarrow R—CH(OH)R' \xrightarrow{[O]} R—CO—R'$$

Cadmium alkyls offer an important alternative method which is discussed on p. 35.

The rate of reaction of an ester with a Grignard reagent depends considerably on steric factors, formates reacting rapidly with two moles of reagent to form secondary alcohols:

$$H—CO—OR + R'MgHal \longrightarrow H—\overset{\displaystyle OR}{\underset{\displaystyle OMgHal}{C}}—R' \xrightarrow[\text{(2) acid}]{\text{(1) R'MgHal}} \overset{R'}{\underset{R'}{\diagup}}C\overset{H}{\underset{OH}{\diagdown}}$$

(X)

The rate of the first step now compares with that of the second and reaction between equimolar amounts leads to the formation of much hemiacetal (X) which affords an aldehyde on hydrolysis. The best conditions are inverse addition of the Grignard to the ester at low temperatures ($-50°$) to precipitate the hemiacetal. Further improvement in yields follows the use of orthoformates:

$$(EtO)_3CH + n\text{-PrMgHal} \longrightarrow n\text{-}C_3H_7—CHO$$
$$75\%$$

This reaction is one of ether fission:

$$H—\overset{\displaystyle OEt}{\underset{\displaystyle R}{C}}—OEt \longrightarrow \overset{H}{\underset{R}{\diagup}}C\overset{OEt}{\underset{OEt}{\diagdown}} + EtO—MgHal$$

It must be stressed that ethers with *gem* alkoxy groups are much more labile than the simple ethers owing to the fission of one alkoxy group being assisted by electron donation from its twin. The ring opening of

34

methylenedioxy ethers and the loss of the central alkyl group in 1,2,3-trialkoxyphenyl derivatives may occur during Grignard synthesis by a similar mechanism.

Another route to aldehydes depends on displacement of the carbonyl group of p-dimethylaminobenzaldehyde, which reacts in the usual way to form a secondary alcohol

$$Me_2N—C_6H_4—CHO + R—MgBr \longrightarrow R—CH(OH)—C_6H_4—NMe_2$$

when this product reacts further with a diazonium salt aldehyde is formed; a suggested mechanism for this is:

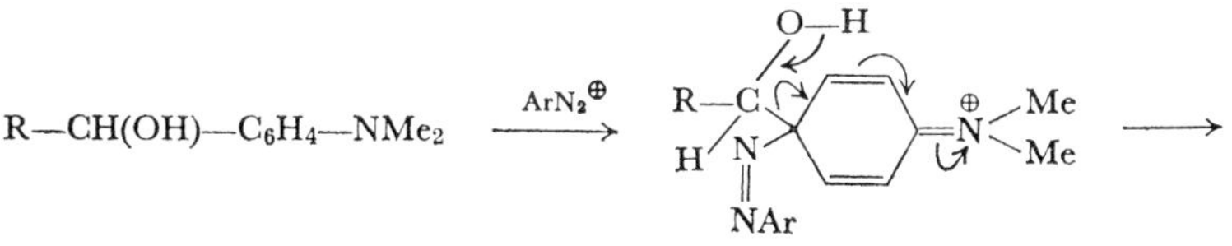

$$RCHO + ArN_2—C_6H_4—NMe_2$$

To keep the right perspective it must be noted that Grignard syntheses for aldehydes are of small weight when one considers all the available methods. An interesting route for the conversion of acid chlorides is:

$$Ph—CO—Cl \; Al^{\ominus}(Ot\text{-}Bu)_3H \longrightarrow Ph—CHO + Cl^{\ominus}$$

and a similar hydrogenolysis of esters has been mentioned above (p. 29).

Acid Chlorides react rapidly with Grignard reagents to yield tertiary alcohols, but the intermediate ketones can be isolated in good yield if cadmium alkyls are used:

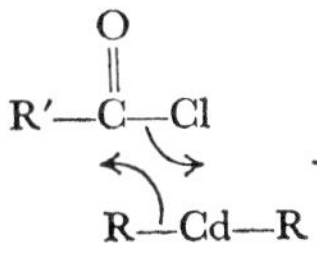

(Gilman and Nelson, 1936)

Following the exchange reaction with the Grignard (p. 12), and after completion has been established by a negative Gilman test (p. 26), the solvent is changed to an aromatic hydrocarbon. This solvent leads to precipitation of the ketone as an insoluble complex which helps to prevent the continuation of the reaction. Some examples of synthesis by this route follow:

$$n\text{-}Pr—CO—Cl + (i\text{-}Pr)_2Cd \longrightarrow n\text{-}Pr—CO—i\text{-}Pr \quad 60\%$$

$$EtO_2C—(CH_2)_8—CO—Cl + Me_2Cd \longrightarrow EtO_2C—(CH_2)_8—CO—Me \quad 84\%$$

35

The mechanism of reaction given above (Y) is evidently a simplification since cadmium and zinc alkyls purified by distillation do not react unless a Lewis acid such as magnesium bromide is added; fortunately this type of catalyst is formed during the preparation by exchange.

Nitriles provide an alternative and older route (Blaise, 1901) to ketones, which is preferred if the acid chloride is more difficult to obtain. A range of phenyl alkyl ketones has been prepared in yields of 70–90% by the addition of phenylmagnesium bromide:

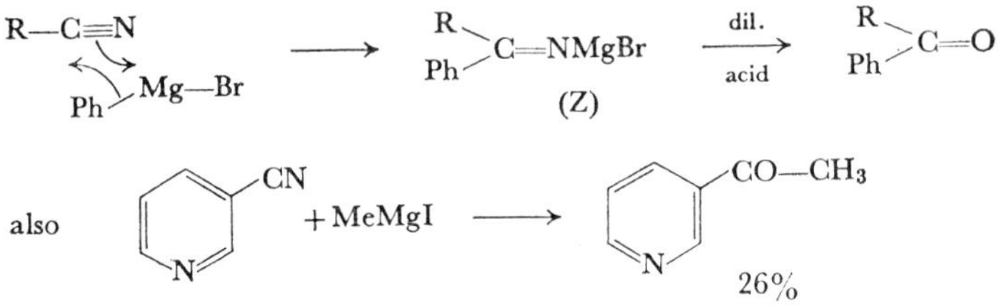

The rates of these reactions are very variable but are usually slower than those of carbonyl compounds. The reaction product (Z) which normally separates from ethereal solution is the magnesium derivative of a ketimine but the free ketimine will be liberated and hydrolysed to the ketone in dilute acid. Ketimines may be isolated from the products if the magnesium derivative is decomposed by ammonium chloride solution. The general superiority of lithium alkyls to Grignards in synthesis is particularly marked in this context:

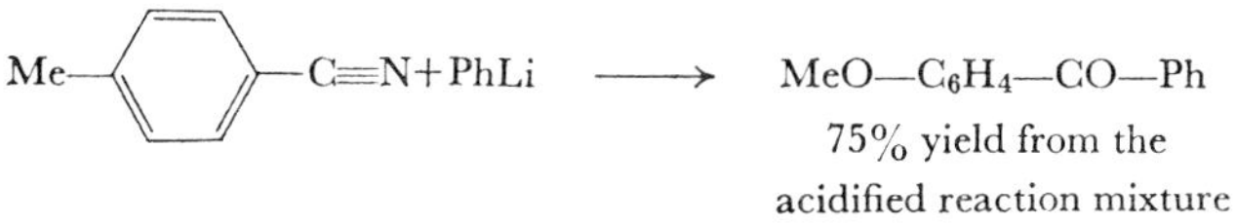

$$\text{Me}-\underset{}{\bigcirc}-\text{C}\equiv\text{N} + \text{PhLi} \longrightarrow \text{MeO}-\text{C}_6\text{H}_4-\text{CO}-\text{Ph}$$

75% yield from the
acidified reaction mixture

The addition of lithium alkyls to azomethines is a related reaction (cf. p. 134):

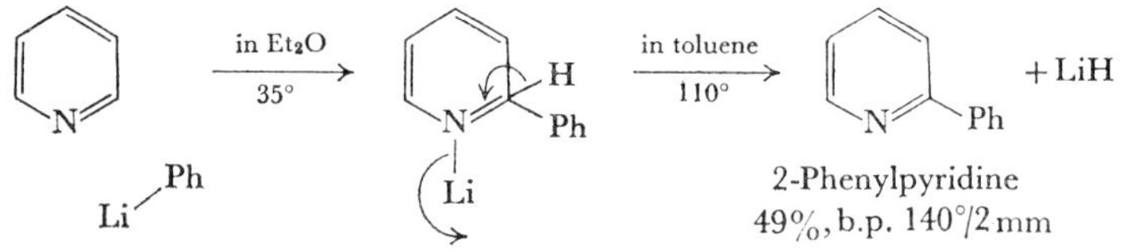

2-Phenylpyridine
49%, b.p. 140°/2 mm

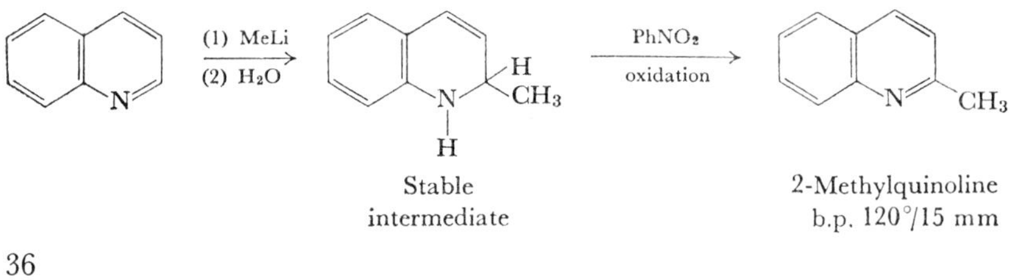

Stable
intermediate

2-Methylquinoline
b.p. 120°/15 mm

36

The Reformatsky Reaction (1887). This is a convenient method for extending a carbon chain by two units by the interaction of an aldehyde or ketone with the zinc derivative of an α-haloester.

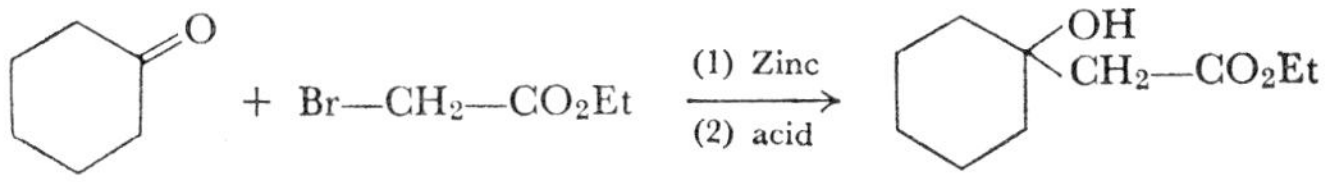

60%
Ethyl-1-hydroxycyclohexylacetate

Acid-washed zinc foil is satisfactory and the reaction is normally carried out in solvent (e.g. benzene). A portion of the solution of ester and carbonyl compound is added to the zinc and once reaction has started it is maintained by the controlled addition of the remainder. In this Grignard-type process addition of the mixed reagents and the use of zinc furthers the desired condensation and reduces the extent of reaction between the metal alkyl moiety and the ester function, although a certain proportion of high molecular weight products is inevitably formed by this side-reaction. Enolization (see p. 26) and coupling may also occur:

$$2\,BrCH_2{-}CO_2Et + Zn \longrightarrow \begin{matrix} CH_2{-}CO_2Et \\ | \\ CH_2{-}CO_2Et \end{matrix} + ZnBr_2$$

If the β-hydroxyester is required the zinc alkoxide must be decomposed with care to avoid the olefin-forming elimination (p. 26); 10% sulphuric acid at 0° generally meets this need. Should elimination occur under acid conditions then a mixture of position isomers is formed, the proportion of βγ-unsaturation varying with the conditions, e.g. when P_2O_5, $SOCl_2$, or a Brönsted acid is chosen as the catalyst, and is possibly the result of reaction under kinetic control:

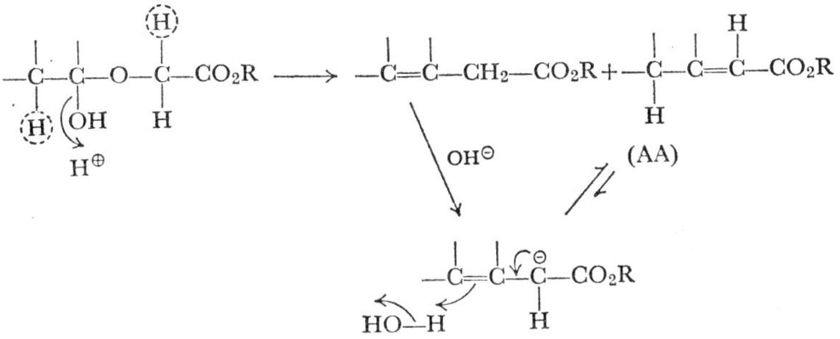

On treatment with bases and during hydrolysis a mixture of unsaturated esters undergoes equilibration by proton transfer affording the stable, conjugated product (AA) as the chief component.

The Reformatsky procedure is rather time-consuming and requires the initial preparation of the α-bromoacid bromide by the Hell, Volhard, Zelinsky route followed by alcoholysis:

$$R—CH_2—CO_2H \xrightarrow[Br_2/P]{} R—CHBr—CO—Br \xrightarrow[R—OH]{} R—CHBr—CO_2R$$

With bromine being preferred the method is costly. The Perkin reaction (p. 129) and Claisen condensation (p. 126) may often be used with advantage, the Reformatsky being reserved for carbonyl compounds having low reactivity to nucleophiles, e.g. acylbenzenes where only the combination of the potential carbanion and oxygen–metal complex formation is effective in driving the reaction to completion.

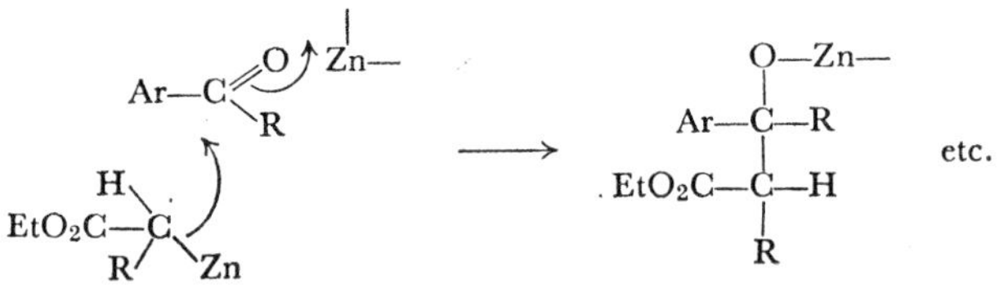

As the reactivity of the carbonyl compound to nucleophilic attack falls so it approaches that of the ester function; we expect therefore that self-condensation of the zinc derivative will be more extensive in this kind of system.

A recent variant of the Reformatsky reaction is the use of bromo-acetonitrile in the synthesis of unsaturated nitriles; older established is an extension due to Blaise (p. 36) for the preparation of β-ketoesters by addition of the zinc derivative to nitriles:

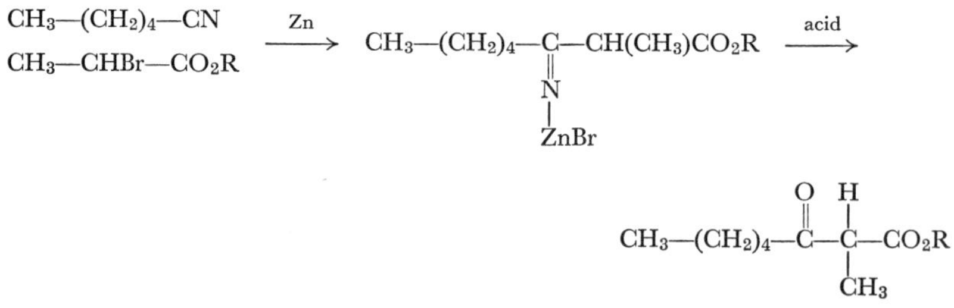

The use of the Reformatsky reaction for chain extension in the synthesis of precursors for vitamin A (cf. p. 58) with side-chain incorporation from metal alkyls is illustrated:

38

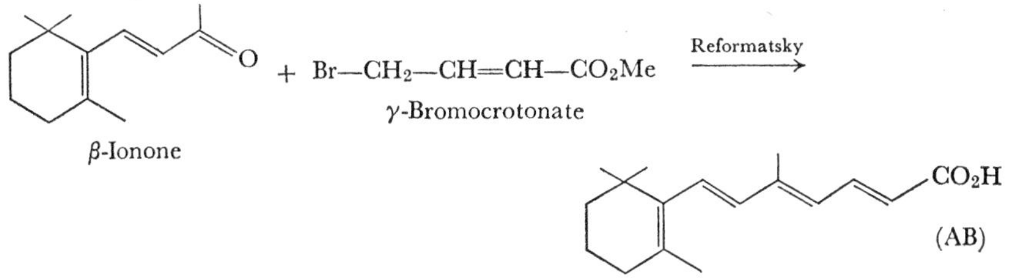
O
+ Br—CH₂—CH=CH—CO₂Me
γ-Bromocrotonate
Reformatsky
β-Ionone
CO₂H
(AB)

The overall yield of ketone (AC) on conversion of the acid (AB) to its chloride and reaction with ZnMeI was 45% compared to 22% with $CdMe_2$

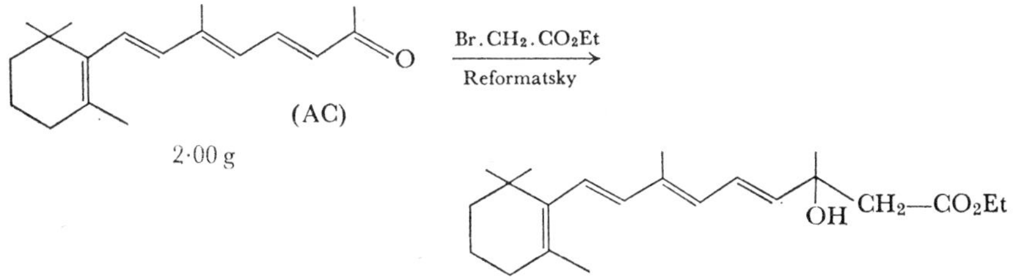
O
Br.CH₂.CO₂Et
Reformatsky
(AC)
2·00 g
OH
CH₂—CO₂Et

0·65 g., b.p. 140°/0·001 mm

Derivatives of Vinyl Halides. It is not possible to obtain satisfactory yields of Grignard reagents from these compounds in ether because olefins and acetylenes are formed by an elimination which probably follows the course:

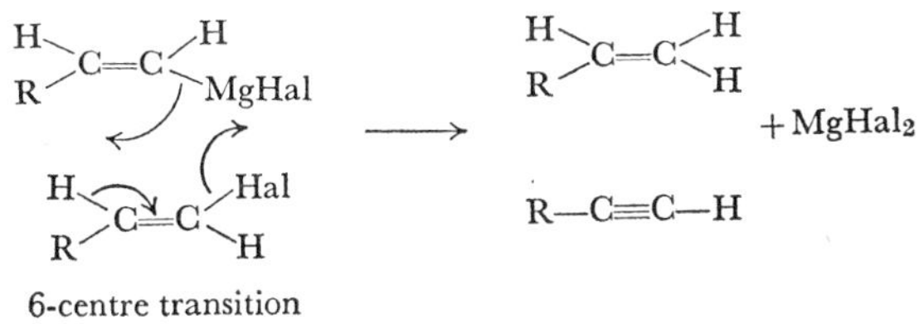
H
R
C=C
H
MgHal
H
R
C=C
Hal
H
6-centre transition
H
R
C=C
H
H
+MgHal₂
R—C≡C—H

This reaction is related to the familiar olefin-forming elimination which follows treatment of *vic*-dibromides with zinc and is also observed in their reaction with magnesium:

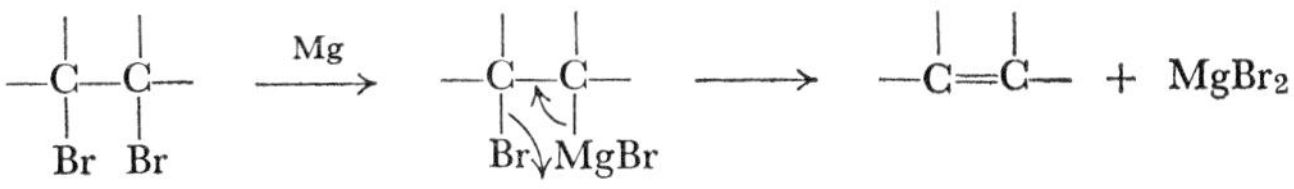
—C—C—
Br Br
Mg
—C—C—
Br MgBr
—C=C— + MgBr₂

Losses in Wurtz reactions of allylic halides may also be rationalized by a mechanism of this kind.

Considerable success in formation of derivatives of vinyl halides was achieved by Braude (1950) who employed lithium metal (see p. 10), but a great improvement of the Grignard method using tetrahydrofuran as a solvent was discovered by Normant in 1953 and has become more important. Normant's method is best applied to vinylic bromides, for although successful for aryl chlorides and vinyl chloride it fails for many alkenylchlorides where the lithio derivatives are still preferred.

Tetrahydrofuran is a stronger base than diethyl ether and will more readily solvate and dissolve vinylmagnesium halides formed on the metal surface under the usual conditions, and so clear solutions of the Grignard compounds are formed. It should be recalled that dioxan, a still more basic ether, disturbs the equilibrium by solvation of magnesium bromide with precipitation of its etherate. The other reaction conditions are very similar to the normal Grignard but the following detailed differences are significant:

(*a*) The Grignard complex may separate from solution on cooling.

(*b*) Working up is best effected in saturated ammonium chloride solution to avoid elimination

$$R—O—MgHal + NH_4Cl \longrightarrow R—OH + NH_3 + MgHalCl$$

(*c*) Tetrahydrofuran (b.p. 66°), although water soluble, may be extracted (e.g. by ether) with the reaction product and if this leads to difficulty in separation another ether may be used to prepare the Grignard: diethyl diethylene glycol, b.p. 162°, is often used.

Substitution of diethyl ether by tetrahydrofuran or other ethers of comparable base strengths is rarely of advantage in the preparation of saturated alkylmagnesium halides and may lead to reduced yields because of a greater tendency to Wurtz coupling.

An interesting feature of nucleophilic substitution at unsaturated centres which is not fully understood is that reaction proceeds with retention of configuration and the same behaviour is found in the formation of vinylmagnesium halides and vinyl lithium compounds, for example:

The *trans* series react similarly, also with retention of configuration.

40

The carbonation illustrated above is general for vinyl Grignards and one expects that they would undergo the same range of reactions as their saturated analogues, although up to the present time only some of these possible applications have been fully explored. Some of the more important reactions are discussed in the sequel.

Application of Vinylmagnesium Halides. αβ-Dihalogenoethers are accessible:

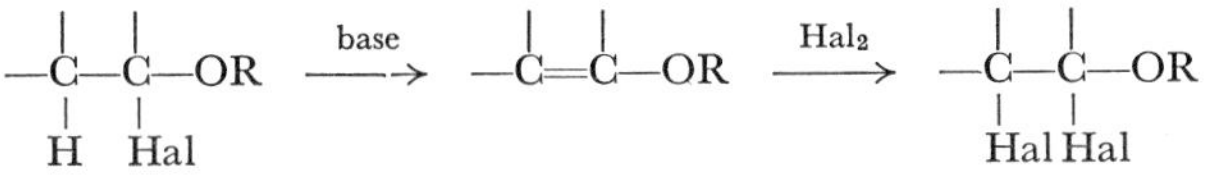

$$-\overset{|}{\underset{\underset{H}{|}}{C}}-\overset{|}{\underset{\underset{Hal}{|}}{C}}-OR \xrightarrow{\text{base}} -\overset{|}{C}=\overset{|}{\underset{\underset{}{|}}{C}}-OR \xrightarrow{\text{Hal}_2} -\overset{|}{\underset{\underset{Hal}{|}}{C}}-\overset{|}{\underset{\underset{Hal}{|}}{C}}-OR$$

and react with the Grignard at the α-carbon

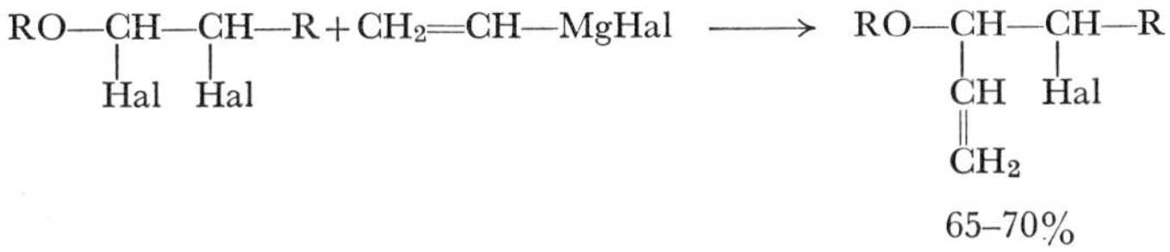

$$RO-\overset{|}{\underset{\underset{Hal}{|}}{CH}}-\overset{|}{\underset{\underset{Hal}{|}}{CH}}-R + CH_2{=}CH-MgHal \longrightarrow RO-\overset{|}{\underset{\underset{\overset{CH}{\underset{\parallel}{CH_2}}}{|}}{CH}}-\overset{|}{\underset{\underset{Hal}{|}}{CH}}-R$$

65–70%

two subsequent reactions are now possible:

(1) Olefin-forming elimination by action of zinc/alcohol or powdered sodium/tetrahydrofuran affording conjugated dienes (cf. p. 39).
(2) Elimination induced by alkali hydroxide/alcohol affording alkoxydienes

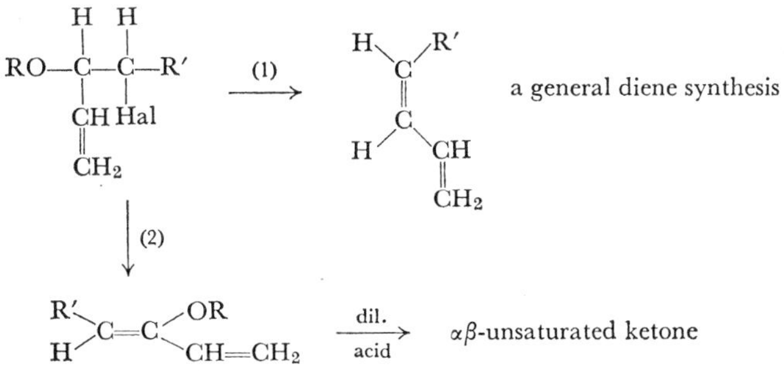

$$RO-\overset{\overset{\displaystyle H}{|}}{\underset{\underset{\overset{CH}{\underset{\parallel}{CH_2}}}{|}}{C}}-\overset{\overset{\displaystyle H}{|}}{\underset{\underset{Hal}{|}}{C}}-R' \xrightarrow{\;(1)\;} \begin{array}{c} H{\diagdown}\quad{\diagup}R' \\ C \\ \parallel \\ C \\ H{\diagup}\;{\diagdown}CH \\ \parallel \\ CH_2 \end{array}$$ a general diene synthesis

$$\Big\downarrow (2)$$

$$\begin{array}{c} R'{\diagdown}\qquad{\diagup}OR \\ C{=}C \\ H{\diagup}\qquad{\diagdown}CH{=}CH_2 \end{array} \xrightarrow[\text{acid}]{\text{dil.}} \alpha\beta\text{-unsaturated ketone}$$

Further development by Diels–Alder addition may yield saturated cyclic ketones.

Conjugated dienones may be derived from 1,3-diketones provided their enolization is blocked by protection of one carbonyl group as the monoacetal or an enol-ether:

4

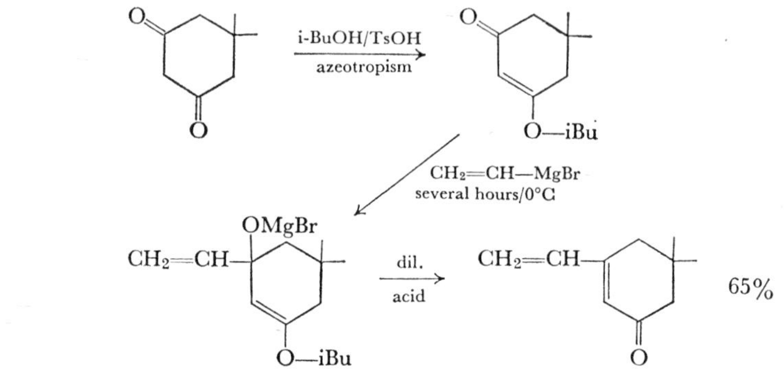

Addition of Metal Alkyls to Alkenes. The addition of alkali alkyls to reactive alkenes such as styrene and butadiene was discovered by Ziegler in 1929. Lithium alkyls are particularly effective because the metal has a higher complexing power than sodium or potassium and ethylene is polymerized, as in the reaction with lithium propyl:

$$\begin{matrix} Li—Pr \\ CH_2{=}CH_2 \end{matrix} \longrightarrow Li—CH_2—CH_2—Pr \xrightarrow[(n-1)C_2H_4]{} Li—(CH_2—CH_2)_n—Pr$$

This experiment was conducted at high pressure in ether by Ziegler and Gellert and the products were confirmed by reaction with paraform-aldehyde and isolation of the alcohols in the range $C_6 \rightarrow C_{12}$ where *n* was $1 \rightarrow 4$.

Aluminium alkyls are used to promote polymerizations of this type, since they are readily available to industry and expensive ethereal solvents are not required. Indeed, undiluted aluminium alkyls react more readily because the affinity of the aluminium atom for π-electrons, on which reaction depends, is reduced by solvation with ether molecules; lithium alkyls also react more readily in the absence of ethers.

Aluminium trialkyls react with aluminium and hydrogen to give dialkylaluminium hydrides:

$$4AlEt_3 + 2Al + 3H_2 \xrightarrow[120°]{} 6Et_2AlH \quad (AD)$$

which combine with alkenes:

$$Et_2AlH + CH_2{=}CH_2 \longrightarrow AlEt_3 \quad (AE)$$

and if aluminium triethyl from another source is used as an initiator the combination of ethylene, aluminium and hydrogen can be accomplished. The reaction (AE) must be carried out below the temperature required for the reaction (AD) if the object is the synthesis of aluminium triethyl

because at 120° this compound itself adds to alkenes as do the homologous aluminium alkyls and a 'growth reaction' can then occur:

$$CH_2{=}CH_2$$

$$Et_2Al{-}Et \longrightarrow Et_2Al{-}CH_2{-}CH_2{-}Et \xrightarrow[CH_2{=}CH_2]{} EtAl(CH_2{-}CH_2{-}Et)_2$$

(AF)   etc.

Heating an aluminium alkyl with an α-alkene can lead to a displacement reaction:

$$Al(CH_2{-}CH_2{-}R)_3 \longrightarrow HAl(CH_2{-}CH_2{-}R)_2 + R{-}CH{=}CH_2$$

$$\Big/ R'{-}CH{=}CH_2$$

$$R{-}(CH_2{-}CH_2)_2{-}Al{-}CH_2{-}CH_2{-}R'$$

which can go to completion and become preparative if an excess of a relatively involatile alkene displaces one of low boiling point: aluminium tri-isobutyl is often used in this way, elimination of the highly branched isobutylene being favoured (see p. 46). The synthetic applications of the growth reaction are more important; it predominates at high pressures when a large excess of alkene is confined in the system and chain lengthening occurs as in (AF) above:

$$Et_2Al{-}CH_2{-}CH_2{-}Et \xrightarrow{n\text{-}C_2H_4} Al \begin{matrix} {-}(CH_2{-}CH_2)_a{-}Et \\ {-}(CH_2{-}CH_2)_b{-}Et \\ {-}(CH_2{-}CH_2)_c{-}Et \end{matrix}$$

$$a+b+c = n+1$$

The molecular weight of the products can be controlled by time, thus after 3 hr at 110 atm and 100° the average molecular weight corresponds to $Al(C_4H_9)_3$. In this way paraffins with an even number of carbon atoms may be obtained within the range C4–C30, but beyond this point the formation of olefin by displacement begins to compete seriously with growth.

Synthesis of paraffins with an odd number of carbon atoms is also possible, not from aluminium trimethyl which is very unreactive, but from aluminium tripropyl:

$$Al(C_3H_7)_3 \xrightarrow{3n\text{-}C_2H_4} \text{n-}Al{-}(CH_2{-}CH_2{-}C_3H_7)_3$$

average composition

It is important here that the displacement reaction should be kept to a minimum because the rapid recombination

$$R_2AlH + CH_2{=}CH_2 \longrightarrow R_2Al{-}Et$$

leads to growth of 'even-numbered' products.

Dimerization in which the aluminium alkyl is formally catalytic was observed by Ziegler in 1952:

$$
\begin{array}{c}
-\overset{|}{Al}-PI- \\
\overset{\nwarrow\;\nearrow}{CH_2\!=\!CH\!-\!CH_3}
\end{array}
\longrightarrow
-\overset{|}{Al}-CH_2-\overset{\overset{\displaystyle H}{|}}{\underset{\underset{\displaystyle C_3H_7}{|}}{C}}-CH_3
\xrightarrow{\;C_3H_6\;}
\begin{array}{c}
CH_3-C\!=\!CH_2 \\
\overset{|}{C_3H_7} \\
+\;\overset{|}{\underset{\diagup}{Al}}-C_3H_7
\end{array}
$$

In the closed system at 200 atm loss of the more volatile alkene is not possible and replacement affords the more branched dimer at 200° (cf. butene). Ziegler discovered that this process is greatly accelerated by addition of Lewis acids to the reaction mixture, and polymerization occurs at about 1 atm in the temperature range 0–100°. The Ziegler catalysts are formed from aluminium alkyls and, most commonly, titanium tetrachloride, although the alkoxides and vanadium chlorides have been used. The mechanism is difficult to establish because most catalysts are insoluble in the hydrocarbon solvents (e.g. heptane) employed and the valency state of the metal is uncertain; titanium alkyls may be involved. The greater rate of reaction results from association between the π-electrons of the alkenes and the metal cation of the catalyst, leaving the alkene more open to attack by carbanion. One possible formulation would be:

$$
\begin{array}{c}
TiCl_4 \\
+\;AlR_3
\end{array}
\longrightarrow
Cl_3Ti^{IV}\!\!\diagdown\;\;\diagup^{Cl}\diagdown Al\diagup
$$

Early products of polymerization of propylene were oils in which the relative configuration of atoms in the chain was random—an atactic polymer. Alkenes polymerized by Ziegler catalysts have a high degree of symmetry, possibly because the large surface of the catalyst encourages

44

regular growth, and polypropylene is obtained as a crystalline isotactic polymer, m.p. 170°. The polymerization is therefore stereospecific and leads to identical configurations at all the tertiary carbon atoms.

ATACTIC
one of the
possible forms

ISOTACTIC

Alternation of configuration gives a syndiotactic polymer.

Boron Alkyls. The addition of diborane to alkenes is related to the reaction between aluminium hydride and alkenes. Hydroboration is however faster and is not restricted to terminal olefins:

$$3R—C\!\!=\!\!C\!\!<\; +BH_3(\text{as } B_2H_6) \longrightarrow \left(R—\underset{|}{\overset{H}{C}}—\underset{|}{\overset{|}{C}}\right)_3 —B$$

Moreover the boron alkyls are more stable to water and air than their aluminium analogues and handling techniques similar to those used for Grignard's are satisfactory. Tri-n-butyl-borane and higher alkyls do not inflame in air.

Hydroboration is an important preparative method for boron alkyls; a convenient procedure is addition of alkene to diborane generated from boron trifluoride etherate and borohydride:

$$12R—CH\!\!=\!\!CH_2+4BF_3.Et_2O+3NaBH_4 \longrightarrow 4(R—CH_2—CH_2)_3B+3NaBF_4+4Et_2O$$

Diethyleneglycol dimethyl ether (diglyme, b.p. 162°) is a good solvent for the borohydride and is usually chosen. After dilution with water products may be obtained by ether extraction. Diborane may be generated *ex situ* from these reagents and streamed into the olefin, which is usually diluted with tetrahydrofuran as diborane has a high solubility in this ether.

There is no growth reaction between alkylboranes and alkenes analogous to that of aluminium alkyls but displacement is observed and has preparative uses:

$$3C_8H_{17}—CH\!\!=\!\!CH_2+(n\text{-}C_5H_{11})_3B \xrightarrow{160°} C_3H_7\overset{\uparrow}{—}CH\!\!=\!\!CH_2+(n\text{-}C_{10}H_{11})_3B$$

1-Decene   1-Pentene

45

Addition of boron hydrides to olefins goes through a reversible four-centre addition:

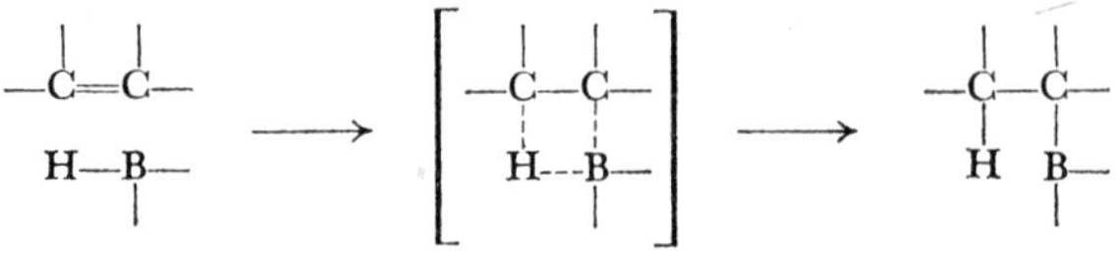

and in the above reaction decene and pentene are in competition, the equilibrium being displaced in favour of decylborane formation by removal of the more volatile pentene; this is strictly hydride donation not carbanion donation. If equilibrium is established in a closed system between two alkenes and diborane the more thermodynamically stable alkene will predominate, whilst the major boron alkyl will have boron bonded at a terminal position. The relative ease of displacement of olefins is:

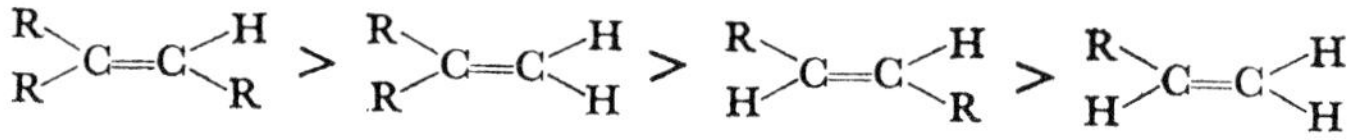

and the facile elimination of isobutylene from aluminium isobutyl is also rationalized.

An important consequence of the reversibility of boron hydride addition to alkenes is that contra-thermodynamic shifts of double bonds can be accomplished by heating the substrate with an excess of boron hydride in a high boiling ether:

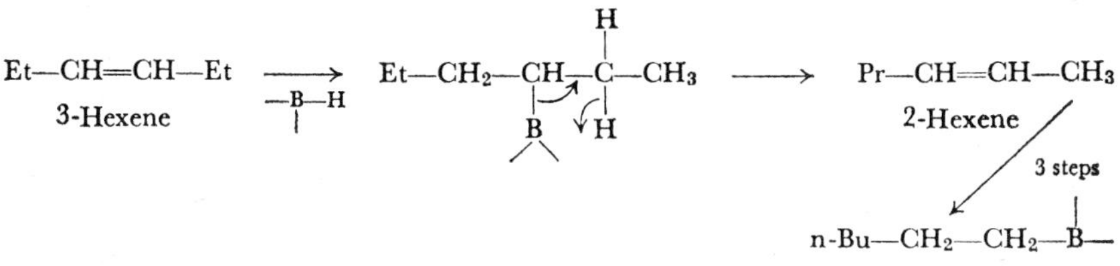

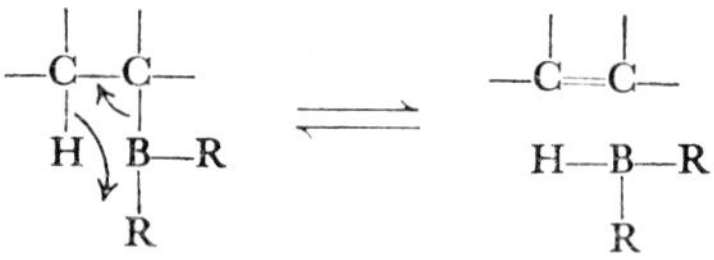

90% conversion to the 1-hexylboron derivative occurs at $150°$. Isomerization is faster than displacement because it is catalysed by the excess of alkyl boron hydride; no such excess is possible in the presence of free alkene and the rate of a displacement is governed by the slower reversal of the last stage of hydroboration. The terminal olefin may be liberated by distillation from an excess of a higher boiling olefin, e.g. 1-decene, when a simple displacement will occur.

Derivatives of unstable exocyclic olefins may also be obtained from their endocyclic isomers:

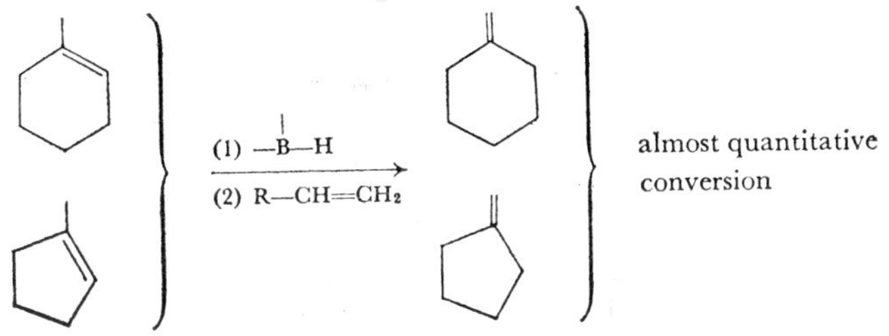

(1) —B—H
(2) R—CH=CH₂

almost quantitative conversion

Hydrogenation of olefins without use of a surface-active catalyst is possible by decomposition of boron alkyls by refluxing their solution in diglyme, or triglyme, b.p. 216°, with a carboxylic acid:

$$R-CH=CH_2 \xrightarrow[\substack{| \\ -B-H}]{} R-CH_2-CH_2-B- \xrightarrow[R-CO_2H]{} R-CH_2-CH_3$$

Coupling Reactions have been shown to be common in metal alkyl chemistry, but since few useful syntheses have been derived from them, a reference to the fruitful coupling reaction which is possible with boron alkyls concludes this section.

Olefins may be coupled by hydroboration and destruction of excess hydride by the addition of water to the solution (in diglyme) which is then made alkaline and silver nitrate solution added. After stirring at room temperature for about an hour the coupled product may be extracted by a hydrocarbon solvent:

$$2n\text{-}C_4H_9-CH=CH_2 \longrightarrow n\text{-}C_{12}H_{26}$$
Dodecane, 66%

Yields are generally better for the less-hindered olefins. Crossed coupling between two different olefins may be useful particularly as the statistical yield of 50% may be increased by an excess of the more accessible component:

$$4R_1-CH=CH_2 + 4R_2-CH=CH_2 \longrightarrow \substack{2R_1-(CH_2)_4-R_2 \\ R_1-(CH_2)_4-R_1 \\ R_2-(CH_2)_4-R_2}$$

This reaction, catalysed by silver oxide and hydroxide ion, is evidently a coupling of alkyl radicals present in high concentration and probably

47

derived from the intermediate unstable silver alkyls. Addition of carbon tetrachloride leads to capture of chlorine and formation of alkylchlorides whilst free radical acceptors, e.g. styrene, inhibit the coupling reaction. The potentialities of this reaction lie in the stability of a number of functional groups, including esters and acetals, under hydroboration conditions. In general the rate of reaction of functional groups with diborane is in the order:

$$-CO_2H > \underset{H}{-\overset{|}{C}}{=}\overset{|}{C}- > \underset{R}{R-\overset{|}{C}}{=}O > R-\overset{|}{C}{=}O > -C{\equiv}N > \underset{O}{-\overset{|}{C}}{-}Cl$$

Further Reading

GENERAL

G. E. COATES, *Organometallic Compounds*. Methuen, London, 2nd edit., 1960.

J. EISCH and H. GILMAN, *Adv. Inorg. Chem. Radiochem.*, 1960, **2**, 61.

J. H. HARWOOD, *Industrial Applications of the Organometallic Compounds*. Chapman and Hall, London, 1963.

D. T. HURD, E. G. ROCHOW and R. N. LEWIS, *The Chemistry of Organometallic Compounds*. Reinhold, New York, 2nd edit., 1964.

M. KHARASCH and O. REINMUTH, *Grignard Reactions of Non-metallic Substances*. Prentice-Hall, New York, 1954.

D. SEYFERTH and R. B. KING, *Annual Survey of Organometallic Chemistry*, Vol. 1. Elsevier, London, 1965.

H. ZEISS (edit.), *Organometallic Chemistry*. Reinhold, New York, 1960.

TOPICS

C. E. H. BAWN and A. LEDWITH, *Quart. Rev.*, 1962, **16**, 361 (stereoregular polymerization).

E. A. BRAUDE, *Progr. Org. Chem.*, 1955, **3**, 172 (lithium alkyls).

W. COOPER, *Progr. High Polymers*, 1961, **1**, 281 (stereoregular polymerization etc.).

H. D. KAESZ, *J. Chem. Educ.*, 1963, **40**, 159 (transition metal derivatives).

H. NORMANT, *Adv. Org. Chem.*, 1960, **2**, 1 (vinyl Grignards).

M. SCHLOSSER, *Angew. Chem.*, Intern. Edit., 1964, **3**, 287 (sodium and potassium alkyls).

D. A. SHIRLEY, *Org. Reactions*, 1954, **8**, 28 (cadmium and zinc alkyls).

R. L. SHRINER, *Org. Reactions*, 1942, **1**, 1 (Reformatsky reaction).

U.S. INDUSTRIAL CHEMICALS CO., *Sodium Dispersions*.

G. ZWEIFEL and H. C. BROWN, *Org. Reactions*, 1963, **13**, 1 (hydroboration).

PROBLEMS

1. Suggest an order for the rate of formation of the Grignard derivatives of the following halides under comparable conditions:

Me—I   n-Bu—Cl   Ph—Cl   n-Bu—Br   s-Bu—Cl   Ph—CH₂—Cl

What changes could be made in the conditions to accelerate the rate of the slowest of these reactions?

Why are homologues of methyl iodide unsatisfactory precursors for the synthesis of lithium and magnesium alkyls?

2. Why is reduction of carbonyl compounds not observed with MeLi or MeMgI?

3. Write an ionic mechanism for the reaction:

$$PhCH_2—Mg—Cl + t\text{-}BuBr \longrightarrow Ph—CH_2—Br + t\text{-}BuMgCl$$

How would you confirm that exchange had occurred?

H. M. Walborsky and A. E. Young, *J. Amer. Chem. Soc.*, 1964, **86**, 3293.

4. Account for the following reactions:

(a)

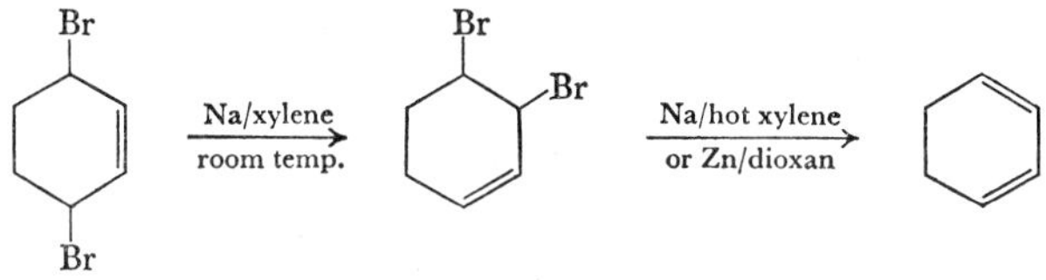

(b)

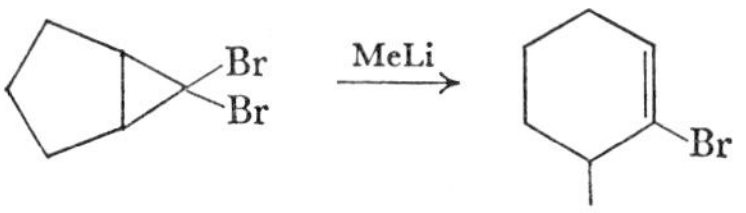

W. R. Moore and H. R. Ward, *Chem. and Ind.*, 1961, 594.

(c)

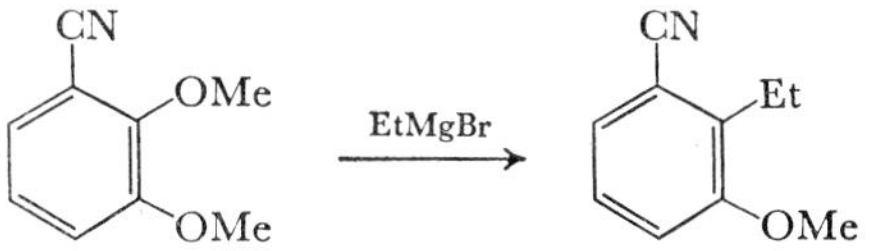

J. F. Bunnett and R. E. Zahler, *Chem. Rev.*, 1951, **49**, 286.

(d)

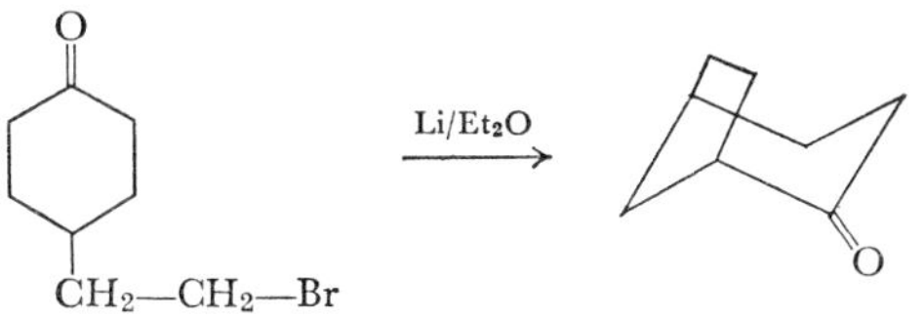

M. S. Newman and Y. T. Yu, *J. Amer. Chem. Soc.*, 1952, **74**, 507.

(e)

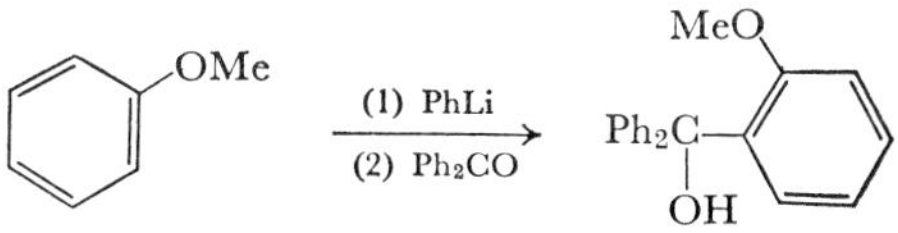

E. A. Braude, *Progr. Org. Chem.*, 1955, **3**, 202.

(f)

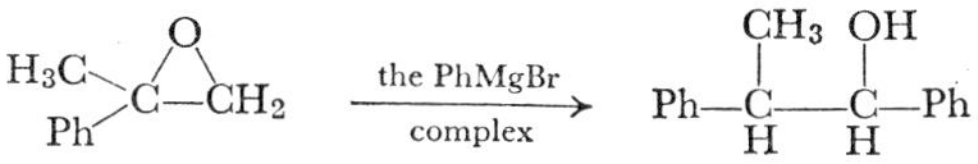

M. Kharasch and O. Reinmuth, *Grignard Reactions of Non-metallic Substances*, p. 965. Prentice-Hall, New York, 1954.

(g) $MeO—CH_2—Ph \xrightarrow{Ph—Li} Ph—CH(OH)—Me$ Wittig rearrangement.

49

Metal Alkyls

5. Predict the products of the following reactions:

(a) Addition of iodine to PhMgBr/Et$_2$O

(b)

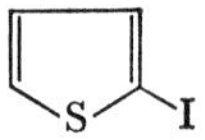

(1) Mg
(2) sulphur
(3) MeI

(c) (CH$_2$=CH)$_4$Sn + PhLi ⟶

D. Seyferth and M. A. Weiner, *Chem. and Ind.*, 1959, 402.

(d)

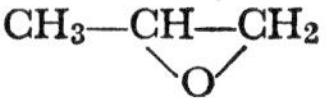

$$CH_3—CH—CH_2 \xrightarrow{\text{n-PrMgCl}}$$

M. Kharasch and O. Reinmuth, *Grignard Reactions of Non-metallic Substances*, p. 961. Prentice-Hall, New York, 1954.

(e)

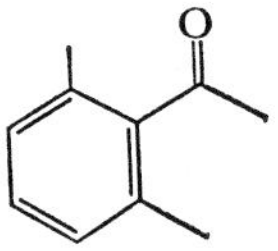

and MeMgI(IE)

L. H. Schwartzman and B. B. Corson, *J. Amer. Chem. Soc.*, 1954, **76**, 781.

(f)

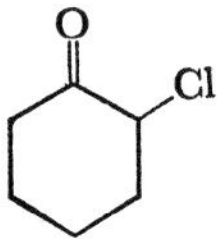

and t-BuMgCl

J. W. Cornforth, Mrs. R. H. Cornforth and K. K. Mathew, *J. Chem. Soc.*, **1959**, 114.

(g)

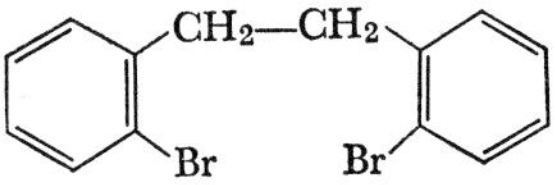

(1) BuLi
(2) (BuO)$_3$B ⟶

E. E. Van Tamelen, G. Brieyer and K. G. Untch, *Tetrahedron Letters*, 1960, No. 8, p. 14.

(h)

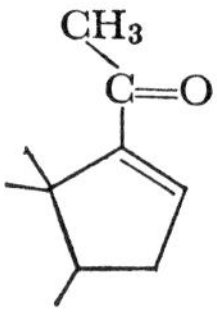

MeMgI/Et$_2$O/THF
+ cuprous chloride ⟶

K. Heusler *et al.*, *Helv. chim. Acta*, 1959, **42**, 2051.

(i)

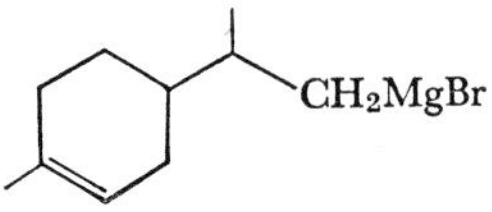

(1) (CH$_3$)$_2$C=CH—CN/benzene
(2) dil. acid

S. M. Mukerjee, *J. Indian C. S.*, 1948, **25**, 163.

50

6. Suggest syntheses for the following compounds:

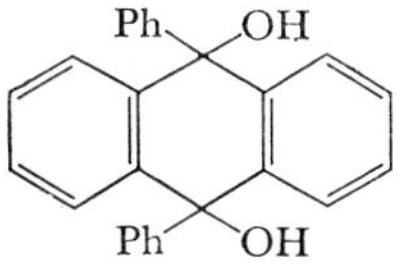

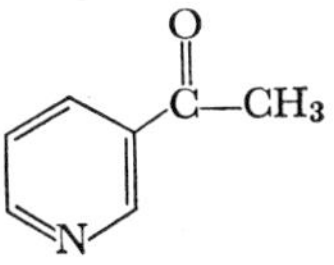

$CH_3—CH=CH—CO—CH_3$

e.g. H. Normant, *Adv. Org. Chem.*, 1960, **2**, 40.

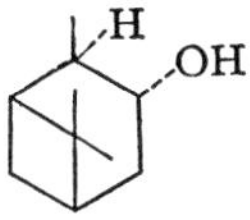

e.g. H. C. Brown and G. Zweifel, *J. Amer. Chem. Soc.*, 1961, **83**, 2544.

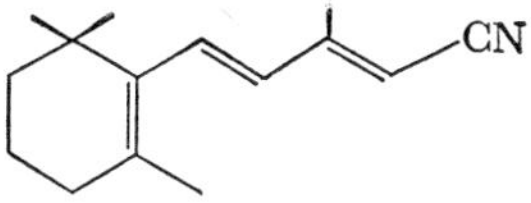

e.g. K. Eiter, E. Truscheit, and H. Oediger, *Angew. Chem.*, 1960, **72**, 951.

$ClCH_2—CH_2—C(OH)(n\text{-}Bu)_2$

Ch. Weizmann and E. Bergmann, *J. Chem. Soc.*, **1936**, 401.

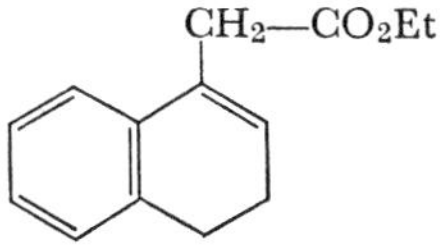

e.g. R. L. Shriner, *Org. Reactions*, 1942, **1**, 9.

$HO—C(Me)_2—C(Et)_2—OH$ Meerwein, *Annalen*, 1913, **396**, 200.

7. The hexameric form of LiEt in benzene solution is thought to have an octahedral structure. Draw a figure showing the most probable co-ordination pattern.

CHAPTER 3

METAL ACETYLIDES

Preparation. The acetylenes are strong acids on the hydrocarbon scale (p. 3) and on treatment with a Grignard reagent they undergo metathesis:

$$RC{\equiv}CH + R'MgX \longrightarrow RC{\equiv}CMgX + R'H{\uparrow}$$

The procedure most commonly used is the passage of acetylene into an ethereal solution of ethylmagnesium bromide, which affords the ether-insoluble acetylene dimagnesium bromide $BrMgC{\equiv}CMgBr$ and the equivalent of ethane is evolved. A solution of the acetylide can be obtained by changing the solvent to benzene or tetrahydrofuran, and in solution or as an oil it reacts with electrophilic reagents in a way that is closely analogous to the Grignard reagents themselves.

Acetylene monomagnesium bromide can be prepared by addition of ethylmagnesium bromide in small amounts to one equivalent of acetylene in tetrahydrofuran at about room temperature, but generally it has no advantage in use over the monosodium derivative which is the normal product of reaction of one equivalent of sodamide with acetylene or a monoalkyl acetylene. Sodium acetylide is obtained as a white suspension in liquid ammonia somewhat discoloured by the iron used to generate the base (see p. 177). As acetylene is a stronger acid than ammonia, hydrogen is evolved and the acetylide is formed when the gas is streamed into a solution of sodium in liquid ammonia (see p. 177) but some sodium remains unreacted and can cause side-reactions.

Some Reactions and Synthetic Applications of Acetylides. Haloacetylenes are formed by halogenation of the metal derivatives:

$$C_5H_{11}-C{\equiv}CMgBr + Br_2 \xrightarrow[-30°]{NH_3} C_5H_{11}-C{\equiv}C-Br + MgBr_2$$
b.p. 69°/25 mm, 70%

A better method is the conversion of the Grignard into the mercury acetylide with mercuric chloride and reaction of this with bromine in carbon tetrachloride. Ether is the solvent of choice for the reaction of chlorine with the acetylenic Grignard reagent.

The electronegativity of the acetylide carbon atom makes the displacement of a halide ion from haloacetylenes very difficult and net

52

substitution commonly follows an addition–elimination mechanism. This stabilization of negative charge makes the acetylides less reactive than other metal alkyls (p. 4), for example in solvents like benzene they react very sluggishly with alkyl halides although the sodio-derivatives are effective in liquid ammonia:

$$\text{n-BuBr} + \text{NaC}{\equiv}\text{CH} \xrightarrow[\text{(2) dil. HCl}]{\text{(1) NH}_3 \text{ reflux}} \text{n-BuC}{\equiv}\text{CH}$$

1-hexyne
b.p. 71°, 87%

Once the first alkylation is complete addition of another equivalent of sodium and another alkyl halide affords an unsymmetrical dialkyl acetylene without isolation of the monoalkyl compound; this procedure is inapplicable to the dimagnesium bromide. The lower reactivity in hydrocarbons, even with a favourable leaving group, is shown by the high temperature required for the second alkylation step conducted in toluene:

$$\text{Ph--C}{\equiv}\text{C--Na} + \text{n-Bu--OTs} \xrightarrow[80°]{3 \text{ hr}} \text{Ph--C}{\equiv}\text{C--Bu}$$

70%

The choice of liquid ammonia as solvent while accelerating metathesis has disadvantages in that branched-chain halides undergo base-catalysed elimination and yields are low for higher homologues of n-decyl halides, which have limited solubility. Loss by olefin formation from secondary halides can be reduced by working with lithium acetylides which are soluble in dioxan:

$$\text{n-C}_4\text{H}_9\text{--C}{\equiv}\text{CH} \xrightarrow[\text{(--NH}_3\text{)}]{\text{LiNH}_2/\text{dioxan}} \text{n-C}_4\text{H}_9\text{--C}{\equiv}\text{C--Li} \xrightarrow{\text{CH}_3\text{CHBr--CO}_2\text{Et (0·44 mol)}}$$

$$\overset{\displaystyle \text{OH}}{\underset{\displaystyle \text{C}_6\text{H}_9}{\text{C}_6\text{H}_9\text{--C--CHBr--CH}_3}}$$

b.p. 115°/0·4 mm, 90%

Insolubility in ammonia may be overcome by the use of dimethyl-formamide as a co-solvent:

$$\text{n-C}_{18}\text{H}_{37}\text{--Br} + \text{NaC}{\equiv}\text{CH} \xrightarrow{\text{DMF}} \text{C}_{18}\text{H}_{37}\text{--C}{\equiv}\text{CH}$$

Stearyl bromide

n-Eicosyne-1
b.p. 135°/0·2 mm, 75%

53

Stereoselective synthesis of olefins is possible from dialkylacetylenes which yield *cis*-olefins following their adsorption on the surface of a metal catalyst and addition of two hydrogen atoms to the same side of the molecule. A series of *cis*-unsaturated acids of possible dietary importance in mammals were prepared by Baker and Gunstone:

$$\text{n-}C_5H_{11}\text{—}C\equiv CH \xrightarrow[\text{I—(CH}_2)_6\text{—Cl}]{\text{NaNH}_2} C_5H_{11}\text{—}C\equiv C\text{—(CH}_2)_6\text{—Cl}$$

(1) NaCN/NaI
(2) KOH hydrolysis

$$\textit{cis}\text{-tetradec-8-eonic acid} \xleftarrow[\text{catalyst}]{H_2} C_5H_{11}\text{—}C\equiv C\text{—(CH}_2)_6\text{—}CO_2H$$

Tetradec-8-ynoic acid, 80%

(A)

Small amounts of *trans*-alkenes can be estimated from their clearly resolved infrared absorption at 970 cm^{-1} due to C—H deformation at the double bond.

The use of 1-chloro-6-iodohexane illustrates a method of elaborating a carbon skeleton to produce an unsymmetrical product. A special catalyst (A) was needed because one of normal activity would cause some hydrogenation of the double bond in the required product; with Lindlar's catalyst (palladium on calcium carbonate partially poisoned by a lead salt) the rate of both hydrogenation steps is slower, but the relative rate for the triple bond is increased and little reduction of olefin occurs if one equivalent of hydrogen is supplied. The small amount of *trans*-isomer isolated is typical and could result from addition of hydrogen in two steps with isomerization of the hemi-hydrogenated molecule on the catalyst:

Metal

cis-Addition of hydrogen is also possible by hydroboration (p. 47)

$$C_2H_5\text{—}C\equiv C\text{—}C_2H_5 \xrightarrow[\text{(B}_2\text{H}_6)]{BF_3/BH_4^{\ominus}/\text{diglyme}}$$

3-Hexyne

$$\underset{H}{C_2H_5}\!\!\diagdown C=C \diagup \!\!\overset{C_2H_5}{B\text{—}}$$

AcOH/0°   H$_2$O$_2$ | pH9

$$C_2H_5\text{—}CH=CH\text{—}C_2H_5 \qquad C_3H_7COC_2H_5$$
cis-3-hexene, 68%

where the alternative oxidative degradation (p. 23) affords a route to ketones. Aldehydes can be obtained from terminal acetylenes but modification is needed because diborane gives a twofold addition:

$$R-C\equiv CH \xrightarrow{B_2H_6} R-\underset{\underset{H}{|}}{\overset{\overset{H}{|}}{C}}-\underset{\underset{B<}{|}}{\overset{\overset{H}{|}}{C}}-B<$$

which is avoided by using a bulky dialkylborane:

$$2(CH_3)_2C=CHCH_3 \xrightarrow{B_2H_6} [(CH_3)_2CH-CH(CH_3)_2]BH$$
di-(3-methyl-2-butyl) borane

$$\searrow C_4H_9C\equiv CH$$

$$CH_3-(CH_2)_4-CHO \xleftarrow{H_2O_2} C_4H_9-CH=CH-B<\overset{R}{\underset{R}{}}$$
88%

Pure *trans*-olefins are obtained on reduction of an acetylene by a solution of a metal, usually sodium or lithium, in liquid ammonia. This process is comparable to Birch reduction (p. 176) and involves the addition of two electrons to the triple bond, where one recalls that the terminal atoms readily accumulate negative charge following nucleophilic attack, followed by abstraction of protons from the solvent:

$$R-C\equiv C-R \underset{\rightleftharpoons}{\xrightarrow{+2e}} \overset{H-NH_2}{\underset{R}{}}\overset{\ominus}{\underset{R}{C=C}}\overset{R}{\underset{\ominus}{}} H-NH_2 \longrightarrow \overset{H}{\underset{R}{}}C=C\overset{R}{\underset{H}{}} + 2NH_2^{\ominus}$$

Full electronic charges may not be developed at the ends of the bond before proton abstraction begins, but both carbon atoms must acquire substantial charge since reduction is complete in ammonia without the addition of a stronger acid (see p. 179) and this is consistent with maximum separation of charges leading to a *trans* relation between the added protons. In the following example the existing negative charge on the terminal function protects it from reduction by electron addition:

$$C_3H_7-C\equiv C-(CH_2)_4-C\equiv C^{\ominus}Na^{\oplus} \xrightarrow{\begin{array}{l}(1)\ Na/NH_3\\(2)\ NH_4Cl\\(3)\ Et_2O\ extn.\\ from\ aqueous\end{array}} \overset{C_3H_7}{\underset{H}{}}C=C\overset{H}{\underset{(CH_2)_4-C\equiv CH}{}}$$

undeca-7(*trans*)-en-1-yne
b.p. 74°/16 mm, 59%

55

Carbonation. $\alpha\beta$-Acetylenic acids are conveniently obtained by carbonation of metal acetylides. The sodio-derivatives are rather unreactive and lithium or Grignard compounds are preferable:

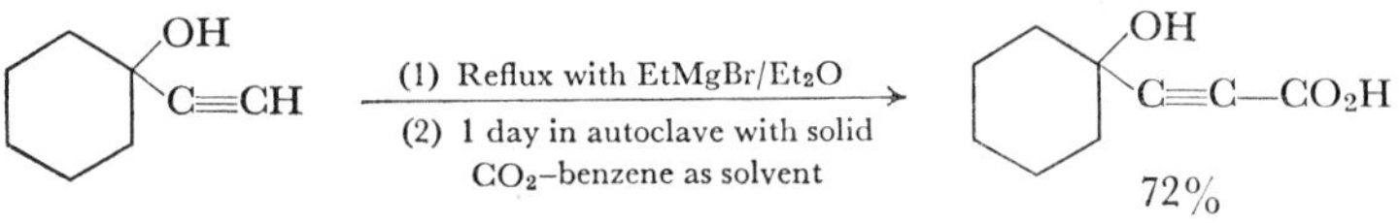

$$\underset{\text{(2) 1 day in autoclave with solid}}{\overset{\text{(1) Reflux with EtMgBr/Et}_2\text{O}}{\xrightarrow{\hspace{2cm}}}}$$
CO₂-benzene as solvent

72%

The further reaction of the metal carboxylate with the Grignard reagent to form a ketone and subsequent products is not a serious competitor here (cf. p. 31).

Allenic acids can be obtained from $\alpha\beta$-acetylenic acids which have a γ-hydrogen atom by treating them with sodamide/liquid ammonia:

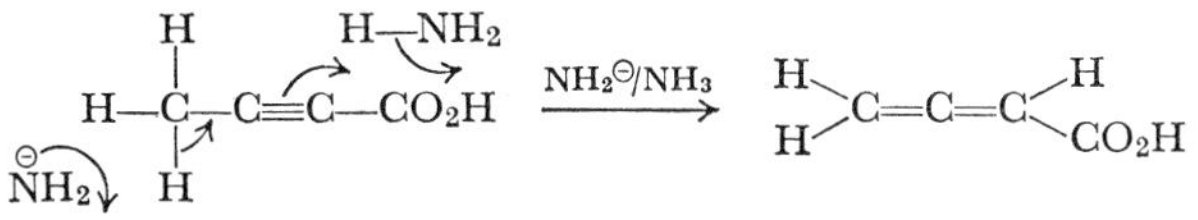

i/r peak at 2240 cm^{-1}

Tetrolic acid, m.p. 76°

i/r peaks 1950, 1970 cm^{-1}
no u/v absorption > 215 mμ

buta-2,3-dienoic acid, m.p. 66°

The reversal of this isomerization occurs when the antibiotic nemotinic acid (B) is converted into the more extensively conjugated isonemotinic acid (C) by dilute aqueous alkali:

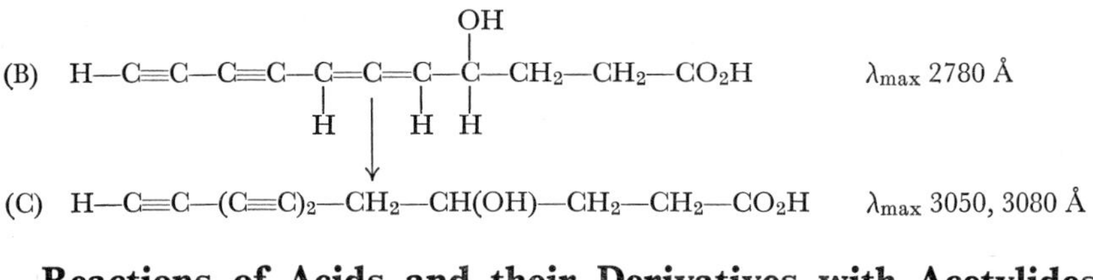

(B) $\quad$ H—C≡C—C≡C—C=C—C—$\overset{\text{OH}}{\underset{\text{H}}{\text{C}}}$—CH₂—CH₂—CO₂H $\qquad \lambda_{max}$ 2780 Å
$\qquad\qquad\qquad\quad \underset{\text{H}}{|} \quad \underset{\text{H}}{|}\ \underset{\text{H}}{|}$

(C) $\quad$ H—C≡C—(C≡C)₂—CH₂—CH(OH)—CH₂—CH₂—CO₂H $\qquad \lambda_{max}$ 3050, 3080 Å

Reactions of Acids and their Derivatives with Acetylides. There is no counterpart in this field to the important ketone synthesis from acid chlorides and cadmium alkyls (p. 35) since the exchange with cadmium chloride is unsuccessful. Silver acetylides have been used with some success in organic solvents using acid chlorides as starting materials; acid anhydrides also react at low temperatures with sodium acetylides and Grignards:

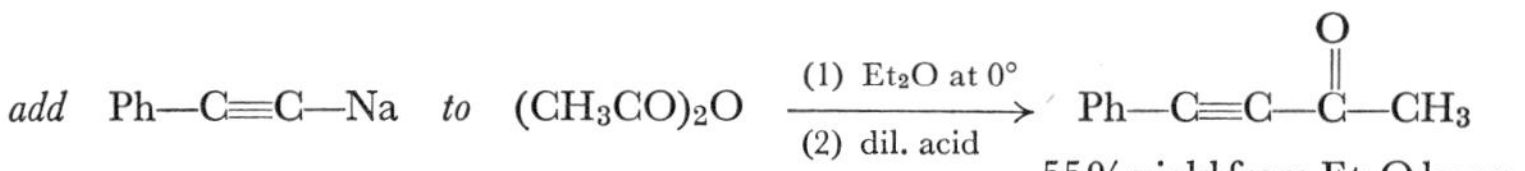

add $\quad$ Ph—C≡C—Na $\quad to \quad$ (CH₃CO)₂O $\xrightarrow[\text{(2) dil. acid}]{\text{(1) Et}_2\text{O at 0°}}$ Ph—C≡C—$\overset{\overset{\text{O}}{\|}}{\text{C}}$—CH₃

55% yield from Et₂O layer
b.p. 122°/14 mm

The tendency for the ketone to react with a further molecule of the acetylide is not so marked as with saturated alkyls (p. 24) indicating a lower reactivity in the acetylide. The most important method of ketone synthesis is by oxidation of the corresponding secondary alcohol (G below).

Acetylides react with orthoformates to give acetals (cf. p. 34):

$$HC{\equiv}C{-}CH_2CH_2{-}C{\equiv}CH \xrightarrow[\text{(2) EtI(I equiv.)/Et}_2\text{O}]{\text{(1) to sodio deriv.}} Et{-}C{\equiv}C{-}CH_2CH_2{-}C{\equiv}CH$$

(1) EtMgBr/Et₂O
(2) HC(OEt)₃ reflux in ether
(3) NH₄Cl/H₂O

$$Et{-}C{\equiv}C{-}CH_2CH_2{-}C{\equiv}C{-}CH(OEt)_2 \longleftarrow$$
2,6-Nonadiynal diethylacetal
b.p. 105°/0·03 mm, 81%

The free aldehyde is obtained on treatment with oxalic or tartaric acid, but the acetal group is frequently retained in order to protect the carbonyl group during subsequent steps in a series of reactions. Formates themselves are not generally useful because the carbonyl group of intermediate (D) is more reactive than in ketones (see above) and interacts with a second molecule of the Grignard:

$$R{-}C{\equiv}CMgBr + H.COEt \longrightarrow \left[R{-}C{\equiv}C{-}\underset{O}{\overset{}{C}}{-}H \right] \xrightarrow{R{-}C{\equiv}CMgBr}$$
(D)

$$R{-}C{\equiv}C{-}\underset{OH}{\overset{H}{C}}{-}C{\equiv}C{-}R$$
(E)

Penta-1,4-diyn-3-ol (E; R=H) is an important intermediate (see p. 60 for an example) obtained in 40% yield from ethyl formate and acetylene monomagnesium bromide.

Reactions with Aldehydes and Ketones. These are analogous to those of the simple Grignard compounds (p. 24) and the formation of alcohols by this route is of great importance:

$$CH_3{-}CH{=}CH{-}CHO + NaC{\equiv}CH \longrightarrow CH_3{-}CH{=}CH{-}\underset{H}{\overset{OH}{C}}{-}C{\equiv}CH$$
(F) (G)

(1) dissolve in acetone add CrO₃/dil.H₂SO₄ at 5°
(2) dilute with H₂O, ether extract

$$CH_3{-}CH{=}CH{-}CO{-}C{\equiv}CH$$
b.p. 76°/44 mm 79%

5

Oxidation of alcohols as in (G) above is easier when an aryl residue is substituted for the allyl group and is harder when a saturated residue replaces it. An alternative method of oxidation of acetylenic alcohols is the use of 'active' manganese dioxide in an organic solvent.

Many of the methods dependent on acetylides were developed by Heilbron and his school. An important synthesis was that of vitamin A by Isler (1947):

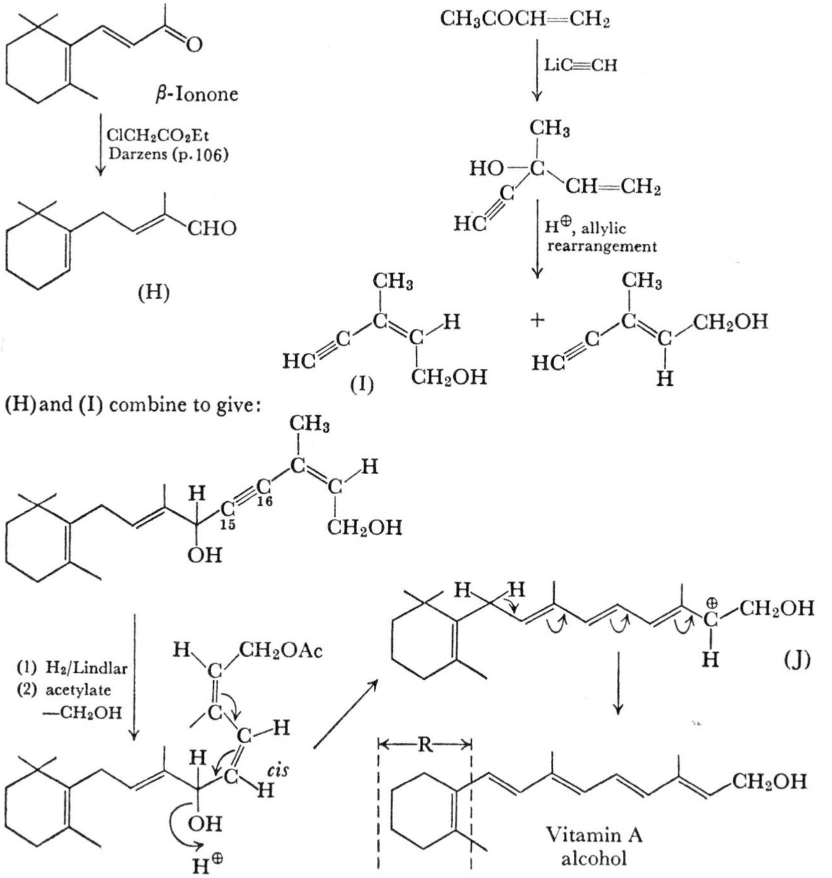

Here hemi-hydrogenation of the triple bond and elimination of water produces the required degree of unsaturation, whilst acetylation of the primary alcohol prevents its elimination and consequent shift of the unsaturated system so as to include the terminal carbon atom. Although *cis*-addition of hydrogen occurs at C_{15} and C_{16}, dehydration in acid affords the mesomeric carbonium ion which isomerizes with hydrolysis of the acetyl group to the more stable all *trans* product.

58

Carotenoids having forty carbon atoms can be synthesized by the use of acetylenic intermediates, for example, by reaction between acetylene and two 19C polyenealdehydes or from diacetylene and two 18C methyl ketones, which can themselves be obtained by procedures similar to those used for vitamin A.

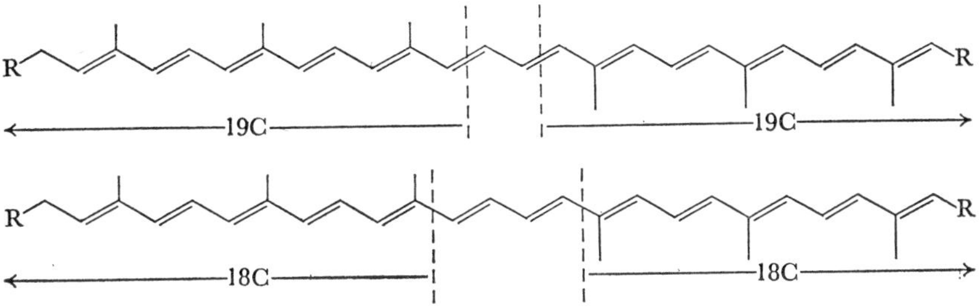

When larger central fragments of the molecule are assembled oxidative coupling of acetylenes (see p. 65) is of value:

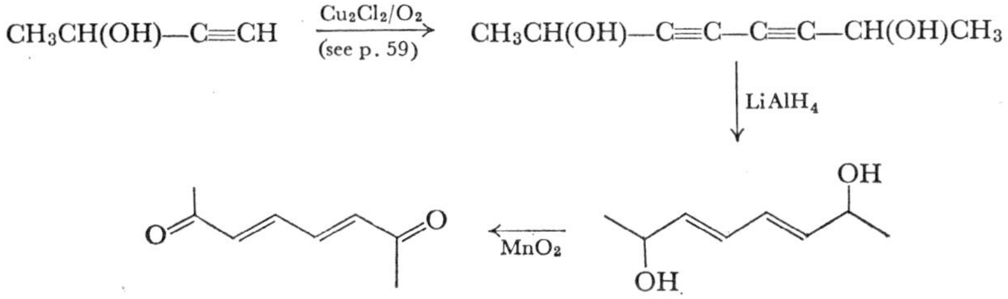

$$CH_3CH(OH)—C{\equiv}CH \xrightarrow[\text{(see p. 59)}]{Cu_2Cl_2/O_2} CH_3CH(OH)—C{\equiv}C—C{\equiv}C—CH(OH)CH_3$$

8C central fragment

The reduction of propargyl alcohols to allyl alcohols in this way is an alternative to Lindlar reduction and is complementary to it in that it gives *trans*-addition.

Wittig reagents (p. 112) are important in syntheses of this type; one example is the following variant on the route to vitamin A:

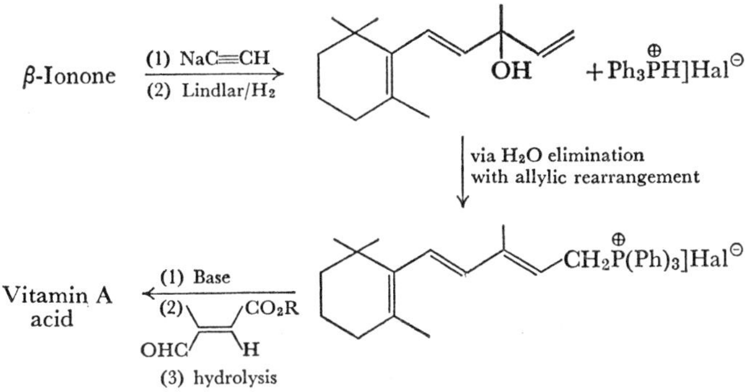

59

Polyacetylenes have been synthesized by the Oxford school; thus penta-1,4-diyn-3-ol (J) was converted into its Grignard derivative and combined with 6,6-dimethylhepta-2,4-diynal (K):

$$CH_3CH{=}CH{-}CHO \xrightarrow{\text{t-BuMgCl}} CH_3CH{=}CHCH(OH)\text{t-Bu}$$
(55 g)   (32·5 g)

(1) Br$_2$/CHCl$_3$
(2) NaNH$_2$/NH$_3$

$$\text{t-BuC}{\equiv}\text{C}{-}\text{C}{\equiv}\text{CCHO} \xleftarrow[\text{(2) HC(OEt)}_3]{\text{(1) EtMgBr}} \text{t-BuC}{\equiv}\text{C}{-}\text{C}{\equiv}\text{CH}$$
(K) b.p. 40°/0·2 mm, 3·3 g   5·5 g, b.p. 43°/50 mm.

(J) HC≡C—CH(OH)—C≡CH
as Grignard

$$\text{t-Bu(C}{\equiv}\text{C)}_2\text{CH(OH)C}{\equiv}\text{CCH(OH)C}{\equiv}\text{CH} \xrightarrow[\text{pyridine}]{\text{SOCl}_2} \text{t-Bu(C}{\equiv}\text{C)}_2{-}\overset{|}{\underset{|}{\text{C}}}{-}\text{C}{\equiv}\text{C}{-}\overset{|}{\underset{|}{\text{C}}}{-}\text{C}{\equiv}\text{C}$$

B$^\ominus$ H   H

Cl   Cl

2 elim. steps
catalysed by Al$_2$O$_3$

$$\text{t-Bu(C}{\equiv}\text{C)}_{10}\text{t-Bu} \xleftarrow{\text{couple}} \text{HC}{\equiv}\text{C(C}{\equiv}\text{C)}_4\text{t-Bu}$$
(L)

The pentayne (L) underwent oxidative coupling on treatment with cupric acetate/pyridine (p. 66) to give the decayne as an orange solid decomposing at 100°; its ultraviolet spectrum has a series of sharply resolved peaks in the range 2180–3200 Å and the molar extinction rises to 850,000. Polyacetylenes which lack bulky end groups polymerize rapidly when exposed to light; t-butyl groups cause a greater separation of the polyne chains in the crystal lattice and this would inhibit cross-linking.

The acetate unit is a common precursor for fatty acids and poly-acetylenes. The latter are probably intermediates in the biosynthesis of many naturally occurring thiophen and furan derivatives whose formation has been demonstrated *in vitro*, for example:

$$\text{Ph}{-}\text{(C}{\equiv}\text{C)}_2{-}\overset{cis}{\text{CH}{=}\text{CH}}{-}\text{CH}_2\text{OH} \xrightarrow{\text{OH}^\ominus} \text{Ph}{-}\text{C}{\equiv}\text{C}{-}\text{C}{\equiv}\text{C}{-}\text{C}$$

H—OH
H
O—CH$_2$
C—H

Ph—C≡C—CH$_2$— (furan ring with O)   ←   Ph—C≡C—CH=C—O—H   OH$^\ominus$

H
HO

Benzene rings can also be formed from polyacetylenes:

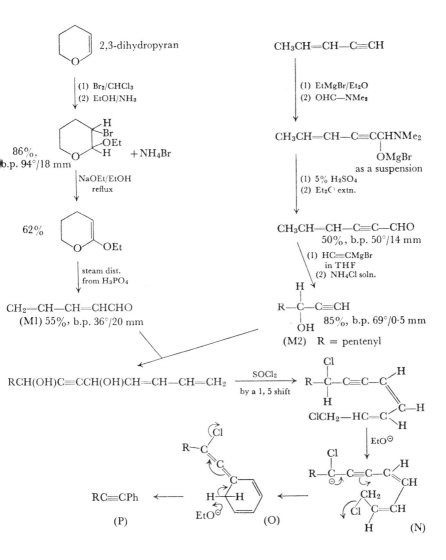

The conjugate base (N) is resonance stabilized but a small amount of the less-stable allenic intermediate (O) in equilibrium leads to formation of the most stable structure (P) with its benzene ring. Cyclization to the six-ring is preferred and should be contrasted with the behaviour of the linear precursor of (L) which must remain acyclic. A related route to benzene derivatives is the base-catalysed cyclization of diynes:

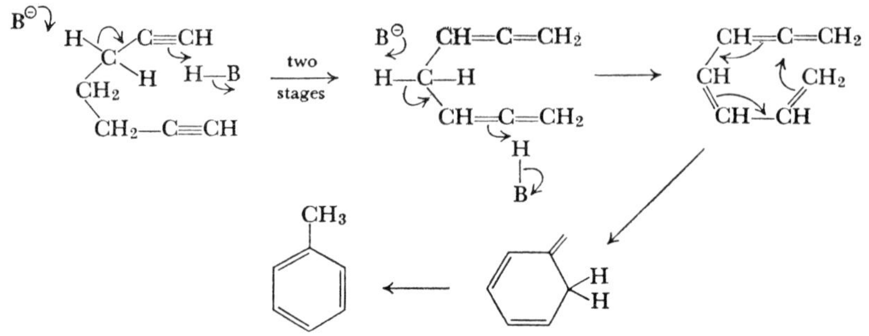

homologues tend to give *ortho*-substituted products. Formally charged acetylides are present in equilibrium but are not considered because the charge would inhibit the *assumed* movement of electrons.

Ethynyl Ethers. Ethoxyacetylene is most often used and it is prepared from chloroacetal by a one- or two-stage base-catalysed elimination:

First stage (Q)

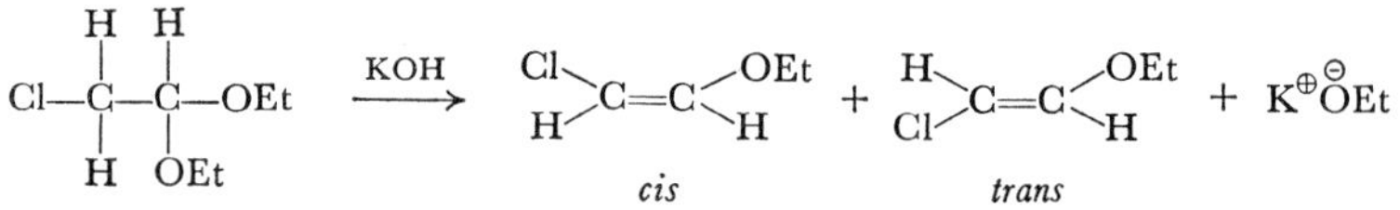

In the presence of hydroxide the second stage (R) only proceeds from the *cis*-isomer in the mixture, where the abstracted proton and the leaving chloride ion are *trans* related. Use of sodamide forces the elimination from the *trans*-isomer and it will therefore convert the chloroacetal

Second stage (R)

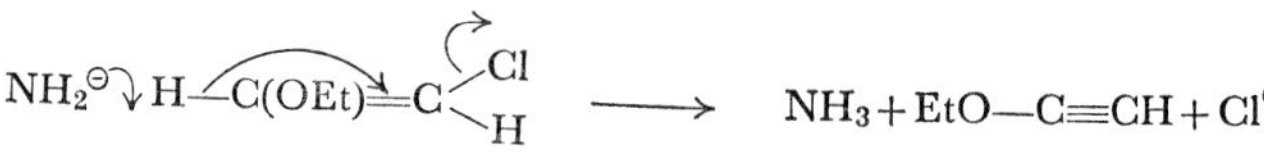

into ethoxyacetylene in one operation; the solution in liquid ammonia can be used directly but it will contain ethoxide ion formed in (Q). If the free base causes side-reactions these can be avoided by isolating the mixed ethyl β-chlorovinyl ethers and completing the elimination with one equivalent of sodamide. The ethynyl ethers can themselves be isolated by treatment of the residue from evaporation of ammonia with water or ammonium chloride solution; in an acid medium rapid solvolysis occurs:

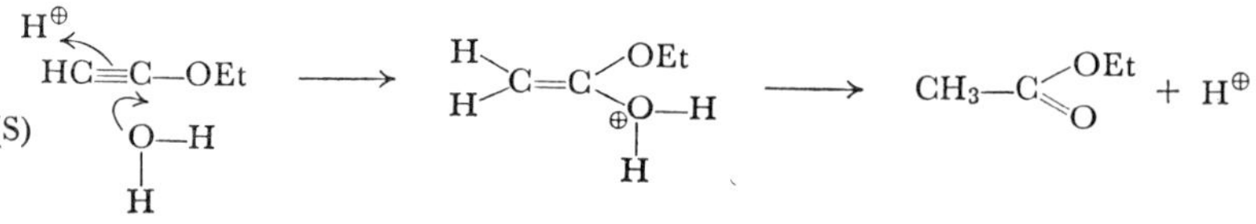

Ethoxyacetylene boils at 51° and the triple bond is characterized by an infrared band at 2150 cm^{-1}; it must be stored at 0° if it is to be kept for any length of time. A Grignard reagent is readily formed on treatment with ethylmagnesium bromide in ether and addition of benzene gives a more concentrated solution. The addition to carbonyl compounds occurs at room temperature and is of general application save that for aldehydes the lithium derivative in ether or sodium ethoxyacetylide in ammonia are preferred, since magnesium bromide in the Grignard equilibrium (p. 21) catalyses the further addition of aldehyde to the initial product (see Problem 2c).

The synthesis of citral affords an early example of ethoxyacetylene chemistry:

$$\text{Acetone} \xrightarrow{\text{NaC}\equiv\text{CH}} \underset{\text{H}_3\text{C}}{\overset{\text{H}_3\text{C}}{>}}\overset{\overset{\text{OH}}{|}}{\text{C}}\text{-C}\equiv\text{CH} \xrightarrow[\text{in H}_2\text{O}]{\text{Zn/Cu}} \underset{\text{H}_3\text{C}}{\overset{\text{H}_3\text{C}}{>}}\overset{\text{OH}}{\underset{\text{CH}=\text{CH}_2}{\text{C}}}$$

PBr$_3$

(1) CH$_3$.CO.CH$_2$.CO$_2$Et
NaOEt

(2) acetate fission in Ba(OH)$_2$

$$\underset{\text{H}_3\text{C}}{\overset{\text{H}_3\text{C}}{>}}\text{C}=\text{CH}-\text{CH}_2\text{Br}$$

By 1:2 shift

(1) EtO.C≡CMgBr   (2) NH$_4$Cl soln.

(1) H$_2$/Lindlar

(2) cold dil. HCl

73%, b.p. 80°/0·1 mm

68%

Citral isomers,
b.p. 115°/18 mm

This illustrates the use of the reagent as a potential enol-ether; other functional groups are obtained on modifying the final stages. Thus if a more active hydrogenation catalyst is used a saturated ether results, whilst decomposition in dilute aqueous acid gives an αβ-unsaturated ester (see structural formulae at top of p. 64).

The products sometimes include the corresponding β-hydroxyesters which are not themselves dehydrated under the conditions; they may be formed from the intermediate (T) by deprotonation and keto-enol tautomerism.

Ethoxyacetylene was used by Stork for the synthesis of *dl*-griseofulvin

63

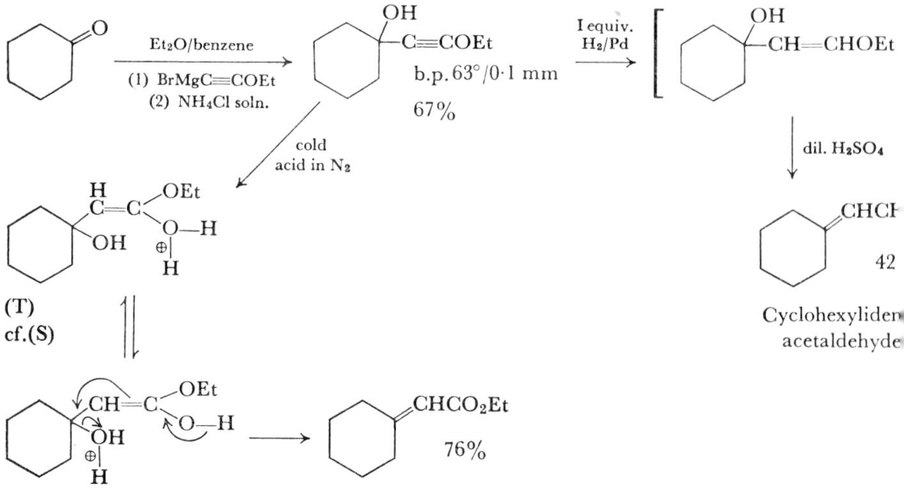

Et₂O/benzene
(1) BrMgC≡COEt
(2) NH₄Cl soln.

OH
—C≡COEt
b.p. 63°/0·1 mm
67%

1 equiv.
H₂/Pd

OH
—CH=CHOEt

dil. H₂SO₄

cold
acid in N₂

H   OEt
 C=C
      O—H
OH ⊕|
     H

(T)
cf.(S)

=CHCHO
42

Cyclohexyliden
acetaldehyde

CH=C—OEt
      O—H
OH
⊕|
H

=CHCO₂Et
76%

(X) the antifungal antibiotic. One principal precursor was the cou-maranone (U) which was prepared as follows:

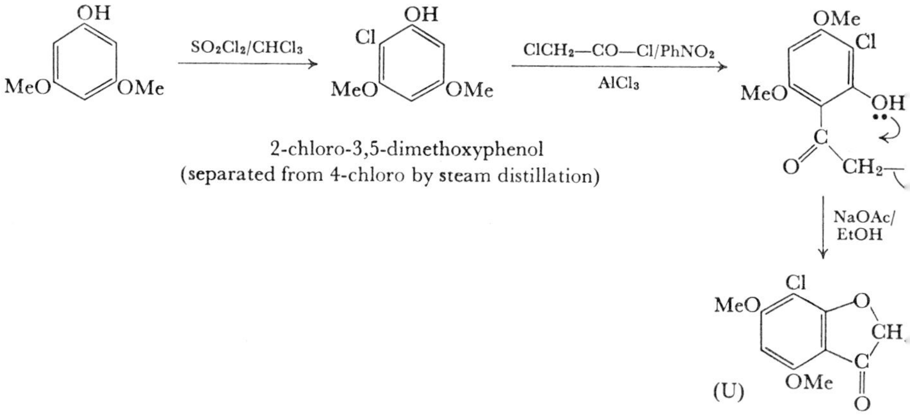

OH
MeO   OMe

SO₂Cl₂/CHCl₃

Cl   OH
MeO   OMe

2-chloro-3,5-dimethoxyphenol
(separated from 4-chloro by steam distillation)

ClCH₂—CO—Cl/PhNO₂
AlCl₃

OMe
        Cl
MeO
           OH
     C
   O   CH₂

NaOAc/
EtOH

Cl
MeO   O
             CH
        C
   OMe   ‖
          O

(U)

The other principal precursor was the alkoxyethynyl ketone (V):

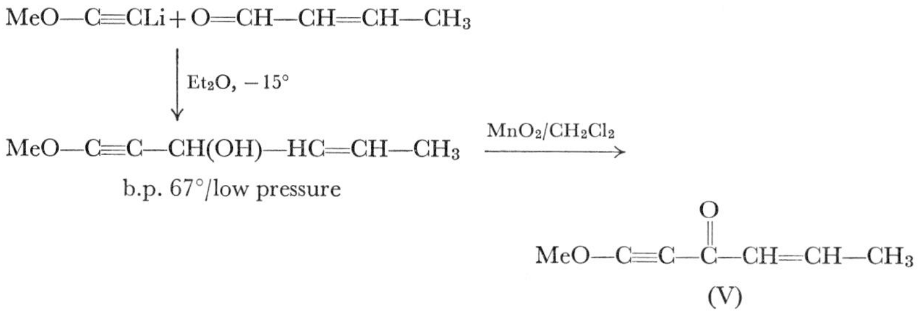

MeO—C≡CLi + O=CH—CH=CH—CH₃

Et₂O, −15°

MeO—C≡C—CH(OH)—HC=CH—CH₃
b.p. 67°/low pressure

MnO₂/CH₂Cl₂

                    O
                    ‖
MeO—C≡C—C—CH=CH—CH₃
                  (V)

Michael addition of the conjugate base of (U) to the unsaturated ketone (V) followed by a second intramolecular addition afforded griseofulvin in one step:

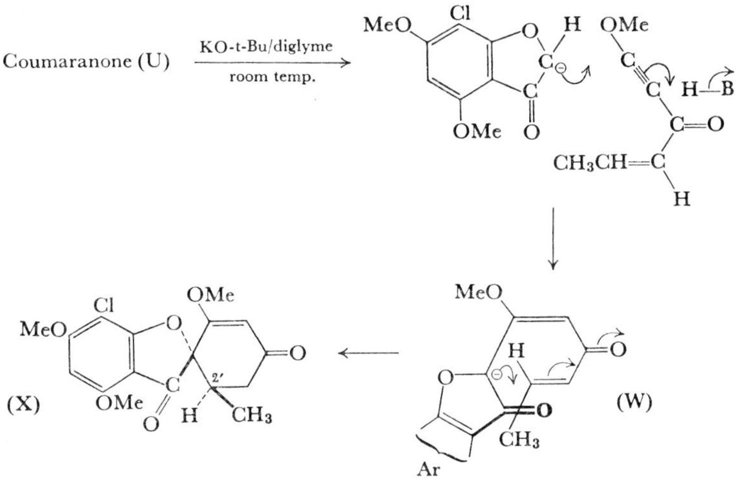

The success of the synthesis depended on the first addition occurring at the triple bond which is normally the case since this is more electronegative, although the destabilizing effect of the ethoxyl group could conceivably have changed the order of events. The formation of griseofulvin as the sole product can be attributed to the transition state (W) in which the spirane is closed from above the plane of the paper and where maximum delocalization of the negative charge is possible over the parallel π-orbitals (cf. p. 97). Inspection of ball-and-spring models shows that in a transition state for attack from below the plane of the paper, leading to the 2′-epimer of griseofulvin, the carbonyl group of the coumaranone is directed away from the enone and the stabilization it affords in (W) would then be absent.

A further application of ethoxyacetylene is the initiation of acylations leading to the formation of anhydrides and amides; this has been extended to the synthesis of peptides (see structural formulae at top of p. 66).

This mechanism is not proved, but following successive additions to the acetylene attack within a four-centred transition (Y) is reasonable because the geminal oxysubstituents assist breaking of the C—N bond.

Coupling Reactions. Passing reference has been made (pp. 59, 60) to the copper-catalysed coupling of acetylenes due originally to Glaser (1869). This is a valuable method of aggregating terminal acetylenes; one effective procedure is to dissolve the substrate in ammoniacal

65

$$\underset{\substack{\text{Benzyloxycarbonylglycyl-}\\\text{L-phenylalanine}}}{\underset{\xleftarrow{\hspace{0.5cm}} R \xrightarrow{\hspace{0.5cm}}}{Ph-CH_2-O-\overset{O}{\overset{\|}{C}}-\underset{H}{N}-CH_2-\overset{O}{\overset{\|}{C}}-\underset{H}{N}-\underset{\underset{\substack{CH_2\\|\\Ph}}{|}}{CH}}} + H-C{\equiv}C-OEt + \underset{CH_2-CO_2Et}{NH_2}$$

$$\Big\downarrow \text{30 min reflux}$$

$$\left[\underset{\substack{O\quad CH_2\\\quad\ |\\\quad\ Ph}}{\overset{H}{\underset{H}{>}}C{=}C\overset{OEt}{\underset{O-\overset{|}{C}-CH-NH-CO.CH_2.NH.R}{<}}}\right]$$

$$\underset{\text{CH}_3-\overset{OEt}{\overset{|}{C}}{=}O \text{ (volatile)}}{}$$

+

$$\underset{\substack{\text{Benzyloxycarbonylglycyl-}\\\text{L-phenylalanylglycine ethyl ester}}}{\underset{CH_2.Ph}{EtO_2C-CH_2-\overset{H}{N}-CO.\overset{|}{CH}-NH-CO.CH_2-NHR}}$$

$$\underset{\substack{\text{m.p. }116°\ [\alpha]_D{-}12°,49\%\ (Y)}}{}$$

$$\underset{\substack{HN^Y\ CO-\overset{|}{CH}-NH-COCH_2NHR\\\quad\ CH_2CO_2Et}}{CH_3-\overset{OEt}{\overset{|}{C}}{\frown}O\quad CH_2Ph}$$

cuprous chloride solution at pH 6·5 and shake in air, or better oxygen, until uptake of gas ceases:

$$HO-CH_2-C{\equiv}CH \longrightarrow HO-CH_2-C{\equiv}C-C{\equiv}C-CH_2OH$$
$$88\%$$

Alcohols can be added as co-solvents and solutions of lower pH have often proved satisfactory (see however pp. 68–69 and problem 5*e*). In an alkaline medium retrocondensation can occur:

$$OH^{\ominus}\curvearrowright H{-}\overset{\curvearrowleft}{O}{-}CH_2{-}\overset{\frown}{C}{\equiv}CH \longrightarrow H_2O+H.CHO+{}^{\ominus}C{\equiv}CH$$

A superior coupling procedure discovered by Eglinton and Galbraith (1959) employs a solution of cupric acetate in pyridine, which dissolves a wide range of substrates and prevents undesirable precipitation of copper derivatives. An example of chain extension by this method has been given (p. 60) and intramolecular coupling is also useful for the synthesis of cyclic structures. As cyclooctyne is the smallest ring which can accommodate a triple bond (cf. p. 174) cyclic diynes formed by coupling must necessarily be many membered and oligomers will be formed by intermolecular reaction in preference to the closure of strained rings. A striking application was the synthesis by Sondheimer's group of the larger annulenes, monocyclic conjugated polyolefins, including benzene and cyclooctatetraene, as the best-known members. Cyclotetradecaheptaene ((Z) p. 68) was obtained as follows:

$$CH_2{=}CH{-}CH{=}CH_2 \xrightarrow{Br_2} \underset{H}{\overset{BrH_2C}{>}}C{=}C\underset{CH_2Br}{\overset{H}{<}} + BrMgC{\equiv}CH \text{ excess in THF}$$

in the presence of Cu_2Cl_2

$$\underset{H_2C}{\overset{H}{>}}C{=}C\underset{H}{\overset{CH_2C{\equiv}CMgBr}{<}} \quad \underset{\text{with } HC{\equiv}CMgBr}{\overset{\text{exchange}}{\longleftarrow}} \quad \left[\underset{H_2C}{\overset{H}{>}}C{=}C\underset{H}{\overset{CH_2C{\equiv}CH}{<}} \right]$$

$$\overset{|}{C}\equiv\overset{|}{C}{-}H \quad \text{additional}$$

$BrCH_2CH{=}CHCH_2Br$
$+$ $HC{\equiv}CMgBr$

$$\underset{CH_2}{\overset{H}{>}}C{=}C\underset{H}{\overset{CH_2C{\equiv}CCH_2}{<}}C{=}C\underset{CH_2}{\overset{H}{<}}$$

(AA)

The intermediate triyne (AA) was isolated in 12% yield with m.p. 72° and was characterized by its ultraviolet absorption, which gave no evidence of conjugation, and by its conversion into n-tetradecane on complete hydrogenation. The function of cuprous chloride in the second step is to enhance the rate of reaction of the allylic bromide by co-ordination of $Cu^\oplus$ ion with the leaving bromide ion (cf. p. 73), the alternative more facile reaction in liquid ammonia (p. 53) being inapplicable because of ammonolysis of the halide (see structural formulae at top of p. 68).

(AA) was treated with cupric acetate/pyridine to give ((AB) top of p 68), in which two of the triple bonds are isomerized via allenes to dienes by base (pp. 56, 62), yielding the completely conjugated red compound (AC or an isomer). The [14]-annulene (Z) was obtained by hemi-hydrogenation of the remaining triple bond using Lindlar's catalyst.

Cyclotetradecaheptaene contains $(4n + 2)$ π-electrons, but although it therefore conforms with Hückel's rule for aromaticity $(n = 3)$ hydrogen–hydrogen interactions make it non-planar and inhibit complete de-

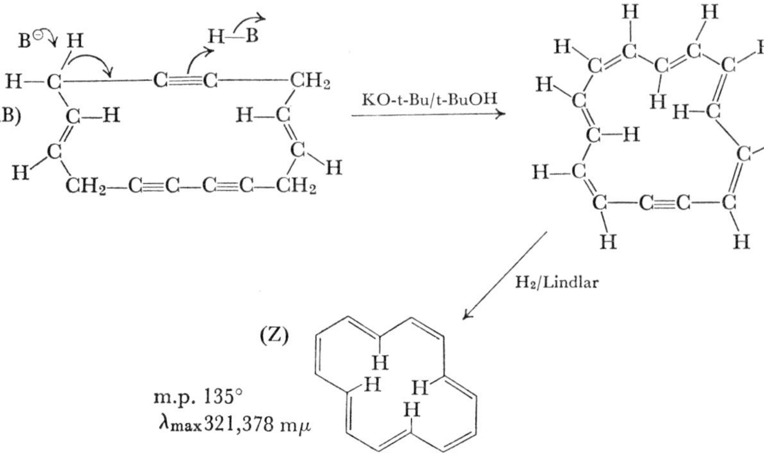

(AB)

KO-t-Bu/t-BuOH

(AC)

H₂/Lindlar

(Z)

m.p. 135°
λ_{max}321,378 mμ

localization round the ring; there is no evidence of a ring current from its NMR spectrum and it is less stable than [18]-annulene which is an aromatic compound.

The mechanism of the coupling in basic media is probably as outlined:

$$R-C\equiv CH \rightleftharpoons R-C\equiv C^{\ominus}+H^{\oplus} \quad (AD)$$

$$R-C\equiv C^{\ominus}+Cu^{\oplus\oplus} \longrightarrow R-C\equiv C\cdot +Cu^{\oplus}$$

$$2R-C\equiv C\cdot \longrightarrow R-C\equiv C-C\equiv C-R$$

that is in sum:

$$2R-C\equiv C-H+2Cu^{\oplus\oplus} \longrightarrow R-C\equiv C-C\equiv C-R+2H^{\oplus}+2Cu^{\oplus}$$

regeneration of the required cupric ion in anhydrous pyridine solution occurs by uptake of oxygen:

$$Cu_2(OAc)_2+2AcOH \xrightarrow[{[O]}]{} 2Cu(OAc)_2+H_2O$$

The dissociation (AD) is catalysed by cuprous ions which are always present in small amounts in the cupric salts used. When R = alkyl the acetylide is destabilized (cf. p. 6); the reaction is then very slow and alkyl acetylenes couple more readily in an acid medium when the rate may be effected by complex formation:

$$\begin{array}{ccc} R-C\equiv C-H & \longrightarrow & R-C\equiv C^{\ominus}+H^{\oplus} \\ \downarrow & & \\ \overset{.}{C}u^{\oplus} & & Cu^{\oplus} \end{array}$$

68

Strongly acidic conditions will impede loss of a proton from such a complex and can also lead to dehydration of alcohols and anionotropic rearrangement.

Cadiot–Chodkiewicz Coupling (1957). This is an important modification particularly useful for the synthesis of unsymmetrical diynes; it depends on preferential coupling between a bromoacetylene (see p. 52) and a cuprous acetylide. A catalytic amount of cuprous chloride is added to a solution of the acetylene in water or alcohol, followed by a solution of the bromocomponent:

First stage

$$HO—CH_2—C\equiv CH \; \underset{}{\overset{Cu^\oplus}{\rightleftharpoons}} \; HO—CH_2—C\equiv C—Cu + H^\oplus$$

Second stage

$$HO—CH_2—C\equiv CCu + BrC\equiv C—CH_3 \longrightarrow HO—CH_2—C\equiv C—C\equiv C—CH_3 + CuBr$$
$$89\%$$

When bromocompounds are used the reaction generally proceeds at a satisfactory rate at room temperature, whilst iodocompounds react too rapidly for convenience and chlorocompounds too slowly. The reaction is halted by the addition of cyanide to trap the cuprous ions, followed by extraction of the products. Two other necessary conditions are the presence of an equivalent of base, usually a primary alkylamine, to take up the liberated acid and a reducing agent, such as hydroxylamine, to prevent the oxidation of cuprous ions. Ethers or dimethylformamide can also be used as solvents and a wide range of functional groups can be incorporated provided that they do not interact with the base:

$$Me_2N—CH_2—C\equiv CH + Br(C\equiv C)_2—CH_3 \xrightarrow{H_2O} Me_2N—CH_2—(C\equiv C)_3—CH_3$$
$$91\%$$

$$H_2N\underset{\underset{O}{\parallel}}{C}—C\equiv CH + BrC\equiv CPh \xrightarrow{DMF} H_2N\underset{\underset{O}{\parallel}}{C}—C\equiv C—C\equiv C—Ph$$
$$76\%$$

Carbonyl compounds are best obtained by the oxidation of coupled alcohols.

Unwanted self-coupling of the bromoacetylene will follow its reduction:

$$R—C\equiv C—Br + 3Cu^\oplus \longrightarrow R—C\equiv C—Cu + Br^\ominus + 2Cu^{\oplus\oplus}$$

This is minimized by inverse addition of the bromocompound and by choice of the lowest convenient temperature for Cadiot–Chodkiewicz

69

coupling which is normally more facile than the reduction. Symmetrical coupling is easily detected because the reducing agent is consumed and the solution is coloured blue by cupric ions.

Straus Coupling (1905). This is a side-reaction of frequent occurrence during oxidative coupling: it is a dimerization, furthered by strong acidity, which does not consume oxygen although both cuprous and cupric ions are apparently required as catalysts.

$$2Ph-C\equiv C-Cu \xrightarrow{AcOH} Ph-C\equiv C-\overset{\overset{\displaystyle H}{|}}{C}=CH-Ph + Cu_2(OAc)_2$$

Straus coupling also competes in the Cadiot–Chodkiewicz procedure if cupric ions are allowed to accumulate.

An example of industrial importance is the Straus coupling of acetylene, which is streamed through an acid solution of cuprous chloride in ammonium chloride:

$$2HC\equiv CH \xrightarrow{60°} \overset{H}{\underset{H}{>}}C=CH-C\equiv CH + CH_2=CH-C\equiv C-CH=CH_2$$

Vinylacetylene   Divinylacetylene (C_6H_6)
10% conversion/cycle

The divinylacetylene formed by a second coupling step is separable by distillation and a small amount of acetaldehyde formed by hydration:

$$HC\equiv CH + H_2O \longrightarrow CH_3-C\overset{\displaystyle O}{\underset{\displaystyle H}{\diagup}}$$

is removed by washing with bisulphite. Vinylacetylene occurs with diacetylene in the electric arc synthesis of acetylene from natural gas; it reacts with hydrogen chloride to form chloroprene:

$$CH_2=CH-C\equiv CH \xrightarrow{HCl} CH_2=CH-\overset{\overset{\displaystyle Cl}{|}}{C}=CH_2$$

which is the unit in the synthesis of the oil-resistant synthetic rubber, neoprene. Another valuable intermediate is acrylonitrile (p. 157) obtained from acetylene and hydrogen cyanide under conditions similar to those used for Straus coupling:

$$HC\equiv CH + HCN \xrightarrow[\text{(2) }H_2O\text{ extraction of}]{\text{(1) }Cu_2Cl_2/NH_4Cl/HCl} 2\% \text{ solution of } CH_2=CH-CN$$

10 equiv.   gas stream   separated by distillation

Oligomerization of Acetylenes. In 1940 Reppe discovered that acetylene was tetramerized by nickel(II) complexes to form cyclooctatetraene (AE) in yields up to 70%. A typical catalyst is the bis(salicylaldehydato)

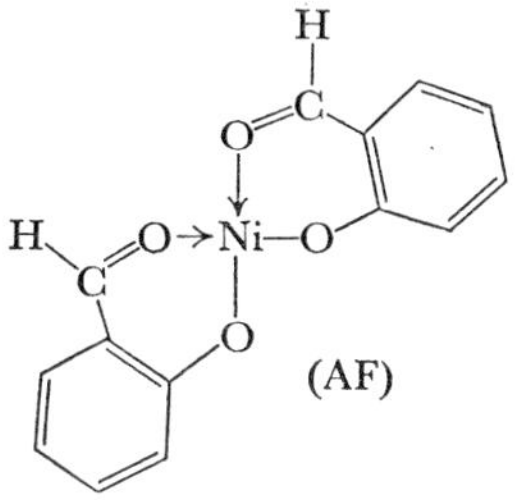

(AF)

complex (AF) and under typical conditions this is warmed with a solution of acetylene in an ether or benzene for several hours and the products separated by distillation after filtration from insoluble polymers.

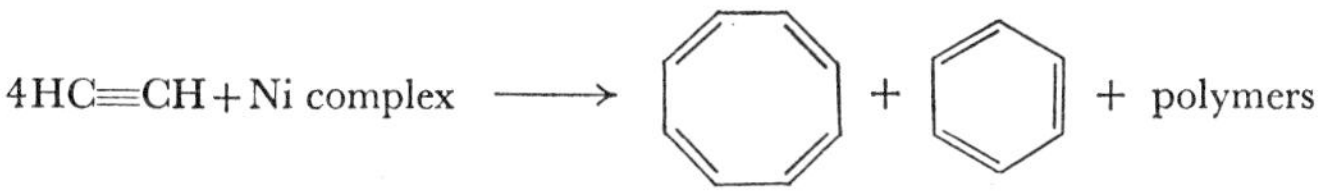

$$4HC\equiv CH + Ni \text{ complex} \longrightarrow \bigcirc + \bigcirc + \text{ polymers}$$

(AE) b.p. 142°, 70%   15%

It is very improbable that four acetylene molecules will collide in correct alignment for a cyclic tetramerization to occur in such high yield and Reppe suggested that the reaction occurred within a metal complex. This view is now widely supported by experiment, for example, very stable complexes are ineffective as catalysts because the acetylene molecules cannot displace the ligand: the salicylaldiminato analogue of (AF, —CH=NH for —CH=O) is inactive for this reason. The nickel atom will co-ordinate with solvent molecules and the salicylaldehydato complex (AF) will attain six-co-ordination closely approaching octahedral symmetry (AG), either by association with two solvent molecules or by additional solvent participation with displacement of a carbonyl group.

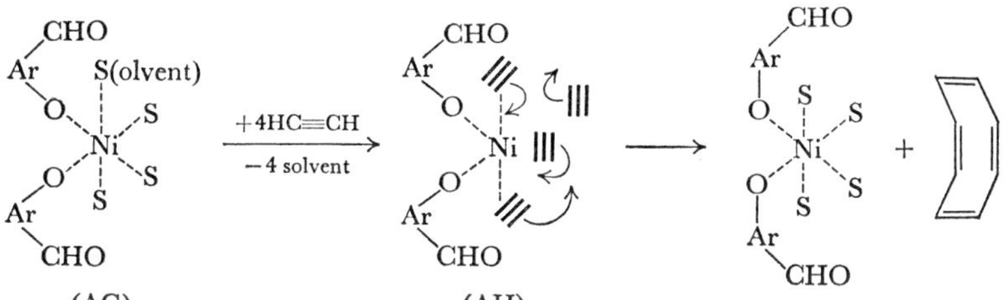

(AG)   (AH)

71

Provided acetylene molecules can displace the solvent four of them can be co-ordinated in a configuration (AH) which facilitates the elimination of cyclooctatetraene, whilst vacant sites are taken up by solvent and/or acetylene molecules and a new sequence can then begin. Displacement of strongly co-ordinated basic solvents such as pyridine is difficult and their use inhibits the reaction; compare here the inactive iminato-complex.

The above views on mechanism are substantiated by the finding that triphenylphosphine diverts the system to benzene synthesis:

$$3 \text{ g of (AF) in THF (100 ml)} + Ph_3P \text{ (I equiv.)} \xrightarrow[90°]{15 \text{ hr}} \text{benzene (8 g)}$$

in an autoclave under N_2 (5 atm)   *no* cyclooctatetraene
and acetylene (10 atm, 20°)

This must result from the blocking of one site in the complex by strong co-ordination of the phosphine, leaving a maximum of three sites for acetylene which can undergo cyclic trimerization when in the configuration (AI). Trimerization of alkylacetylenes to symmetrical trialkyl-benzenes and, less satisfactorily, mixed condensations of acetylene and alkylacetylenes are possible.

The highly toxic nickel carbonyl (b.p. 43°), formed by direct inter-action between the metal and carbon monoxide, is an important source of co-ordination catalysts since carbon monoxide is displaced by many other ligands:

$$Ni(CO)_4 + Ph_3P \longrightarrow Ni(CO)_3Ph_3P + CO\uparrow$$
(Tetrahedral)

The remaining three molecules of carbon monoxide are displaced on heating to 75° with acrylonitrile, and addition of acetylene (2 mols under pressure) during 6 hr affords 2,4,6-heptatrienenitrile (AJ):

$$Ph_3PNi(CH_2\!=\!CH\!-\!CN)_2 \xrightarrow{HC\equiv CH} CH_2\!=\!CH\!-\!CH\!=\!CH\!-\!CH\!=\!CH\!-\!CN$$
(AJ) b.p. 58°/2 mm, 74%

Carbon monoxide itself condenses with acetylenes as in the synthesis of acrylic acids:

$$H-C\equiv C-(CH_2)_4-CO_2Et$$
$$+ Ni(CO)_4 \text{ in EtOH/H}_2O \text{ acid by AcOH} \longrightarrow$$

$$CH_2=C-(CH_2)_4-CO_2Et$$
$$\underset{CO_2H}{|}$$

b.p. 108°/0·02 mm, 37%

Cyclopropenones have been suggested as intermediates in this reaction:

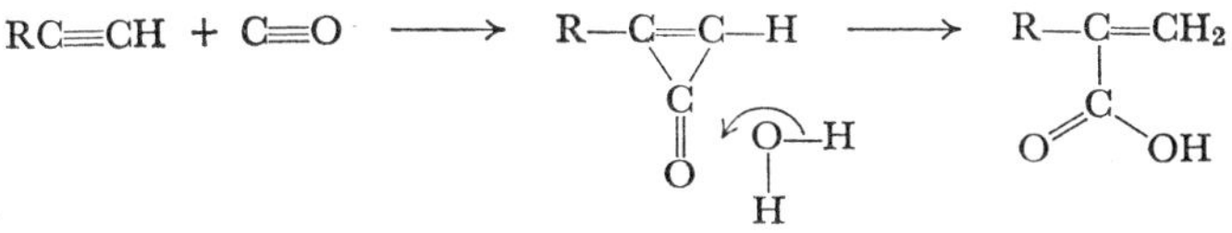

$$RC\equiv CH + C\equiv O \longrightarrow R-\underset{\substack{C\\ \|\\ O}}{\overset{}{C=C-H}} \longrightarrow R-\underset{\substack{C\\ O^{\nearrow}\diagdown OH}}{\overset{}{C=CH_2}}$$

a concerted reaction in a complex is a possible alternative to the two-step process:

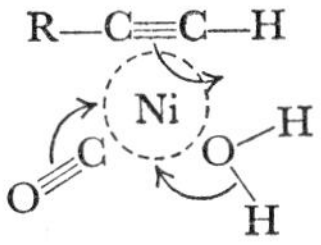

When dry alcohol is used as solvent the acrylic ester is obtained.

The Mechanism of Copper-catalysed Coupling. This is probably similar to the nickel-catalysed oligomerizations, for example one could suggest that Cadiot–Chodkiewicz coupling occurs in polymeric complexes of copper (I):

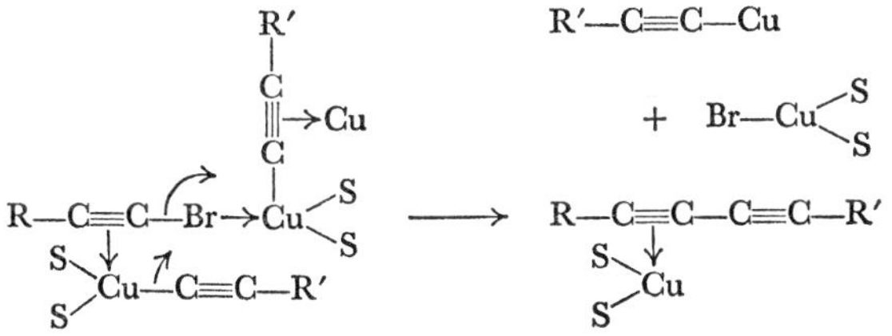

S = solvent

in this way the C-halogen bond is weakened by co-ordination and participation of solvent molecules, to the possible co-ordination number of three or four, lends stability. Polymeric substances of this kind are precipitated if appreciable concentrations of copper salts accumulate during coupling reactions.

6

Metal Acetylides

Further Reading

GENERAL

J. W. COPENHAUER and M. H. BIGELOW, *Acetylene and Carbon Monoxide Chemistry*. Reinhold, New York, 1949.

D. W. F. HARDIE, *Acetylene, Manufacture and Uses*. Oxford, 1965.

R. A. RAPHAEL, *Acetylenic Compounds in Organic Synthesis*. Butterworth, London, 1955.

TOPICS

T. ARENS, *Adv. Org. Chem.*, 1960, **2**, 117 (ethoxyacetylene).

J. D. Bu'LOCK, *Progr. Org. Chem.*, 1964, **6**, 86 (natural occurrence).

G. EGLINTON and W. McCRAE, *Adv. Org. Chem.*, 1963, **4**, 225 (coupling reactions).

SIR EWART R. H. JONES, *Chem. in Britain*, 1966, **2**, 6 (natural occurrence).

T. SCHRAUZER, *Angew. Chem.*, Intern. Edit., 1964, **3**, 185 (co-ordination complexes).

PROBLEMS

1. Suggest syntheses from acetylenic intermediates for:

(a) $H-C{\equiv}C-CH_2OH$ $(CH_3)_2-C(OH)-CO-CH_3$

$H-C{\equiv}C-CHO$ $HO-(CH_2)_4-OH$

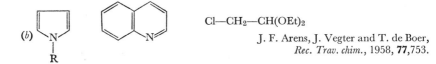

$HC{\equiv}C-C{\equiv}CH$ $CH_2{=}C-CH{=}CH_2$
                                            CH_3

$Cl-CH_2-C{\equiv}C-CH_2Cl$

J. W. Copenhauer and M. H. Bigelow, *Acetylene and Carbon Monoxide Chemistry*. Reinhold, New York, 1949.

(b) $Cl-CH_2-CH(OEt)_2$

J. F. Arens, J. Vegter and T. de Boer, *Rec. Trav. chim.*, 1958, **77**,753.

from propargyl chloride
N. R. Easton and D. R. Cassady,
J. Org. Chem., 1962, **27**, 4713.

2. Write mechanisms for the following:

(a) $R-C{\equiv}C-Cl \xrightarrow{\ KOH/EtOH\ } R-CH_2-CO_2H$

R. A. Raphael, *Acetylenic Compounds in Organic Synthesis*, p. 57. Butterworth, London, 1955 (*b*) $MeO_2C—C≡C—CO_2Me$ $\xrightarrow[Ph_2C=O]{NaNH_2/NH_3}$ $Ph_2C(OH)—C≡C—C(OH)Ph_2$

J. Cymerman Craig and M. Moyle, *Proc. Chem. Soc.*, **1962**, 283.

(*c*) $R—\underset{OMgBr}{CH}—C≡C—OEt + R—CHO$ $\xrightarrow{MgBr_2}$ $R—\underset{\underset{R\,\,H}{\underset{\|}{C}}}{\overset{OMgBr}{\underset{|}{CH}}}—C—CO_2Et$

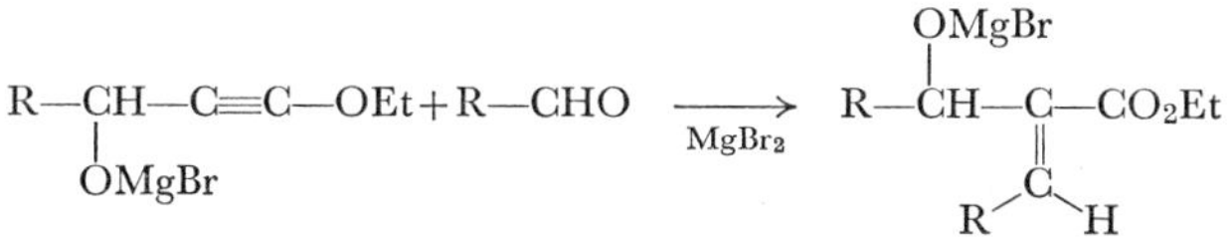

T. Arens, *Adv. Org. Chem.*, 1960, **2**, 176.

(*d*) $\underset{OH}{>C}—C≡C—OEt$ $\xrightarrow{LiAlH_4}$ $\underset{OH}{>C}—CH=CH—OEt +$ $>C=C=C\underset{OEt}{\overset{H}{<}}$

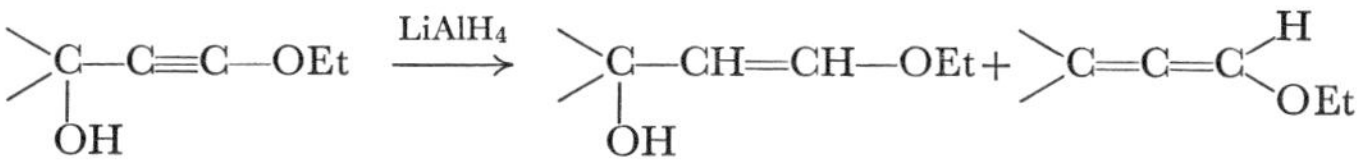

O. Isler and P. Schudel, *Adv. Org. Chem.*, 1963, **4**, 198.

(*e*)

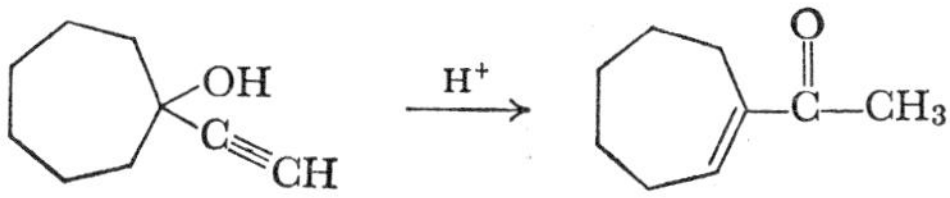

3. How would you synthesize $CH_3—\overset{c}{CH}=CH—C≡C—C≡C—\overset{c}{CH}=CH—CO_2Me$ from $HC≡C—\overset{c}{CH}=CH—CH_2OH$

I. Bell, E. R. H. Jones and M. C. Whiting, *J. Chem. Soc.*, **1958**, 1315.

4. Account for the rearrangement:

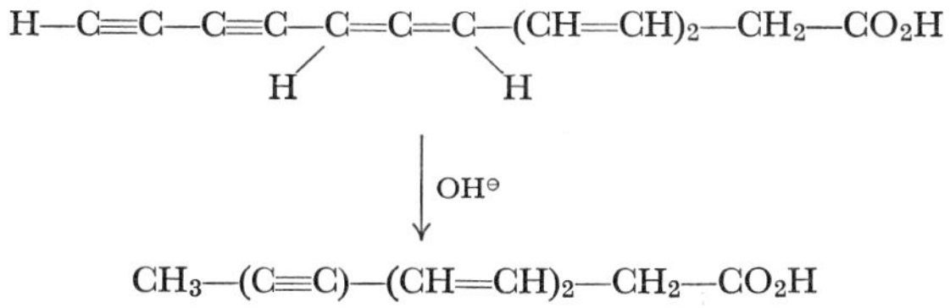

$CH_3—(C≡C)—(CH=CH)_2—CH_2—CO_2H$

J. D. Bu'Lock, E. R. H. Jones, P. R. Leeming and J. M. Thompson, *J. Chem. Soc.*, **1956**, 3768.

5. Suggest mechanisms for:

(*a*) $CH_3—CH=CH—CO—C≡C—OEt$ $\xrightarrow{CH_2(CO_2Et)_2/KOtBu}$

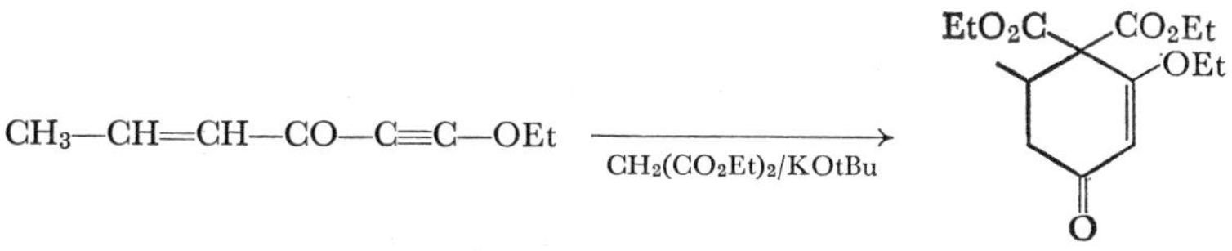

G. Stork and M. Tomasz, *J. Amer. Chem. Soc.*, 1962, **84**, 311.

(*b*) $Ph—CO—CH_2Cl$ $\xrightarrow[heat]{(EtO)_3P}$ $Ph—\underset{O—P(OEt)_2}{\overset{}{C}}=CH_2$ $\xrightarrow{NaNH_2/NH_3}$ $Ph—C≡CH$

$+ EtCl$

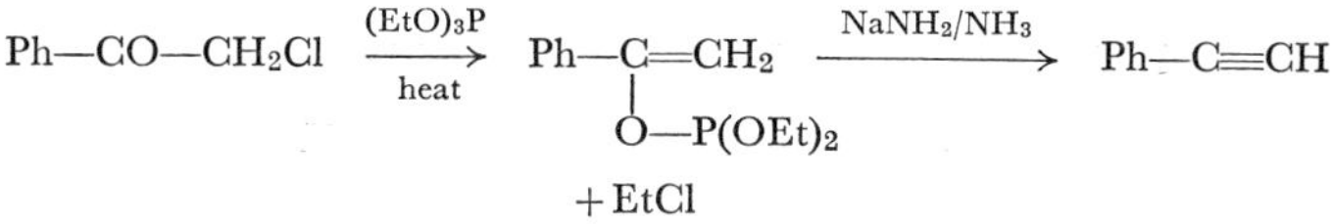

F. W. Lichtenthaler, *Chem. Rev.*, 1961, **61**, 616.

Metal Acetylides

and H—C≡C—CH₂—O—P(OEt)₂ $\xrightarrow[\text{PCl}_3/\text{pyridine}]{}$ CH₂=C=CH—P(O)(OEt)₂

V. Mark, *Tetrahedron Letters*, **1962**, 281.

(*c*)

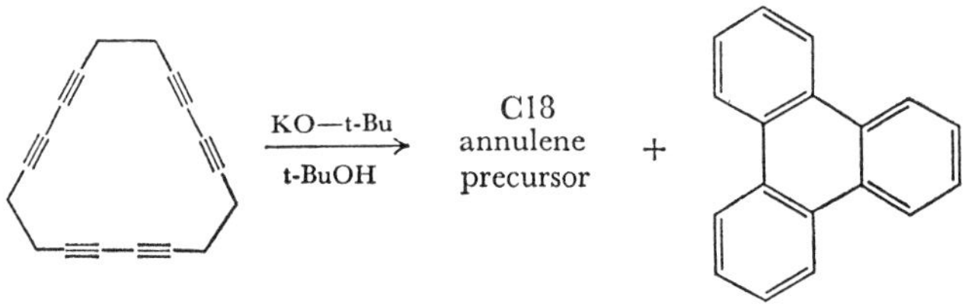

$\xrightarrow[\text{t-BuOH}]{\text{KO—t-Bu}}$ C18 annulene precursor +

G. Eglinton and W. McCrae, *Adv. Org. Chem.*, 1963, **4**, 307.

(*d*) Cu—C≡C—CO₂Me $\xrightarrow{\text{AcOH}}$ MeO₂C—CH=C—CH=CH—CO₂Me
  |
  OAc

M. Akhtar and B. C. L. Weedon, *Proc. Chem. Soc.*, **1958**, 303

CH₃—CH=CH—CH(OH)—C≡CH $\underset{\text{pH 6·5}}{\overset{\text{pH 1}}{\underset{\nwarrow}{\overset{\searrow}{\rightleftarrows}}}}$ CuCl₂/O₂

[CH₃—CH(OH)—CH=CH—C≡C]₂

[CH₃—CH=CH—CH(OH)—C≡C]₂

G. Eglinton and W. McCrae, *Adv. Org. Chem.*, 1963, **4**, 239–240.

(*f*) CH₂=CH—CH₂Cl + HC≡CH + Ni(CO)₄

$\xrightarrow{\text{MeOH}}$ CH₂=CH—CH₂—CH=CH
  \
  CO₂Me

O. Bayer in, J. Houben and T. Weyl, *Methoden der organischen Chemie*, Vol. 4, II, p. 415. G. Thieme, Stuttgart, 4th edit., 1954.

6. The rates of Cadiot-Chodkiewicz coupling of Ph—C≡CH and R—C≡C—C≡CH are greater than that of R—C≡CH; explain this.

7. Deduce a mechanism for:

H—C≡C—OEt $\xrightarrow[\text{2R—CO}_2\text{H}]{}$ CH₃—CO₂Et + R—CO—O—CO—R

and hence rationalize

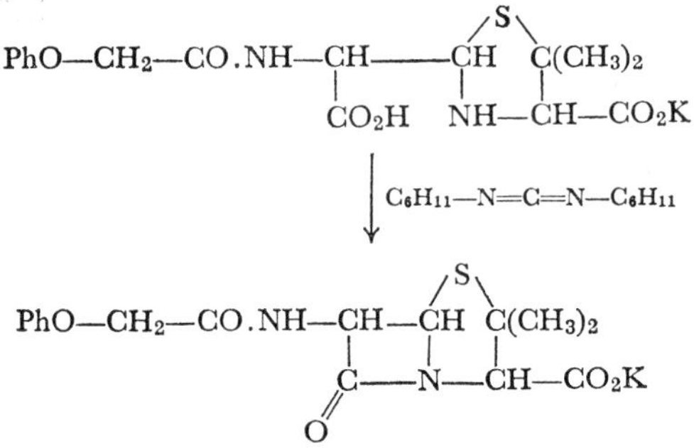

PhO—CH₂—CO.NH—CH——CH C(CH₃)₂
  | | S
  CO₂H   NH—CH—CO₂K

$\downarrow$ C₆H₁₁—N=C=N—C₆H₁₁

PhO—CH₂—CO.NH—CH—CH C(CH₃)₂
  | | S
  C——N—CH—CO₂K
  ‖
  O

J. C. Sheehan, K. R. Henesy-Logan, *J. Amer. Chem. Soc.*, 1957, **79**, 1262.

8. Four molecules of acetone react with the complex

$$Ni^{\oplus\oplus}(H_2N—CH_2.CH_2—NH_2)_3(ClO_4^{\ominus})_2$$

to yield:

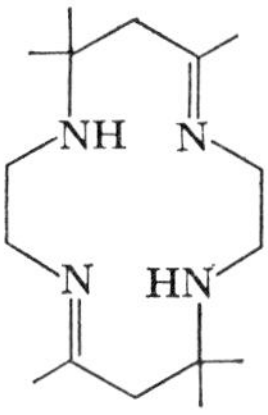

Show how this is formed.

L. J. Andrews and R. M. Keefer, *J. Chem. Educ.*, 1965, **42**, 460.

9. An acetylenic primary alcohol, C_4H_6O, reacted with an acid chloride, $C_{11}H_{17}ClO$, in pyridine and the product (A) underwent copper acetate catalysed coupling in the same solvent to afford a product (B; $C_{15}H_{20}O_2$), m.p. 56°. On hydrogenation of (B) 4 moles of gas were taken up and a product (C) was obtained which had a strong absorption in the infrared at 2900 cm^{-1} but no other peak appeared until that at 1745 cm^{-1}, nor was any peak detectable at 1370 cm^{-1}. Assign structures (A)→(C).

G. Eglinton and W. McCrae, *Adv. Org. Chem.*, 1963, **4**, 304.

CHAPTER 4

CARBANION CHEMISTRY OF ALDEHYDES
AND KETONES

The formation of carbanions by abstraction of a proton from a carbon atom α to the C=O group has been referred to:

$$-\overset{\displaystyle |}{\underset{\displaystyle H}{C}}-\overset{\displaystyle O}{\overset{\displaystyle \|}{C}}- \quad \underset{k_{-1}}{\overset{k_1 \text{ Base}^\ominus}{\rightleftarrows}} \quad -\overset{\displaystyle |}{C}-\overset{\displaystyle O}{\overset{\displaystyle \|}{\underset{\displaystyle \ominus}{C}}}-+\text{BH}$$

$$(1) \qquad\qquad\qquad (2)$$

In protic solvents the carbanion (2) may capture a proton and reform the carbonyl compound (1) or make a nucleophilic attack on a second molecule and form a new C–C bond. The latter course is favoured for aldehydes where the carbonyl group is strongly electrophilic:

$$\underset{\overset{\displaystyle \curvearrowright}{\ominus CH_2-CHO}}{CH_3-C\overset{\displaystyle \diagup O}{\diagdown H}} \quad \underset{k_{-2}}{\overset{k_2}{\rightleftarrows}} \quad CH_3-\overset{\displaystyle O^\ominus}{\underset{\displaystyle H}{C}}-CH_2-CHO \quad \overset{H_2O}{\rightleftarrows} \quad CH_3-\overset{\displaystyle OH}{\underset{\displaystyle H}{C}}-CH_2-CHO+OH^\ominus \quad (A)$$

The product is an aldehydic alcohol or aldol giving the name *aldol condensation* to the reaction. Solvents commonly used include water, alcohol, and aqueous dioxan with metal hydroxides and certain amines as catalysts. No appreciable concentration of carbanion is formed in the presence of excess aldehyde because the condensation rate (k_2) is greater than the uptake of proton (k_{-1}); this was demonstrated by conducting the reaction in deuterium oxide when no significant amount of carbon-bound deuterium was incorporated in the aldehyde.

Ketones do not undergo the reaction under the conditions mentioned above, because the steric and inductive effects of the second alkyl group

$$\overset{\displaystyle R}{\underset{\displaystyle R}{\diagdown\diagup}}C=O$$

make them less susceptible to nucleophilic attack and the equilibrium (A) lies to the left. This difference in reactivity is the basis of the useful,

78

but not infallible, test for aldehydes which undergo a series of aldol condensations in hot alkaline solution affording a coloured unsaturated polymer:

$$(n+1)R.CH_2.CHO \longrightarrow R-CH_2-\left[\begin{array}{c} OHH \\ | \; | \\ C-C \\ | \; | \\ H \; R \end{array}\right]_n CHO \longrightarrow$$

$$R-CH_2-\left[\begin{array}{c} | \\ C=C \\ | \quad | \\ H \quad R \end{array}\right]_n CHO \quad (B)$$

Acetone, the most reactive of simple ketones, can be induced to react if refluxed in a Soxhlet extractor with barium hydroxide in the thimble. A small amount of the condensation product diacetone–alcohol is formed in the thimble:

$$2CH_3-CO-CH_3 \rightleftharpoons CH_3-\overset{\overset{\displaystyle OH}{|}}{\underset{\underset{\displaystyle CH_3}{|}}{C}}-CH_2-COCH_3 \quad 70\%$$

and further contact with the alkali, insoluble in acetone, is prevented by return of product to the flask in acetone solution. The reverse reaction

$$(CH_3)_2-\overset{OH}{\underset{}{C}}-CH_2-CO.CH_3 \longrightarrow CH_3-CO.CH_3 + \overset{\ominus}{C}H_2-CO.CH_3$$

cannot then occur. It will be noticed that reversal by abstraction of a proton from the β—OH group rather than from the α-C atom would lead to reversal in (B) and no doubt this does take place, but elimination of —OH groups and the separation of an insoluble polymer drives equilibrium to the right.

The retro-aldol condensation has been used in the systematic degradation of natural products, for example citral, a conjugated enal undergoes fission on reflux in potassium carbonate solution (see structural formulae at top of p. 80).

Removal of the volatile acetaldehyde displaces the equilibrium and 6-methylhept-5-en-2-one is obtained in 96% yield.

Synthesis by Aldol Condensation. The reader may verify that there are four possible products in a mixed condensation between two different aldehydes with available α-hydrogen; hence this combination

79

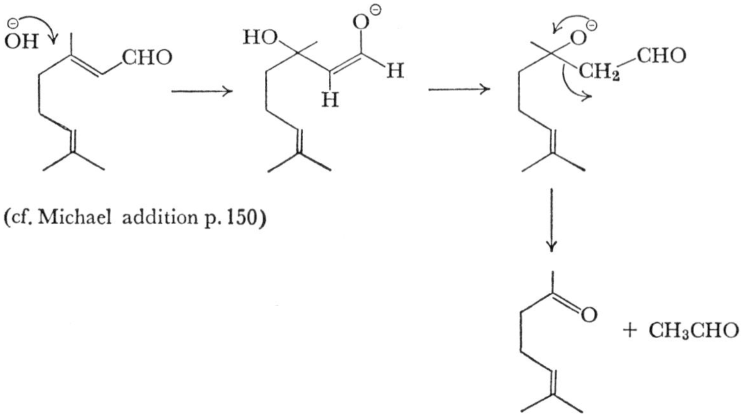

(cf. Michael addition p. 150)

$+ CH_3CHO$

is rarely useful synthetically although acceptable yields of one aldol may be obtained if one of the components is in excess:

$$CH_3.CH_2.CH_2.CHO + CH_3.CHO \xrightarrow[17°]{24\% \text{ NaOH}} CH_3.CH_2-CH \begin{matrix} CHO \\ CHOH \\ | \\ CH_3 \end{matrix}$$

1 mol   4 mol

b.p. 100°/20 mm
40%

Should one component lack α-H it can only act as an acceptor (see also p. 85, 'Cannizzaro') giving rise to only two products and if these are separable, e.g. by distillation, a useful chain extension procedure results:

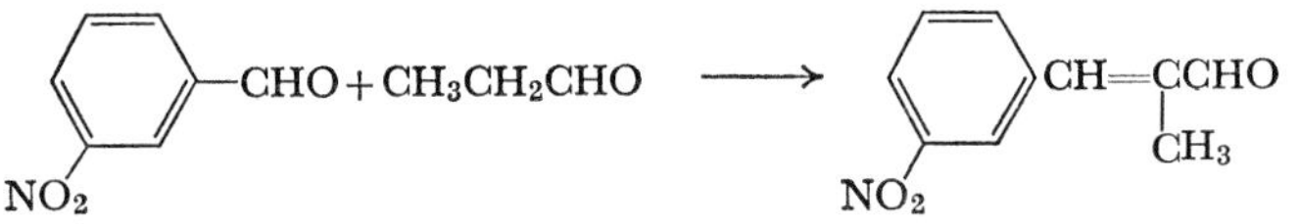

$$\text{(3-NO}_2\text{)C}_6\text{H}_4\text{—CHO} + CH_3CH_2CHO \longrightarrow \text{(3-NO}_2\text{)C}_6\text{H}_4\text{—CH}\!=\!\underset{\underset{CH_3}{|}}{C}CHO \qquad \text{(C)}$$

A variant here is to use a simple nitroalkane as source of the carbanion (p. 2).

$$Ph—CHO + CH_3.CH_2.NO_2 \xrightarrow{Bu.NH_2} Ph—CH\!=\!C.NO_2(CH_3)$$

This has the advantage that the product is readily reduced to the saturated oxime

$$Ph.CH_2—\underset{\underset{CH_3}{|}}{C}\!=\!N.OH$$

whence hydrolysis affords the ketone; alternatively the primary amine may be obtained by catalytic reduction.

It is not usual for the aldol itself to be isolated when an aromatic aldehyde reacts because of the ready elimination of water to give a product stabilized by conjugation. The aldol condensation is also catalysed by acids and here too the subsequent elimination occurs, even in simple systems:

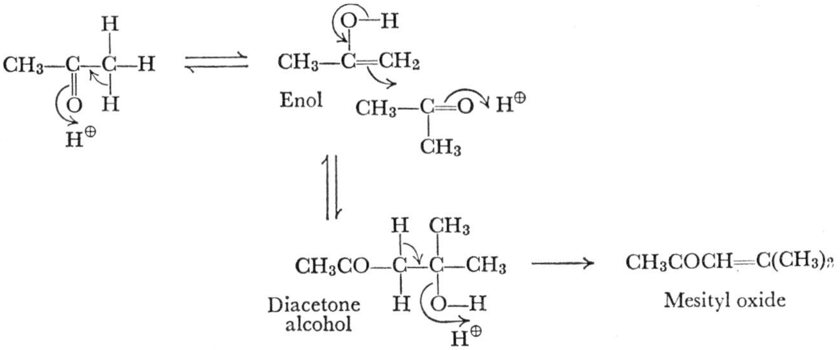

The enol, which may be formed by the loss of a proton from a C—H bond, has an electron-rich C=C and readily reacts with the conjugate acid of acetone.

Compounds having extended conjugation are conveniently prepared from crotonaldehyde, for a stabilized carbanion can be obtained by removal of a proton from the methyl group:

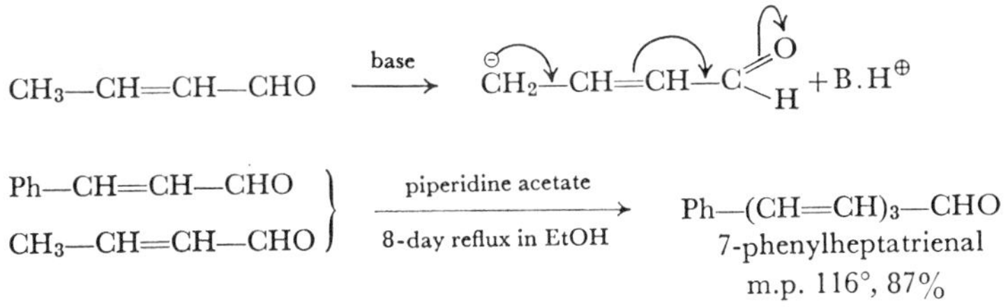

$$CH_3—CH=CH—CHO \xrightarrow{\text{base}} \ominus CH_2—CH=CH—C\!\!\diagdown^O_H + B.H^\oplus$$

$$
\begin{array}{l}
Ph—CH=CH—CHO \\
CH_3—CH=CH—CHO
\end{array}
\left.\right\}
\xrightarrow[\text{8-day reflux in EtOH}]{\text{piperidine acetate}}
$$
Ph—(CH=CH)₃—CHO
7-phenylheptatrienal
m.p. 116°, 87%

Continued condensations with other molecules of crotonaldehyde are also possible.

Because ketones are less susceptible to nucleophilic attack than aldehydes crossed condensations between these compounds are often fruitful:

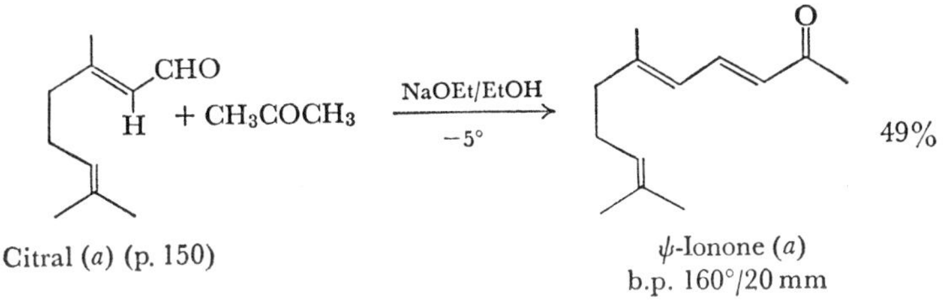

Citral (*a*) (p. 150)   ψ-Ionone (*a*)
b.p. 160°/20 mm

81

Under normal conditions the more reactive aldehyde acts as the acceptor:

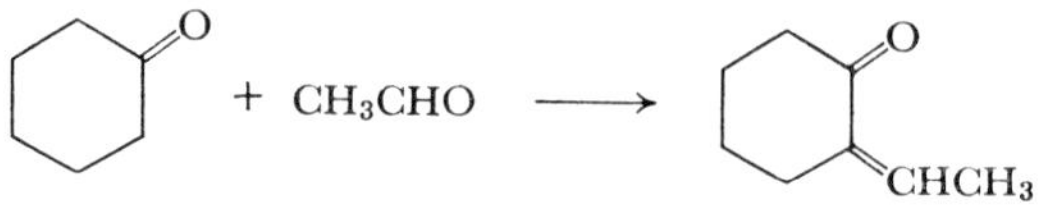

but if a Schiff's base of the aldehyde is used and undergoes exchange with a lithio-amide (this is not itself reactive, see p. 135) then the lithium derivative will react with ketones:

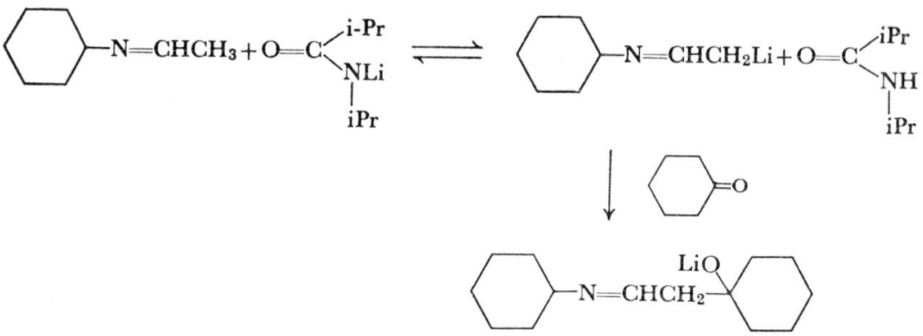

and the crystalline —OLi derivative, m.p. 62°, may be decomposed by dilute acid to the product

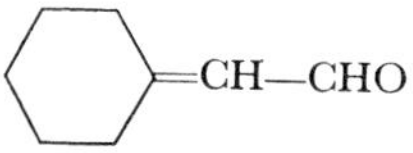

in 92% yield, corresponding to acceptance by the ketone. This method is applicable to ketones of very low reactivity, e.g.

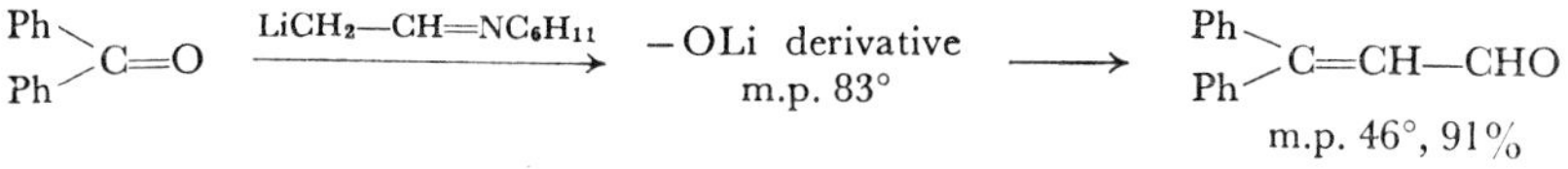

Intramolecular Condensations. Cyclic products are obtained from di-carbonyl compounds, including diketones, and loss by intermolecular reaction is not serious if a strain-free ring is formed (see structural formulae at top of p. 83).

In (D), the dialdehyde is derived by ozonolysis and only one mode of cyclization is possible. In (E), which forms part of the Harvard steroid synthesis, the dialdehyde is obtained by hydroxylation of a double bond in a fourth fused ring, followed by periodate fission of the *vic*-diol. The —CHO groups are not identically situated and both undergo

82

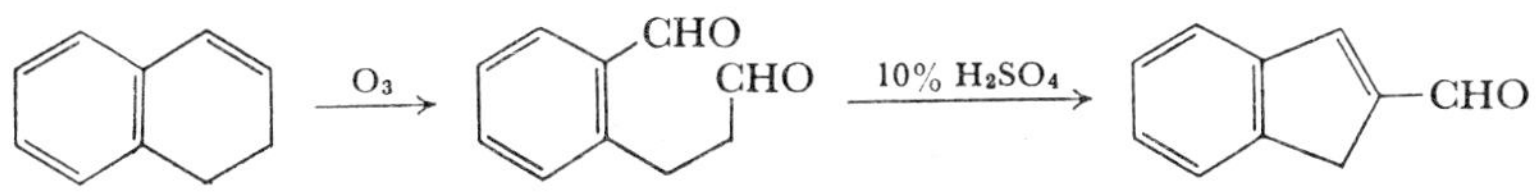

Indene-2-aldehyde

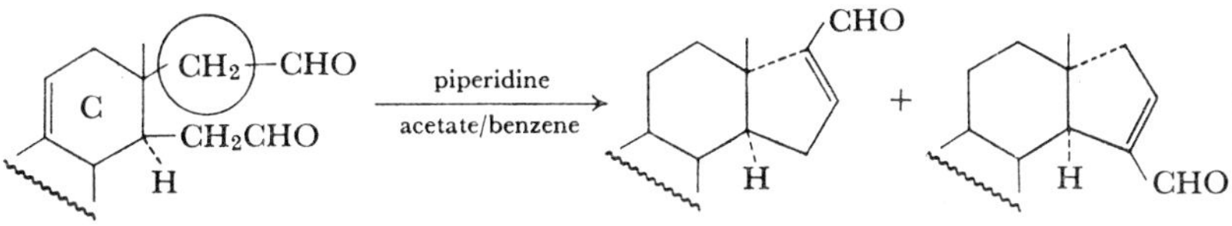

m.p. 129–132°   (1) m.p. 178°, 65%   (2) m.p. 156°, < 35% yield

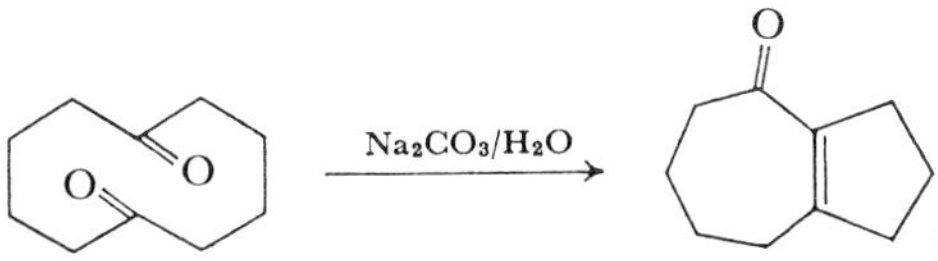

intramolecular attack by carbanion leading to the principal product (1) and also (2). Product (1) is formed in greater yield because there is less hindrance to the approach of base at the outlined α-C atom.

Reactions of Aldehydes which have no α-H Atom. Aromatic aldehydes fall under this head and although their structure precludes aldol condensation this was seen (p. 80) to be advantageous in crossed reactions. Another synthetic outlet for aromatic aldehydes is the *Benzoin Condensation* which leads to union at the aldehydic carbon atoms:

$$2Ph—CHO \xrightarrow[\substack{H_2O/EtOH \\ KCN\ M/7}]{reflux\ in} Ph.CH(OH)—CO—Ph$$

M/5   Benzoin

A mechanism dependent on abstraction of proton to form $Ph—\underset{\ominus}{C}=O$ is unattractive because this carbanion is not resonance stabilized and, further, in an alkaline medium only the weakly basic cyanide ion is effective as a catalyst. The mechanism originally suggested by Lapworth (1903) is in harmony with most of the experimental facts (see structural formulae at top of p. 84).

Following transfer of a proton in (F), the conjugate base of a cyano-hydrin, a carbanion (G) is formed with negative charge now stabilized by the adjacent —CN and Ar— groups (cf. cyanoacetates, p. 145). Nucleophilic attack on a molecule of aldehyde (step H), which is probably rate-determining, and subsequent ejection of cyanide ion (step I) follows.

83

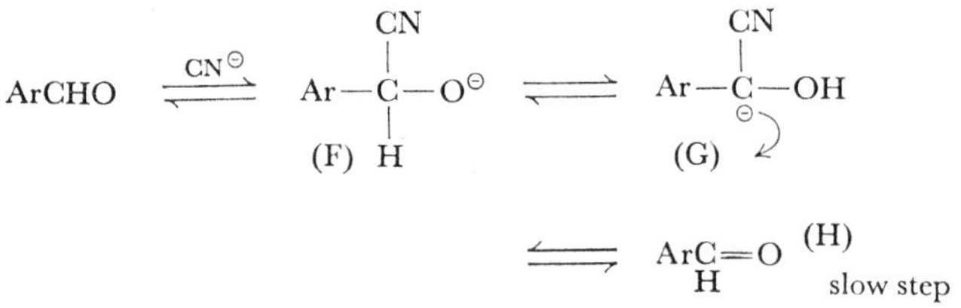

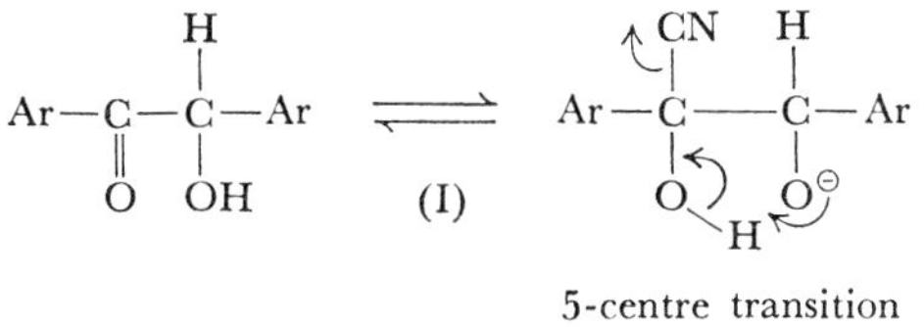

$$ArCHO \underset{\longleftarrow}{\overset{CN^{\ominus}}{\longrightarrow}} \underset{\underset{H}{\underset{|}{(F)}}}{Ar-\overset{\overset{\displaystyle CN}{|}}{\underset{|}{C}}-O^{\ominus}} \rightleftharpoons \underset{(G)}{Ar-\overset{\overset{\displaystyle CN}{|}}{\underset{\ominus}{C}}-OH}$$

$$\rightleftharpoons \quad Ar\underset{H}{\overset{\overset{\displaystyle (H)}{}}{C}}=O \quad \text{slow step}$$

$$\underset{(I)}{Ar-\overset{\overset{\displaystyle H}{|}}{\underset{\underset{OH}{|}}{\overset{\|}{C}}}-Ar} \rightleftharpoons Ar-\overset{\overset{\displaystyle CN}{|}}{\underset{\underset{H}{O}}{C}}\!-\!\overset{\overset{\displaystyle H}{|}}{\underset{O^{\ominus}}{C}}-Ar$$

5-centre transition

The benzoin condensation is reversible and may not proceed far to the right, e.g. with alkyl and ethoxybenzaldehydes. 4-Methoxybenz-aldehyde gives the benzoin in 60% yield but a very strongly electron-donating substituent may prevent reaction. Thus although *p*-dimethyl-aminobenzaldehyde forms a cyanohydrin it cannot condense as in step (H) because the carbonyl carbon of the parent aldehyde is not sufficiently electrophilic. At the other end of the scale reaction is impeded by electron-attracting substituents because the carbanion (G) is too weak a nucleophile, e.g. with *p*-chloro and *p*-nitrobenzaldehydes. In the latter the effect is particularly marked because of the extensive delocalization of charge (cf. p. 2).

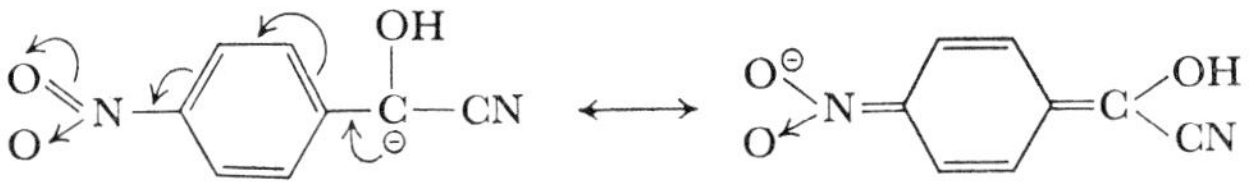

The operation of these two factors has an interesting effect in crossed condensations, which often occur in preference to self-condensation. *p*-Dimethylaminobenzaldehyde affords a strongly nucleophilic car-banion which condenses with piperonal as acceptor:

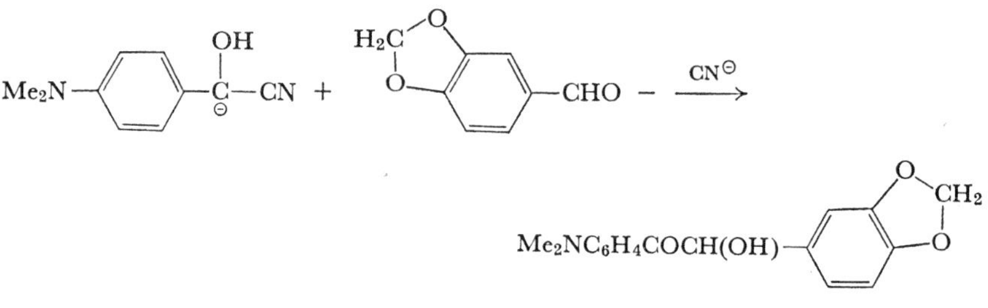

$$Me_2NC_6H_4COCH(OH)$$

40%, m.p. 136°

Piperonal itself gives piperoin, m.p. 120°, in 32% yield. Note also:

$$p\text{-ClC}_6\text{H}_4\text{—CHO} + p\text{-MeO—C}_6\text{H}_4\text{—CHO} \longrightarrow$$
$$\text{ClC}_6\text{H}_4\text{—CH(OH)—CO—C}_6\text{H}_4\text{—OMe}$$
$$70\%, \text{m.p. } 71°$$

This reaction offers a route to unsymmetrical benzophenones where classical Friedel–Craft syntheses are unsatisfactory:

$$\text{Ar—CH(OH)—CO—Ar}' \xrightarrow[\text{oxidation}]{\text{Oppenauer}} \text{Ar—CO—CO—Ar}' \quad a \ benzil$$

(1) strong alkali
(2) acid

$$\overset{O}{\overset{\|}{\text{Ar—C}}}\text{—Ar}' + \text{CO}_2 \xleftarrow{\text{CrO}_3/\text{Ac}_2\text{O}} \overset{\text{Ar}'}{\underset{\text{OH}}{\text{Ar—C—CO}_2\text{H}}} \quad a \ benzilic \ acid$$

Benzils formed by oxidation rearrange in alkali, because nucleophilic attack by OH⊖ ion displaces the aryl residue with its bonding electrons

$$\text{Ar—C—C—Ar} \rightleftharpoons \text{HO—C—C—Ar}$$

and this gives a stable product by its attachment to the adjacent electrophilic C=O group.

The Cannizzaro Reaction. Aromatic and aliphatic aldehydes lacking α-hydrogen react in a strongly basic medium with transfer of hydride from the —CHO group,

$$\text{R—C}\overset{O}{\underset{H}{\diagdown}} \rightleftharpoons \text{R—C—H} \quad \text{C=O} \longrightarrow$$

$$\text{R—C}\overset{O}{\underset{\text{OH}}{\diagup}} + \text{RCH}_2\text{O}^\ominus \longrightarrow \text{RCO}_2^\ominus + \text{RCH}_2\text{OH}$$

forming the carboxylate anion and alcohol irreversibly. In exceptional circumstances this course may be followed even when α-H is available:

$$\overset{\diagup \text{CH}_2\text{—CHO}}{\underset{\diagdown \text{CH}_2\text{—CHO}}{\text{CH}_2}} \xrightarrow{\text{OH}^\ominus} \overset{\diagup \text{CH}_2\text{—CO}_2^\ominus}{\underset{\diagdown \text{CH}_2\text{—CH}_2\text{OH}}{\text{CH}_2}} \xrightarrow[\text{acid}]{\text{dil.}}$$

Glutaraldehyde

85

Of two possible intramolecular reactions the transfer of hydride ion is here preferred to the formation of a strained four-membered ring by aldol cyclization.

The Cannizzaro reaction is not important synthetically, although formaldehyde, which alone yields methanol and formic acid, is sometimes used in crossed reactions to reduce aldehydes:

$$X-C_6H_4-CHO \xrightarrow[\text{30\% NaOH brief reflux}]{\text{H}_2\text{O/MeOH/HCHO}} X-C_6H_4-CH_2OH + HCO_2H$$

X = for example, MeO, —OCH₂O—
yield 85–90%

Formaldehyde being very electrophilic will accept OH⊖ ion rather than the aromatic aldehyde which will subsequently accept H⊖ ion and undergo reduction. It must be pointed out that when an organic liquid phase is present during Cannizzaro reactions a radical transfer probably occurs in this phase.

Reactions of Formaldehyde. This most reactive of carbonyl compounds readily accepts carbanions derived from other aldehydes and ketones (cf. p. 80) in synthetically useful crossed aldolizations:

$$HCHO + CH_3CHO \xrightarrow[\substack{\text{dil. Na}_2\text{CO}_3 \text{ soln.} \\ 40°/24 \text{ hr}}]{J} HOCH_2-\underset{\underset{CH_2OH}{|}}{\overset{\overset{CH_2OH}{|}}{C}}-CHO \xrightarrow{K} C(CH_2OH)_4$$

82%   Pentaerythritol

$$(CH_3)_2CHCHO \xrightarrow{\text{as J}} (CH_3)_2\underset{\underset{CH_2OH}{|}}{C}-CHO \xrightarrow[\substack{\text{excess HCHO, hot} \\ 30\% \text{ KOH soln.}}]{K} (CH_3)_2C\overset{CH_2OH}{\underset{CH_2OH}{\diagdown}}$$

64%
b.p. 101°/2·5 mm

$$CH_3COCH_2CH_3 \xrightarrow{\text{1E HCHO}} CH_3COCH\overset{CH_2OH}{\underset{CH_3}{\diagdown}} \xrightarrow{\text{HCHO}} CH_3CO-\underset{\underset{CH_3}{|}}{C}(CH_2OH)_2$$

b.p. 193°   m.p. 66°

Following aldol condensation in dilute solution (as in J), when all available α-H atoms undergo condensation, the Cannizzaro reaction (K) can be carried out in more concentrated alkali. The products are isolated by extraction (ether, benzene) of the concentrated neutralized solution, or if very water-soluble by evaporation and acetone extraction. Formaldehyde will condense in a similar manner with 'active hydrogen' in other molecules, e.g. nitroparaffins and malonic esters (p. 142).

The Mannich Reaction. In its general form this may be represented as

$$X{-}\overset{|}{\underset{|}{C}}H + H.CHO + HN(R)_2 \longrightarrow X{-}CH_2{-}NR_2 + H_2O \quad (L)$$

where X is a structural element that can stabilize charge. The reaction can be regarded as an aldol condensation followed by water elimination between the aldol—OH group and hydrogen of an $-\overset{|}{N}-H$ group. Secondary amines are most widely used because a further condensation can occur with the second replaceable hydrogen of a primary amine:

$$CH_3.CO.CH_3 \xrightarrow[MeNH_2.HCl]{H.CHO} CH_3{-}CO{-}CH_2.CH_2{-}NHMe \longrightarrow (CH_3{-}CO{-}CH_2{-}CH_2)_2N{-}Me$$

56%

acetophenone behaves similarly.

Further products of reactions involving primary amines may result from intramolecular aldol condensation, as in the reaction between acetaldehyde (2 mols), formaldehyde (2 mols), and methylamine hydrochloride:

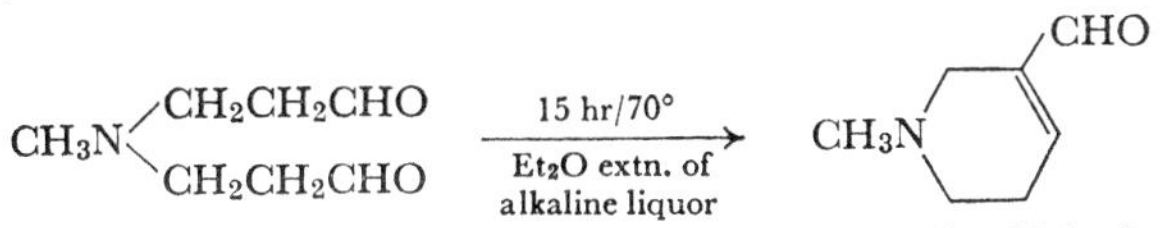

Arecaidinaldehyde
25%, b.p. 50°/0·3 mm

The Mannich reaction may be conducted in alkaline solution as for cyclohexanone and dimethylamine or in acid solution:

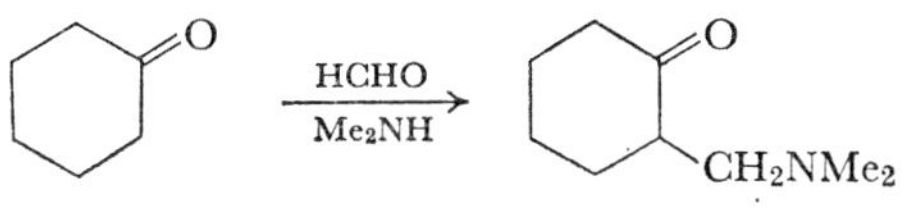

b.p. 100°/13 mm

$$(CH_3)_2CHCHO + (CH_3)_2NH.HCl \xrightarrow[\text{in EtOH}]{\text{HCHO 1 hr reflux}} (H_3C)_2C(CH_2NMe_2HCl)(CHO)$$

the Mannich base separates from the medium as its crystalline hydrochloride, m.p. 152–153° and the free base is isolated by treatment of the salt with aqueous alkali and ether extraction. If required, Mannich products can be reduced to the amino-alcohol by a crossed Cannizzaro reaction:

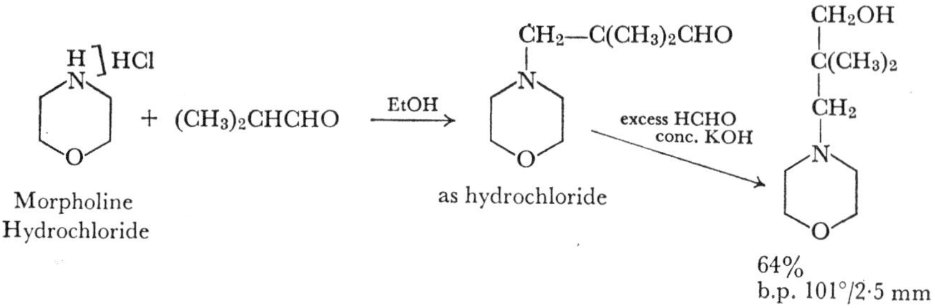

$$\text{Morpholine Hydrochloride} + (CH_3)_2CHCHO \xrightarrow{EtOH} \text{(as hydrochloride)} \xrightarrow[\text{conc. KOH}]{\text{excess HCHO}} \text{64\%, b.p. } 101°/2\cdot5 \text{ mm}$$

Since yields are often affected adversely by impurities in the amine it is most convenient to use pure amine hydrochlorides as starting materials and to operate in an acid medium. Besides the bases used in the above illustrations piperidine and diethylamine have been widely used.

Mechanism of the Reaction with Aldehydes and Ketones. Irrespective of pH the condensation (L) is of first order in X—$\overset{|}{\underset{|}{C}}$—H, H—CHO, and amine, consistent with two reversible steps to produce intermediates. In an acid medium the mechanism differs in detail from that in alkali because the rate, maximal at pH 5, rises until it reaches a new maximum at pH 10·5. The most probable course is nucleophilic attack by the amine on the strongly electrophilic formaldehyde

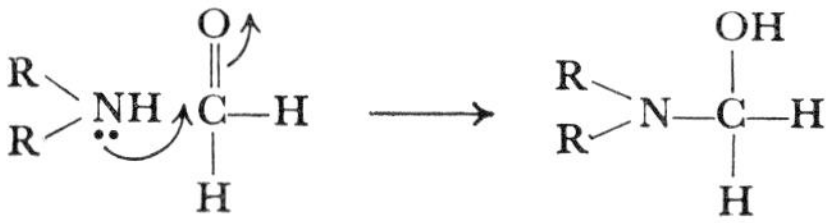

$$\begin{matrix} R \\ R \end{matrix}\!>\!NH + \overset{O}{\underset{\underset{H}{|}}{\overset{||}{C}}}\!\!-\!H \longrightarrow \begin{matrix} R \\ R \end{matrix}\!>\!N\!-\!\overset{OH}{\underset{\underset{H}{|}}{C}}\!-\!H$$

followed in alkali by attack by a carbanion:

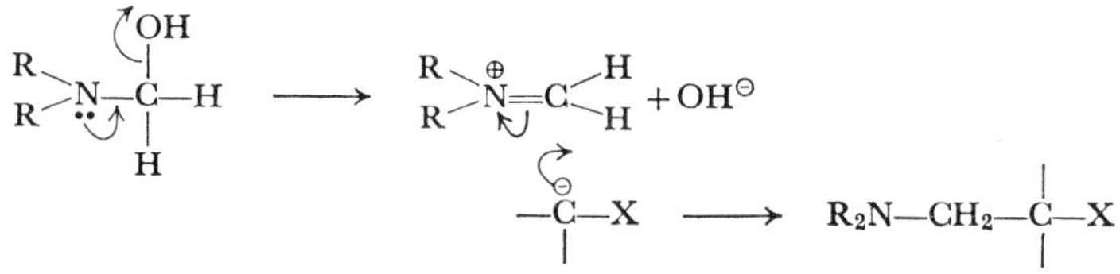

$$\begin{matrix} R \\ R \end{matrix}\!>\!N\!-\!\overset{OH}{\underset{\underset{H}{|}}{C}}\!-\!H \longrightarrow \begin{matrix} R \\ R \end{matrix}\!>\!\overset{\oplus}{N}\!=\!C\!\!<\!\!\begin{matrix} H \\ H \end{matrix} + OH^{\ominus}$$

$$-\overset{|}{\underset{|}{C}}\!-\!X \longrightarrow R_2N\!-\!CH_2\!-\!\overset{|}{\underset{|}{C}}\!-\!X$$

In acid a carbonium–imonium ion interacts with the enol of the 'active' hydrogen component:

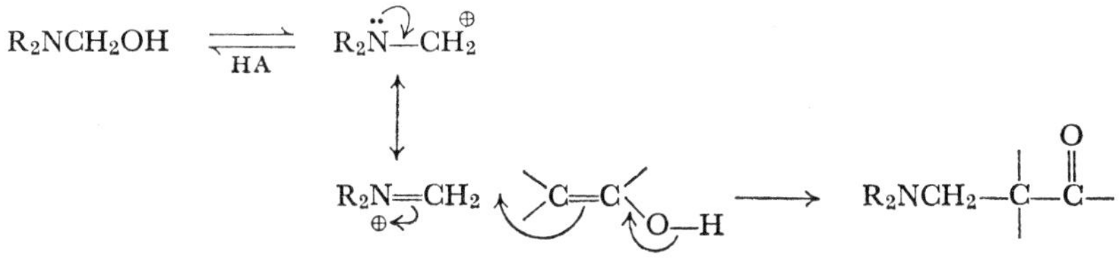

$$R_2NCH_2OH \xrightarrow[\text{HA}]{} R_2\overset{..}{N}\!-\!\overset{\oplus}{CH_2}$$

$$R_2\overset{\oplus}{N}{=\!\!=}CH_2 \;\; \begin{matrix} C=C \\ O-H \end{matrix} \longrightarrow R_2NCH_2-\overset{|}{\underset{|}{C}}-\overset{O}{\overset{||}{C}}-$$

[where in (L)
X is carbonyl]

Conjugated enones are obtained from Mannich bases by an acid- or base-catalysed elimination of a α-hydrogen atom, e.g.

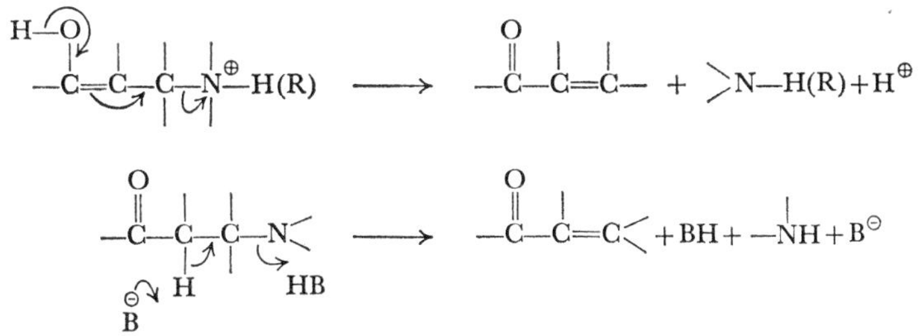

$$-\overset{H-O}{\underset{|}{C}}{=}\overset{|}{\underset{|}{C}}{-}\overset{|}{\underset{|}{C}}{-}\overset{\oplus}{N}{-}H(R) \longrightarrow -\overset{O}{\overset{||}{C}}-\overset{|}{C}{=}\overset{|}{C}{-} + \;\; >N-H(R)+H^{\oplus} \quad (M)$$

$$-\overset{O}{\overset{||}{C}}-\overset{|}{\underset{\underset{B}{\overset{\ominus}{\curvearrowleft}}H}{C}}-\overset{|}{\underset{HB}{C}}-N< \longrightarrow -\overset{O}{\overset{||}{C}}-\overset{|}{C}{=}C< + BH + -\overset{|}{N}H + B^{\ominus} \quad (N)$$

and they can therefore be used as precursors in Michael additions (cf. p. 150). Ketonic Mannich bases are stored as their salts, hydrochlorides of piperidino-bases being particularly convenient. The salts are converted via the free bases into quaternary derivatives with alkyl halides; these in their turn are the precursors of enones formed by mechanism (N) in a basic medium (pp. 159–160).

The Mannich Reaction of Aromatic Compounds. Aromatic amines are not used to catalyse the reaction with carbonyl compounds because they themselves tend to undergo ring alkylation. The acid- or base-catalysed C-alkylation of phenols (cf. p. 168) and other electron-rich aromatic nuclei also occurs:

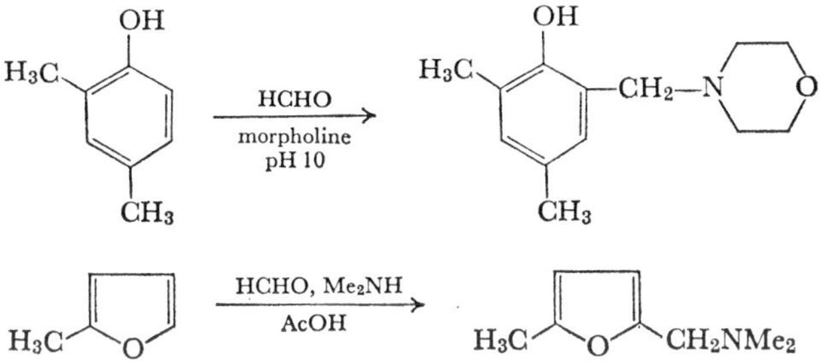

(O)

75%

Compare also the gramine synthesis on p. 160. Only one product can be obtained in the reaction (O) but *ortho*- and *para*-substitution occurs when these positions are free. Burckhalter and his colleagues showed that the reaction was of the first order in each of the reactants— rate $=k$ [formaldehyde] [morpholine] [phenol] by maintaining the conditions and a constant concentration of two reagents in turn. It was further shown that the rate depended on the formation of an intermediate from two molecules of morpholine and one of formaldehyde:

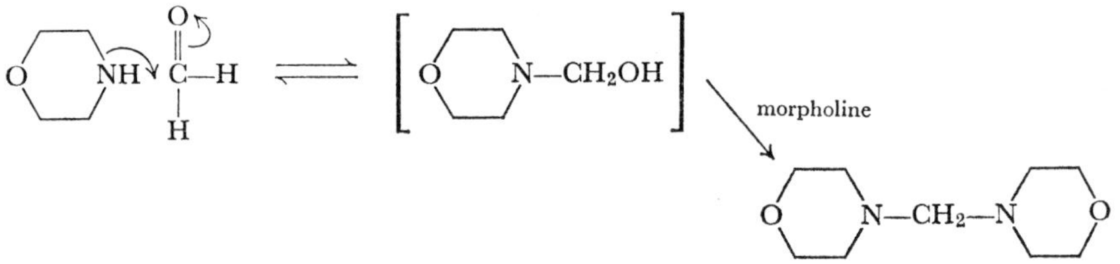

for with the concentration of phenol and formaldehyde fixed at 0·1 M the rate rose to a maximum at a morpholine concentration of 0·2 M, whilst with phenol and morpholine fixed at the former molarity the rate became maximal when the formaldehyde was 0·05 M. In order to account for the dominance of *ortho*-alkylation a six-centred transition state must be assumed for the second step:

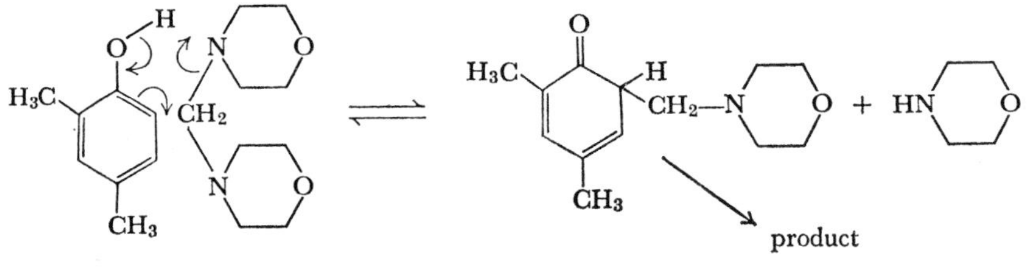

in which the free phenol and free base associate initially through a hydrogen bond. The kinetics were unchanged when the base N,N'-methylene-bismorpholine was used instead of a mixture of formaldehyde and morpholine.

Once a dialkylamino group has been introduced it may be converted into a methyl group or an oxymethylene group:

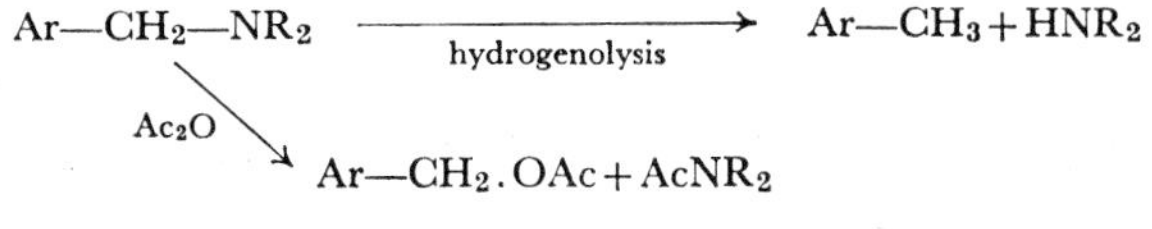

$$Ar—CH_2—NR_2 \xrightarrow{\text{hydrogenolysis}} Ar—CH_3 + HNR_2$$

$$\searrow Ac_2O$$

$$Ar—CH_2.OAc + AcNR_2$$

The Mannich condensation figures largely in the following synthesis of the anti-malarial quinine substitute, camoquin (P):

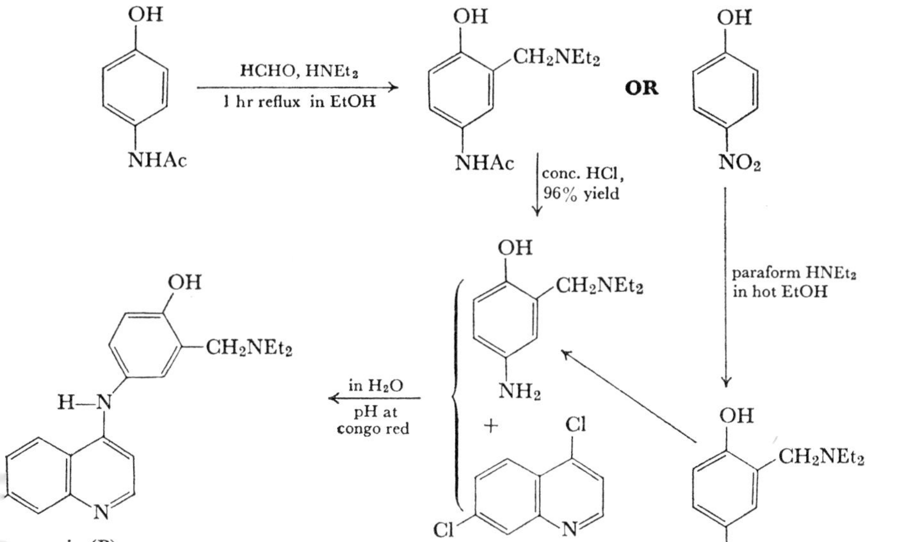

The reaction has also been widely used for the *in vitro* synthesis of alkaloids whose synthesis *in vivo* often takes the same course.

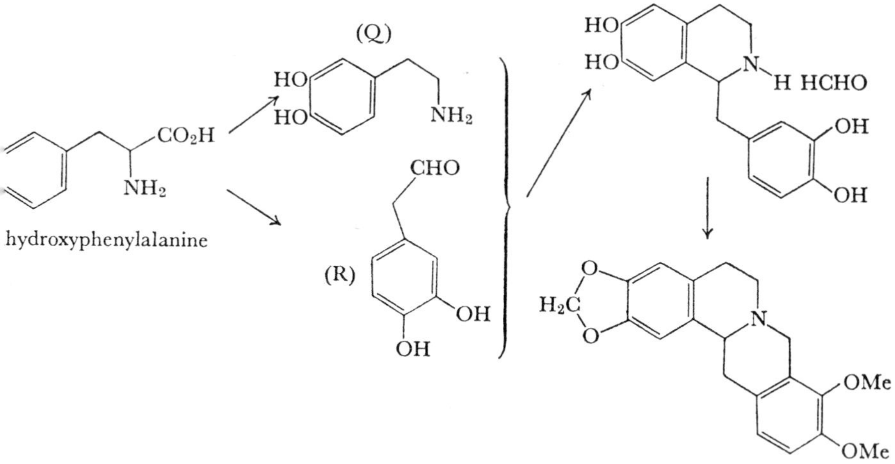

Canadine

91

Alternative modes of enzymic degradation of the amino acid afford the two intermediates (Q) and (R) which combine in a Pictet–Spengler reaction, a general method for the synthesis of isoquinolines, in which the ring is closed through a Friedel–Crafts alkylation by the carbonium–imonium ion (p. 88). The norlaudanosoline formed reacts in the Mannich sense with the biogenetic equivalent of formaldehyde to yield canadine, where the phenolic —OH groups are alkylated. The formaldehyde equivalent is the $-\overset{|}{N}-Me$ compound which is oxidized to the methylol $-\overset{|}{N}-CH_2OH$.

Alkylation Reactions. The conjugate bases of carbonyl compounds may give nucleophilic attack on a species R—X where $X^{\ominus}$ is a readily displaced anion, leading to alkylation of the parent compound

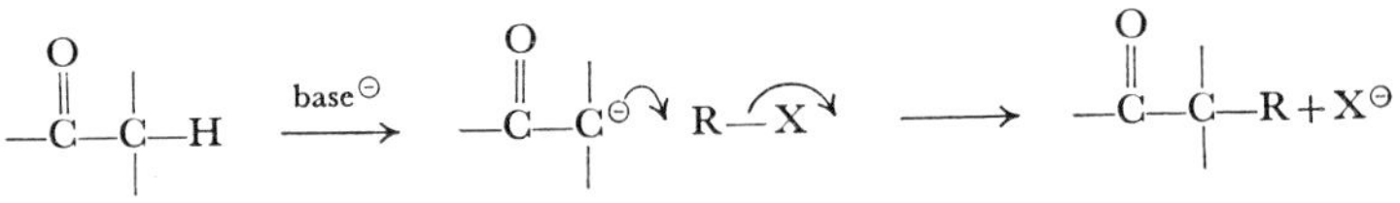

In most instances X is halogen or sulphate.

Two routes (S and T) are possible on alkylation of an unsymmetrical ketone:

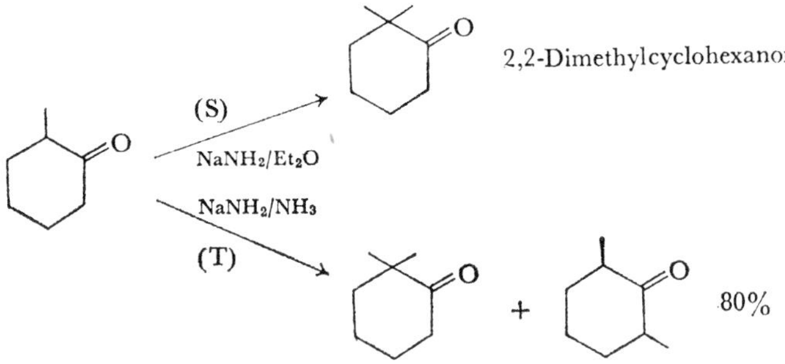

2,2-Dimethylcyclohexanone

20%   2,6-Dimethylcyclohexanone

80%

In (U, X=Me) the more highly substituted enolate reacts:

(U)

92

but the isolation of two isomeric products (route T) derived from a mixture of enols is the general finding, although the route (S) will always predominate if the substituent X, e.g. Ph, can stabilize the enol by conjugation. The ratio of products in a mixture can be varied by switching to a more or a less polar solvent. It is advisable to form the conjugate base of the ketone by addition of one equivalent of base (NaOR, NaNH$_2$, NaH) followed by the alkylating agent, thus minimizing the competing 'aldolization'.

The 2,6-dimethylcyclohexanone formed (in T) is a mixture of *cis*- and *trans*-isomers, which are separable on distillation or through their crystalline oximes, *cis* having m.p. 79° and *trans* 118°. In the presence of excess base the products will be converted into the equilibrium mixture containing 90% of the more stable *cis*-isomer:

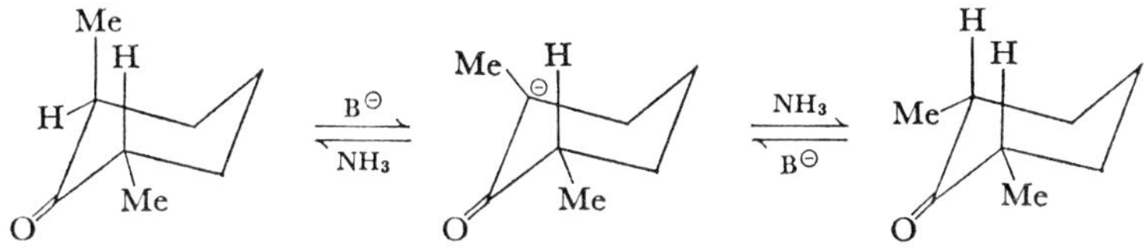

trans
10% at equilibrium

The following scheme for the synthesis of camphene invites comment:

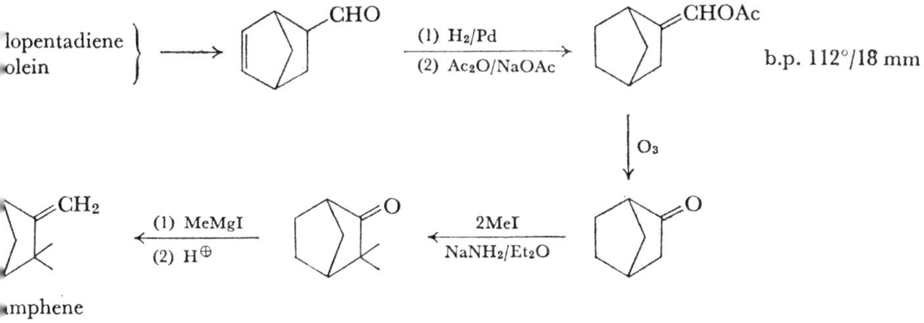

(a) the second and third steps are equivalent to the reversal of a Darzens condensation (p. 106);

(b) a strong base is needed to effect *gem* dialkylation;

(c) bridgehead alkylation does not occur because the carbanion cannot be resonance stabilized without violating Bredt's rule (cf. p. 7);

(d) the last step is better carried out by the Wittig procedure (p. 112).

93

An intramolecular reaction of this kind affords a cyclic product:

Cl(CH₂)₃CO(CH₂)₃Cl — NaOH/MeOH/H₂O →

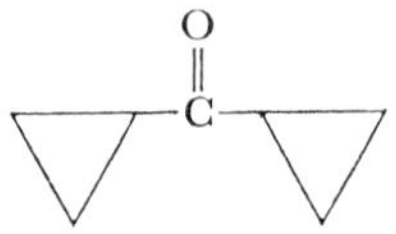

b.p. 72°/33 mm, 52%

Bridgehead Alkylation is frequently needed in the synthesis of natural products, e.g. the contraction of ring B of 9-methyldecalone-1 typifies an approach to the steroids (cf. p. 82). Direct alkylation of *trans*-decalone-1 yields principally the 2-methyl decalone:

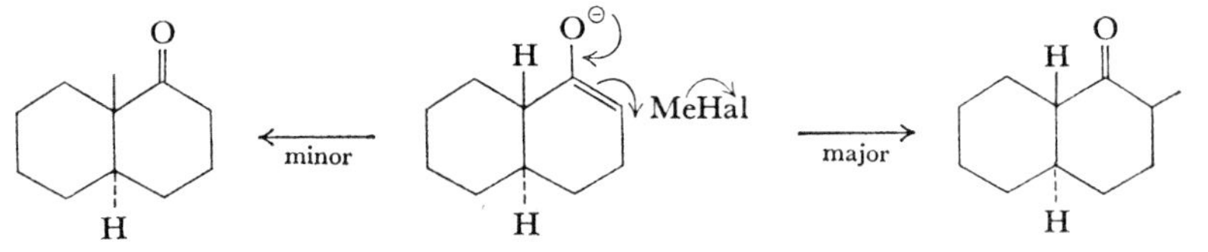

9-Methyldecalone-1   (V)   2-Methyldecalone

this is to be expected since the less hindered position is involved and the enolate shown (V) is more stable than its tautomer with a double bond at the bridgehead. W. S. Johnson and collaborators introduced a blocking group at the reactive site by aldol condensation:

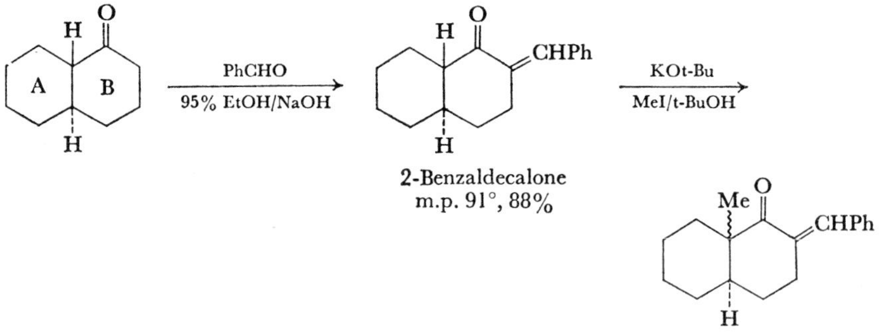

2-Benzaldecalone
m.p. 91°, 88%

Yield: 68% *cis*
23% *trans*

followed by alkylation at the bridgehead C9, which is then the only position at which a resonance stabilized carbanion can be formed. This method has two disadvantages: (*a*) it is difficult to remove the protecting group and (*b*) the proportion of the desired *trans*-isomer is low.

94

Removal of the Protecting Group.

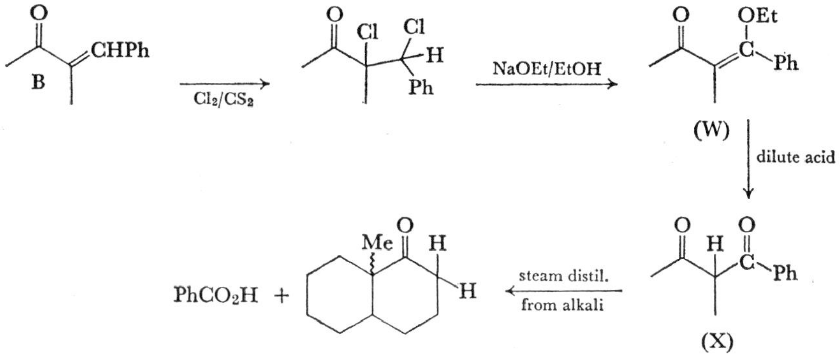

In this sequence the enol ether (W), formed by substitution at the benzylic carbon atom and elimination of hydrogen chloride, need not be isolated; the diketone (X) can also be subjected to the retro-Claisen condensation (cf. p. 138) without isolation although acid hydrolysis of (W) illustrates a viable route to β-diketones. The use of chlorine in the sequence is undesirable because it may react at other sites, for example an oxygenated aromatic nucleus could undergo chlorination, and a number of alternatives have been developed. A widely used technique is the formation of a hydroxymethylene derivative (p. 128):

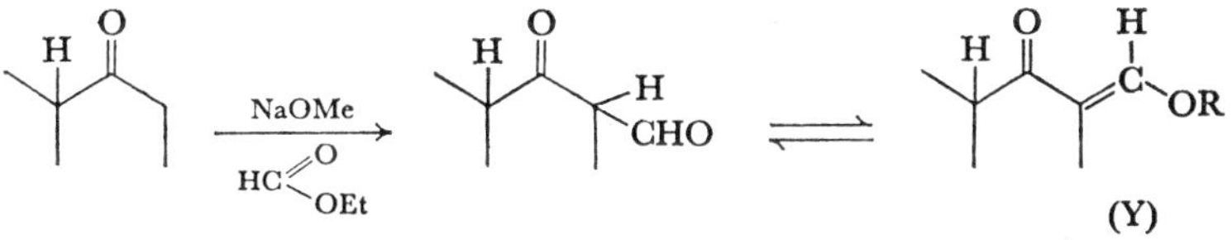

followed by O-alkylation of the enol (Y, R = H); here a bulky alkyl group is better, isopropyl iodide affording 84% of the ether (Y, R = iPr) in contrast to methyl iodide which gave an unsatisfactory mixture containing O- and C-alkylation products in acetone/potassium carbonate (but cf. p. 141). The C-methyl group at the bridgehead can be introduced by treatment of the enol ether with methyl iodide and a strong base (e.g. potassium t-butoxide) but yields are often low because electron donation from the oxygen atom of the protecting group makes abstraction of the α-hydrogen atom by base more difficult:

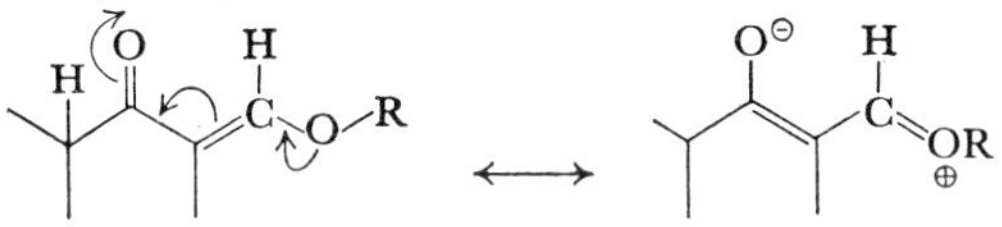

95

The thioethers are superior because the conjugative effect of sulphur is much less than that of oxygen; treatment of both ethers with alkali regenerates the enol which gives product and formic acid on steam distillation via a retro-Claisen condensation:

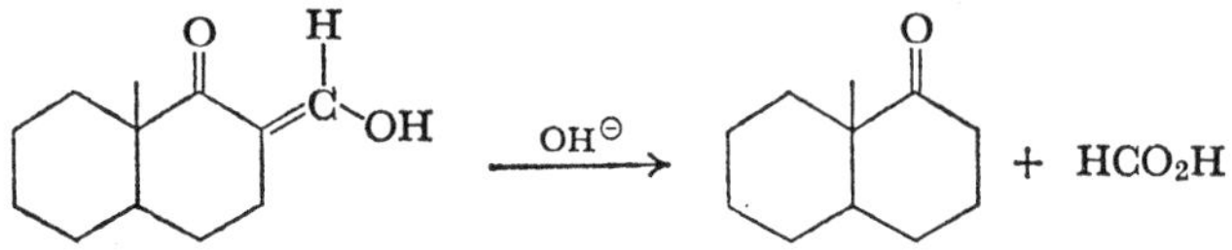

Steric Control of Alkylation. W. S. Johnson showed that the ratio of isomers obtained on alkylation at a bridgehead was independent of electronic factors, for a *p*-nitrobenzylidene blocking group gave the same results as the unsubstituted derivative; variation of the halogen in the methylating agent was also without effect. From the influence of ring substituents on the *cis/trans* ratio from 2-arylidene-1-decalones it was deduced that the transition state for alkylation resembled the reactants more closely than the products. When one considers two transition states, (Z) and (AA), for *cis*- and *trans*-alkylation respectively, which have configurations like the products:

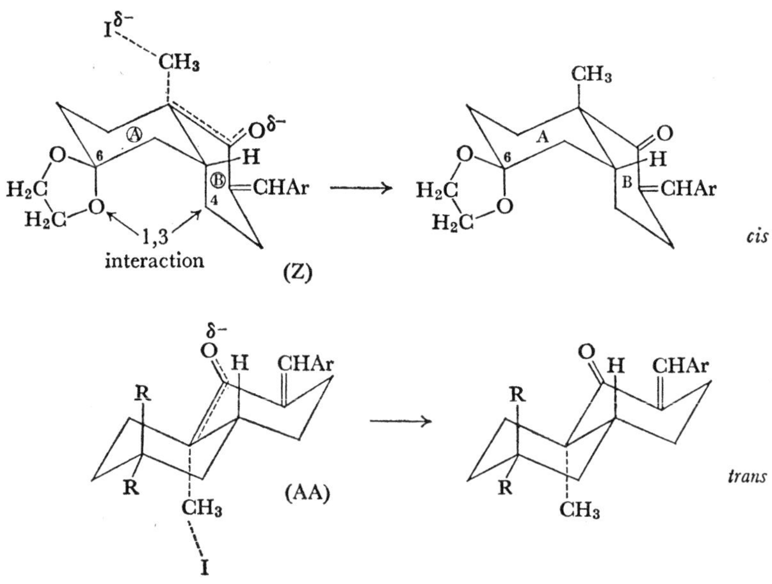

(R,R = —O—CH₂CH₂—O—)

then *gem* disubstitution at C6 would destabilize the transition state for *cis*-alkylation because it includes a large 1–3 interaction with the axially substituted carbon-4 of ring B, leading to a decrease in the amount of *cis* product. In fact, the *cis/trans* ratio rises slightly and hence the above view of the transition state is untenable. The alternative product-like transition state for *cis*-alkylation has the conformation (AB) obtained by 'flipping' (Z); here no 1–3 interaction is possible for C6-disubstituted derivatives which is consistent with the above findings,

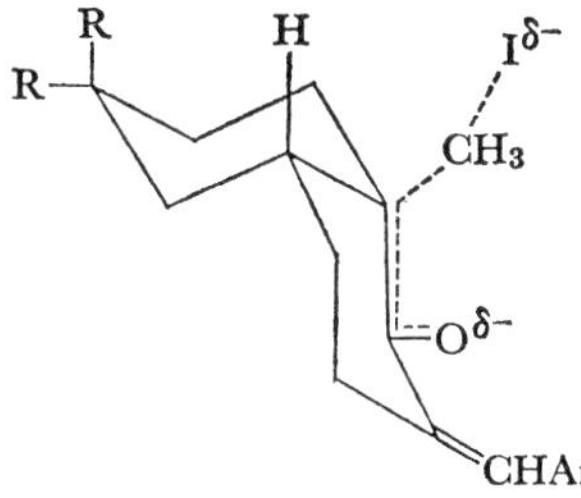

(AB)

(R,R = —O—CH$_2$CH$_2$—O—)

but not with the behaviour of the decalone (AC) *trans*-disubstituted at C3 and/or C4. In this example the alkyl substituents would become axial in the transition state for *cis*-alkylation if this resembled products (AD)

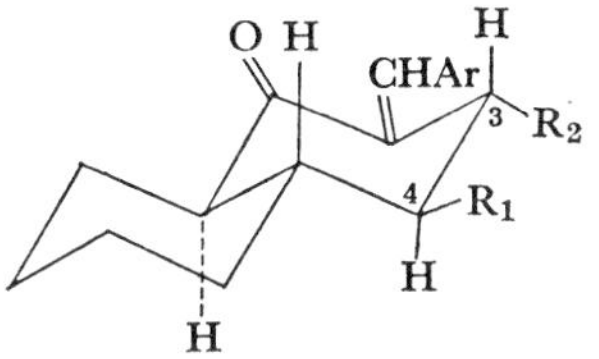

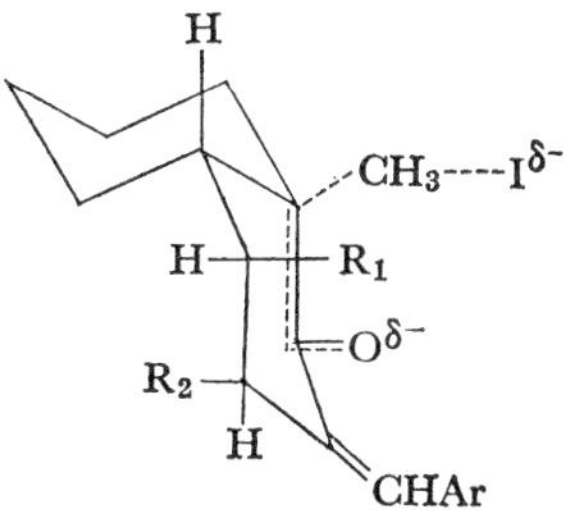

(AC)   (AD)

leading to its destabilization and an increase in the proportion of *trans*-alkylation. In fact for R_1 = —O—tetrahydropyranyl, R_2 = H, the *cis/trans* ratio rose to 9:1, which leaves the transition state (AF below) which resembles reactants as the only acceptable model (see structural formulae at top of p. 98).

The methyl group enters along an axis perpendicular to the C=C bond of the enol giving maximum interaction with its electrons. Entry from above (AE) affords a *trans* product but this approach is hindered by 1–3 repulsive interactions between the methyl group and axial hydrogen atoms at the 4, 5, and 7 positions, therefore the *cis* product formed by approach from below (AF) predominates. The presence of a C=C bond

97

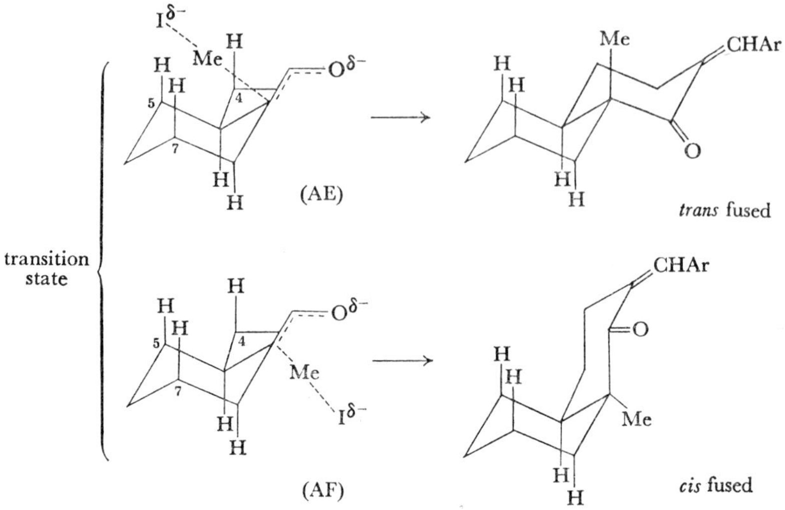
transition state
(AE)
trans fused
(AF)
cis fused
CHAr
Me

between carbon 6 and carbon 7 eliminates one interaction hindering approach from above (AE) and reduces that at carbon 5 where the C—H bond becomes quasi-axial and is tilted away from the incoming group. In fact methylation of ketones of this type gives predominantly the *trans*-isomer consistent with a transition state of type (AE) and as an example of a controlled methylation one can consider the sequence:

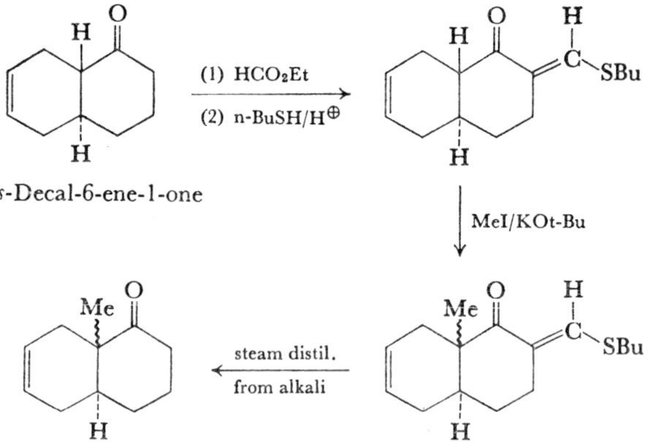
trans-Decal-6-ene-1-one
(1) HCO_2Et
(2) n-BuSH/$H^{\oplus}$
SBu
MeI/KOt-Bu
steam distil.
from alkali
Me

(AG) *cis* and *trans* 88% yield   89% yield of mixed isomers

A point of interest here is that the octalones (AG) were not separable by gas–liquid chromatography, but after hydrogenation to the 9-methyl-decalone two isomers were detected by this technique in a ratio of 3:1.

The major product was shown to be *trans* by degradation to the dicarboxylic acid (AH) of known configuration (see Chapter 5, question 1*e*).

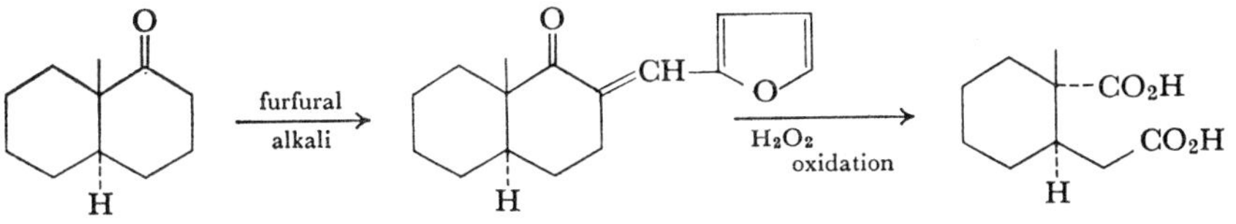

By hydrogenation   m.p. 75°   (AH)

Halogenation. In acid the reaction rate is independent of the halogen
and is the same as the rate of enolization. For a series of methyl ketones,
$R{-}\overset{*}{C}H_2COCH_3$, substitution occurs preferentially at the marked carbon
atom via the more stable enol:

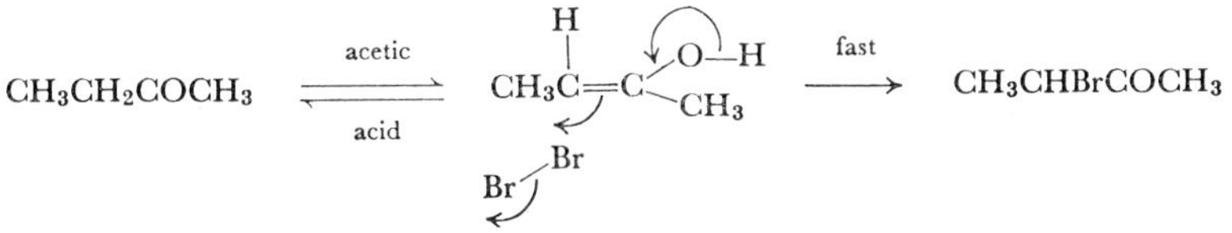

some dibromocompound may be formed, even when only one equivalent
of bromine is used, with recovery of the corresponding amount of
unchanged ketone: with aldehydes the position of substitution is un-
ambiguous. The halogenated products themselves are important intermediates, for example they are readily converted into unsaturated
carbonyl compounds by a base-catalysed elimination:

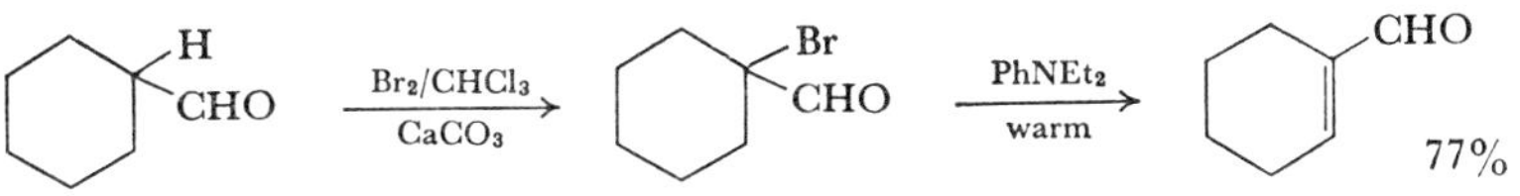

80%   Cyclohexenealdehyde

During halogenation in alkali a proton is abstracted from the less
hindered position and nucleophilic attack on halogen follows:

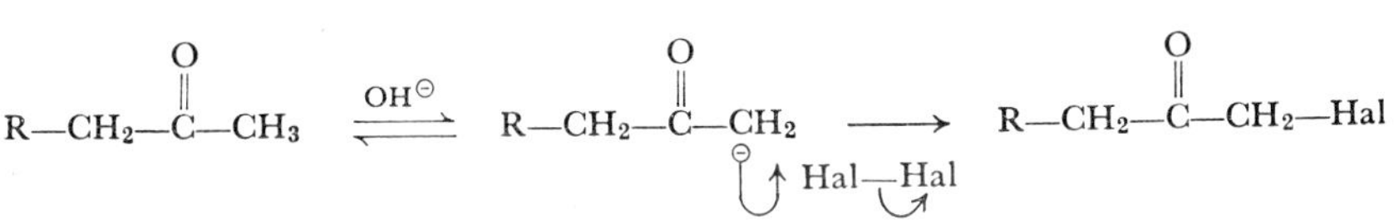

99

When bromine and chlorine are employed it is difficult to control the reaction because removal of a second proton is facilitated by the electron-withdrawing C—Hal bond (cf. Darzen's condensation, p. 106) and the second and third stages are more rapid than the first:

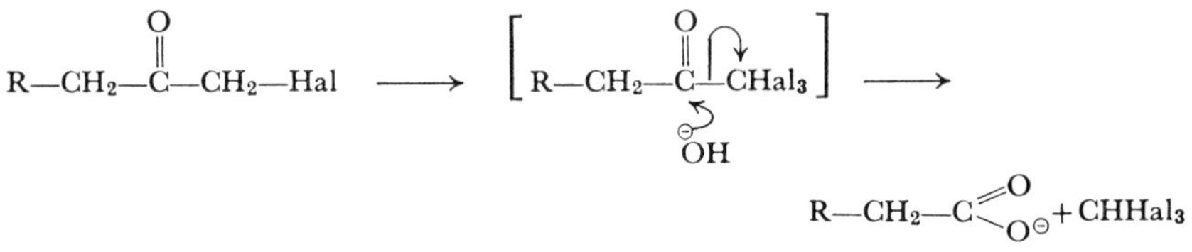

$$R-CH_2-\overset{\overset{\displaystyle O}{\|}}{C}-CH_2-Hal \longrightarrow \left[R-CH_2-\overset{\overset{\displaystyle O}{\|}}{\underset{\underset{\displaystyle OH}{\ominus}}{C}}-CHal_3 \right] \longrightarrow$$

$$R-CH_2-C\overset{\displaystyle O}{\underset{\displaystyle O\ominus}{\diagup}} + CHHal_3$$

furthermore, in alkali the trihalomethyl anion is displaced as a stable leaving group $\ominus CHal_3$ which captures a proton from the solvent, commonly water or aqueous dioxan, affording the haloform. This course clearly cannot be followed for ketones which lack a methyl group where fission of a single carbon fragment is not possible:

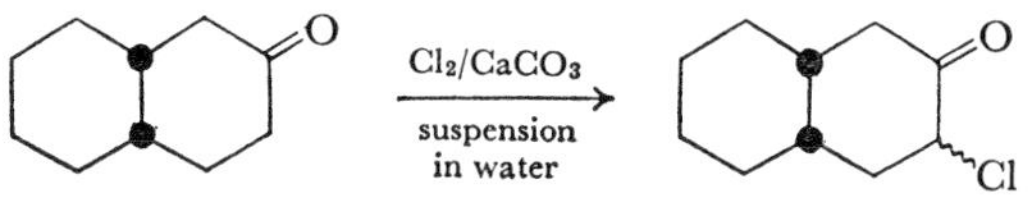

cis-Decal-2-one   66%

The sequential substitution is appreciably slower for iodine than for the other halogens, where the inductive effect of the C—I bond is not so marked and where steric hindrance becomes a factor; as a result partially iodinated ketones may frequently be isolated:

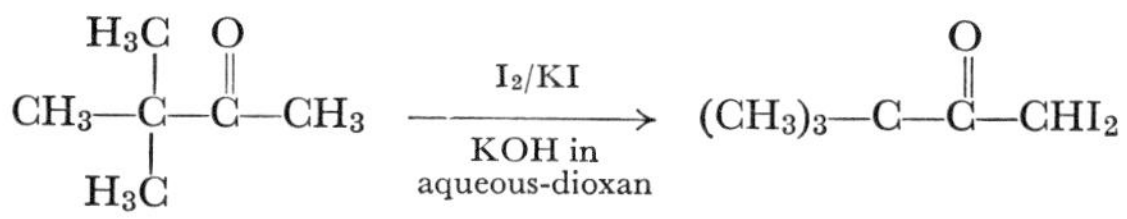

Pinacolone   m.p. 76°

By using half the equivalent of iodine the mono-iodopinacolone, b.p. 49°/2 mm, may be obtained. It follows that if the reaction is to be used as a qualitative test for methyl ketones an excess of iodine is desirable when pinacolone yields iodoform, m.p. 120°, and trimethylacetic acid. The test can fail when applied to highly hindered methyl ketones such as acetomesitylene

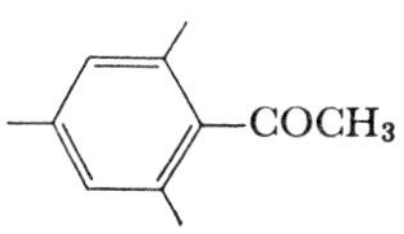

which affords only the di-iodoketone, m.p. 94°.

100

Carbenes (cf. p. 188) strictly fall outside the theme of the text but their growing synthetic importance makes a mention desirable.

If a trihalocarbanion is obtained from a haloform in an aprotic solvent it will be unlikely to capture a proton from the H-base formed but will eject halide ion:

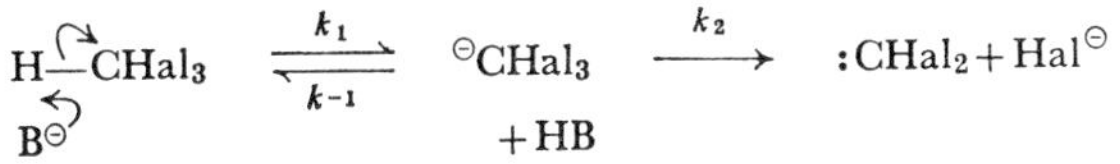

$$H\overset{\curvearrowleft}{\underset{B^\ominus}{-}}CHal_3 \quad \underset{k_{-1}}{\overset{k_1}{\rightleftarrows}} \quad \overset{\ominus}{C}Hal_3 \quad \overset{k_2}{\longrightarrow} \quad :CHal_2 + Hal^\ominus$$
$$+HB$$

The first step, carbanion formation, is easy for iodoform and very difficult for fluoroform, and the relative abilities of halogen atoms to stabilize the carbanion are in the order $I \sim Br > Cl > F$. This may be due to the greater ease of accommodating 10 electrons by d-orbital resonance in the larger halogens:

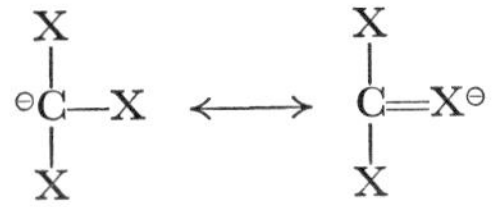

$$\underset{X}{\overset{X}{\underset{|}{\overset{|}{\ominus C}}}} - X \quad \longleftrightarrow \quad \underset{X}{\overset{X}{\underset{|}{\overset{|}{C}}}} = X^\ominus$$

or may reflect their greater polarizability. Stabilization of the dihalo-carbene is in the reverse order, $F \gg Cl > Br > I$, and may be attributed to the relative ability to donate electrons to the carbon mesomerically: $Hal—\overset{..}{C}—Hal \leftrightarrow Hal—\overset{\ominus}{C}=Hal^\oplus$. The orbitals of the small fluorine atom are expected to overlap most effectively with those of the carbon atom. Dihalocarbenes can be trapped as olefin adducts:

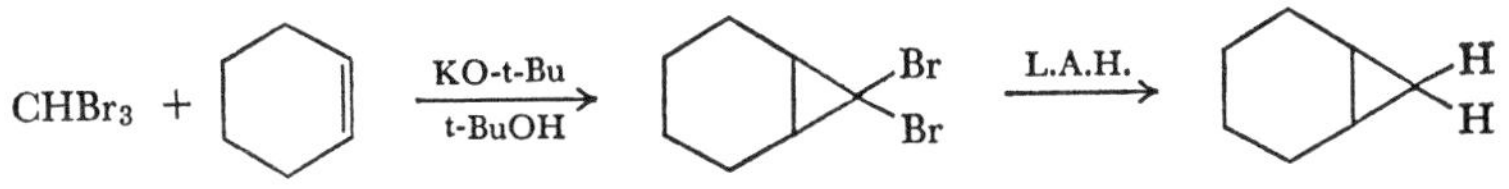

Dibromonorcarane   Norcarane
75%, b.p. 100°/18 mm

these in turn afford cyclopropane derivatives on reduction, for example by lithium aluminium hydride. Carbenes are also obtained following hydrogen exchange between an alkyl halide and a metal alkyl:

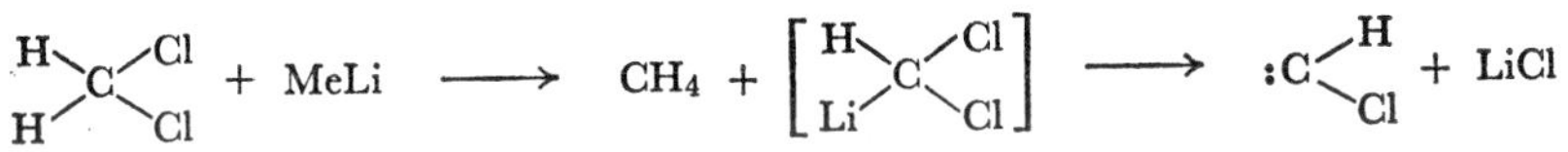

101

Ring expansion of some heterocyclic compounds occurs on reaction with a halocarbene:

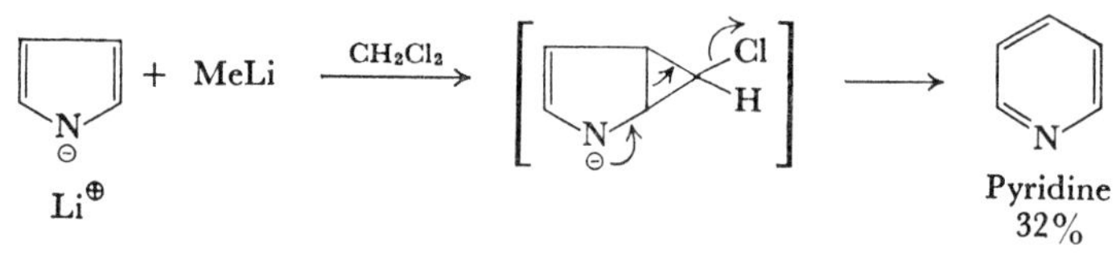

Pyridine
32%

The Reimer–Tiemann Reaction (1876) provides a route to phenolic aldehydes by treatment of a hot alkaline solution of the phenol with chloroform; ethanol and pyridine can be used as co-solvents but the latter is likely to encourage side-reactions.

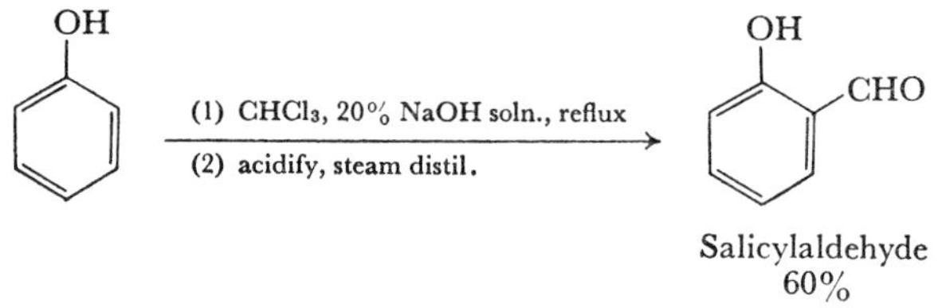

(1) CHCl₃, 20% NaOH soln., reflux
(2) acidify, steam distil.

Salicylaldehyde
60%

A small amount of *p*-hydroxybenzaldehyde, which is not steam volatile, is also formed. Yields of the mixed aldehydes do not usually exceed 50% and the proportion of the *ortho*-isomer, which is the major product from the simpler phenols, falls away when more complex substrates are used; overall yields are also reduced by deactivating substituents such as

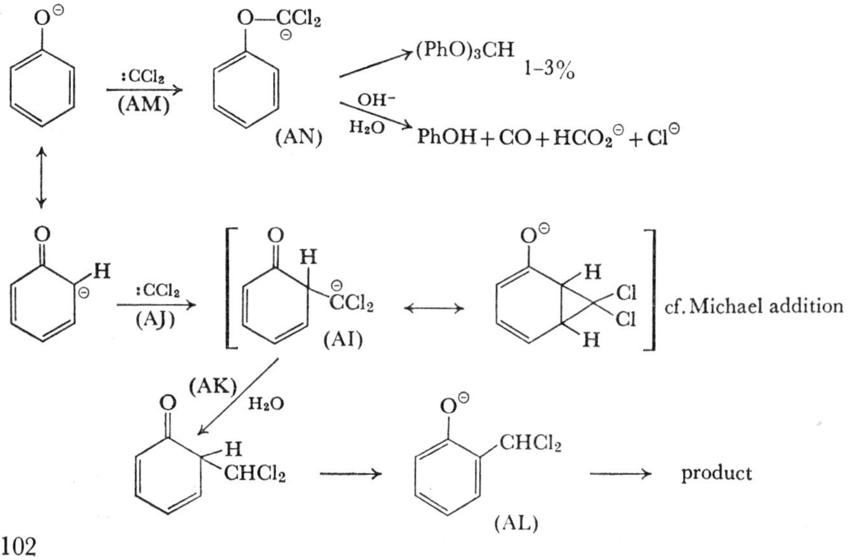

102

—NO$_2$, Hal—, and —CHO groups. In general, working-up entails the removal of excess chloroform and any co-solvent by steam distillation of the liquor, followed by acidification, extraction of products and their separation by distillation or chromatography.

The reaction conditions are typically those for the formation of carbenes (p. 99) and in fact bromoform, iodoform, and trichloroacetic acid have all been employed, the latter decarboxylating to give the trichloromethyl anion (p. 171) and thence dichloro carbene. Hine has interpreted the mechanism as being analogous to haloform hydrolysis save that the Reimer–Tiemann reaction involves attack by the ambident phenoxide ion (see structural formulae at foot of p. 102).

Following proton abstraction from the solvent by the anion (AI) the benzal chloride formed rapidly undergoes hydrolysis to the aldehyde. The two steps (AJ) and (AK) could be concerted:

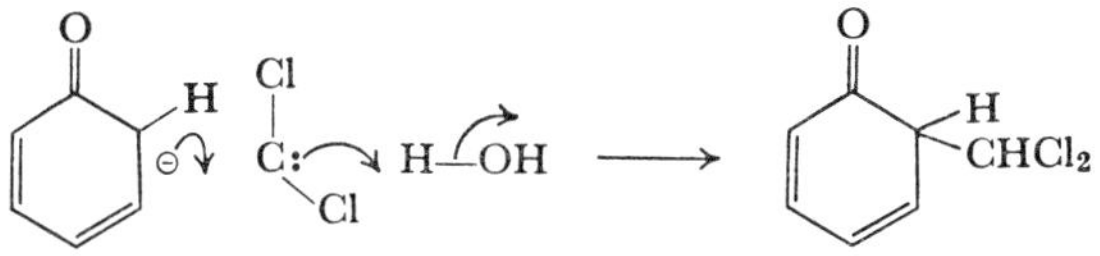

The competing O-alkylation (AM) leads to the formation of a little triphenylorthoformate and products typical of the hydrolysis of the intermediate (AN).

The formation of interesting products from side-reactions is consistent with the above mechanism:

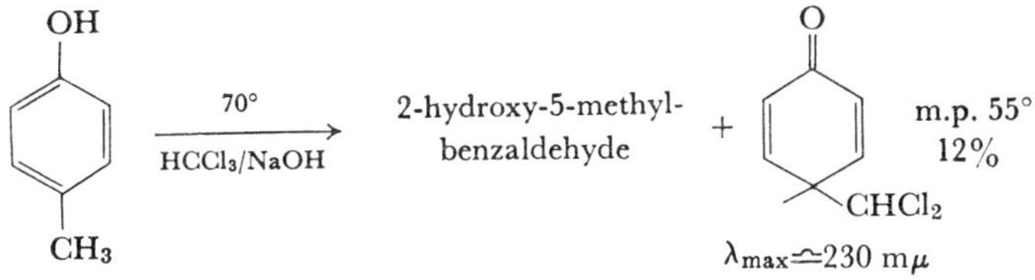

The dichloromethyl dienone results because the proton transfer

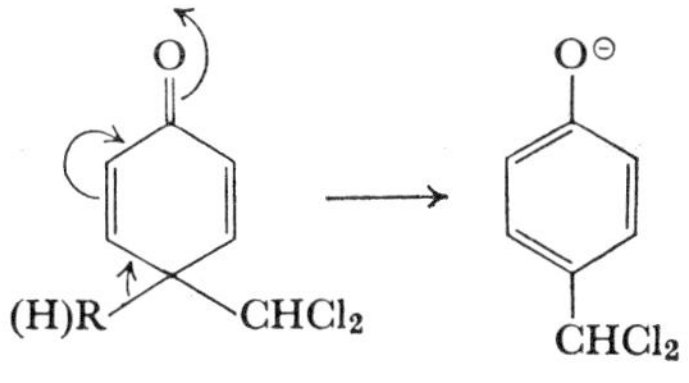

is blocked when R = alkyl. A dienone was the only product isolated in the reaction with 1-methyl-2-napthol:

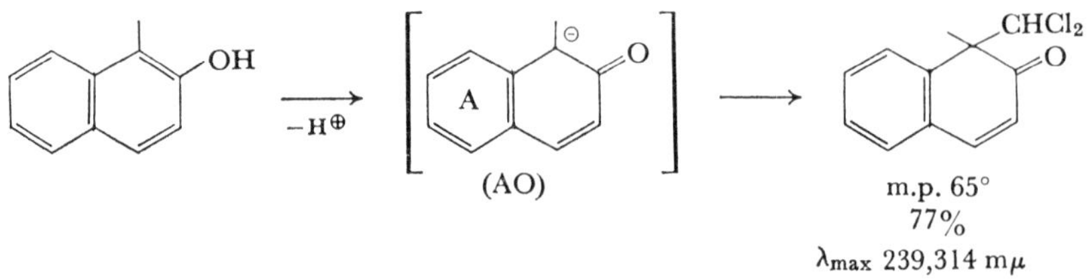

It should be noted that the mesomeric anion (AO) is preferred to

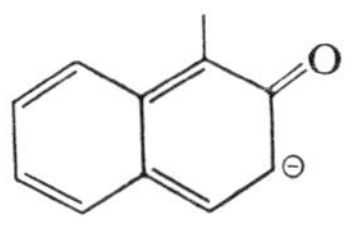

because it retains the aromatic ring A. The reaction of α-tetralol afforded the bridgehead alkylation product (AP):

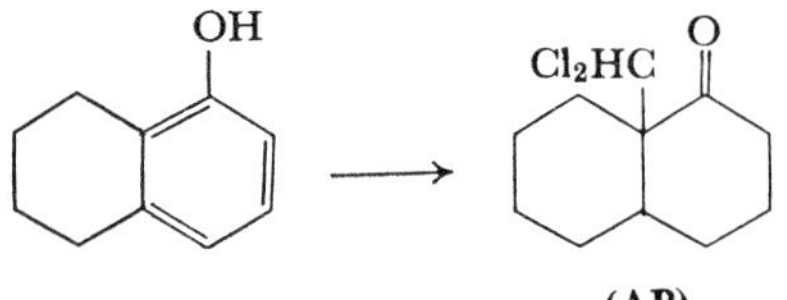

(AP)

together with about four times the yield of combined aldehydes and some orthoformate $(RO)_3CH$. This is the expected result since the precursor of (AP) lacks the particular stability of (AO). The structure of (AP) was proved by hydrogenation/hydrogenolysis with Raney nickel to the known 9-methyldecalone, thus confirming the structural change from an aromatic precursor already indicated by the ultraviolet absorption of the dienone. Applications of this sequence to steroids have had only limited success.

Heterocyclic nitrogen compounds with an acidic hydrogen atom undergo the Reimer–Tiemann reaction:

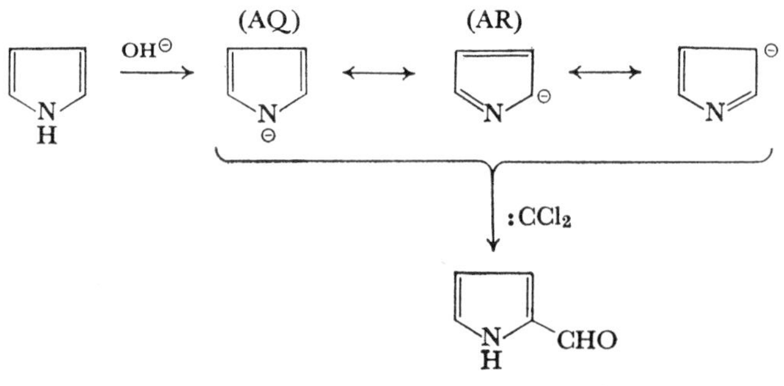

Pyrrole-2-aldehyde, 31%

104

These compounds also undergo the ring expansion referred to on p. 102 following addition of the carbene:

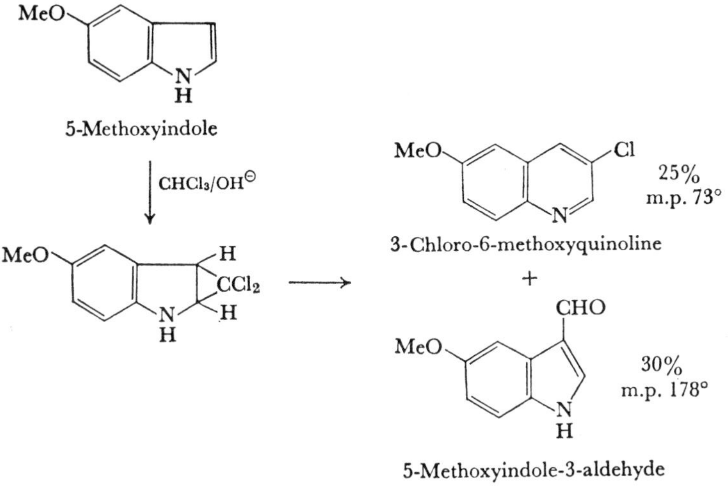
MeO
N
H
5-Methoxyindole
$CHCl_3/OH^{\ominus}$
MeO
H
CCl_2
H
N
H
MeO
Cl
N
25%
m.p. 73°
3-Chloro-6-methoxyquinoline
+
CHO
MeO
N
H
30%
m.p. 178°
5-Methoxyindole-3-aldehyde

The 'normal' reaction, with the conjugate base of the heterocyclic compound, is favoured when there is a large excess of the basic catalyst. The ring expansion is favoured in the absence of strong base in aprotic solvents which encourage addition of carbene:

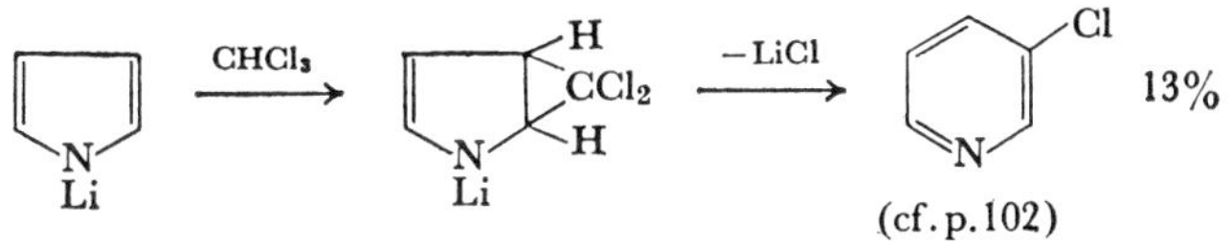
N
Li
$CHCl_3$
H
CCl_2
H
N
Li
−LiCl
Cl
N
13%
(cf. p. 102)

The Duff Reaction (1941) is sometimes superior to the Reimer–Tiemann for the preparation of phenolic aldehydes; it can be carried out in two stages:

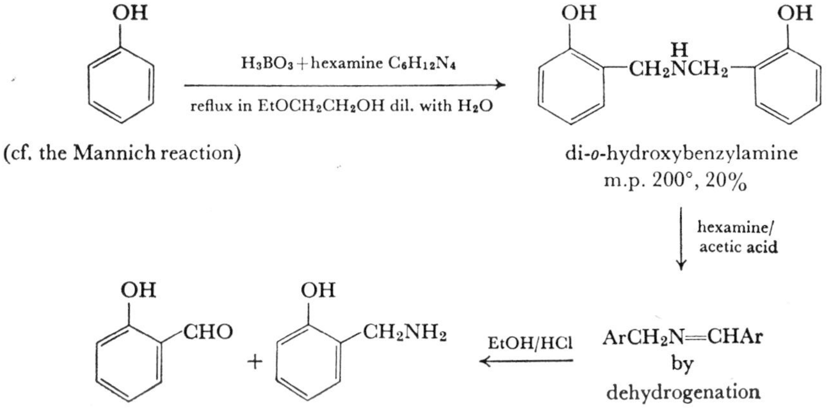
OH
H_3BO_3 + hexamine $C_6H_{12}N_4$
reflux in $EtOCH_2CH_2OH$ dil. with H_2O
(cf. the Mannich reaction)
OH
H
CH_2NCH_2
OH
di-o-hydroxybenzylamine
m.p. 200°, 20%
hexamine/
acetic acid
OH
CHO
+
OH
CH_2NH_2
EtOH/HCl
$ArCH_2N{=}CHAr$
by
dehydrogenation

8

A single-stage procedure using glycerol–boric acid and hexamine gives overall yields of the order of 20% of phenolic aldehydes.

Darzens Condensation (1904). This is principally used in the synthesis of α,β-epoxyesters, or glycidic esters, by reaction of ketones or aromatic aldehydes with an α-haloester and base:

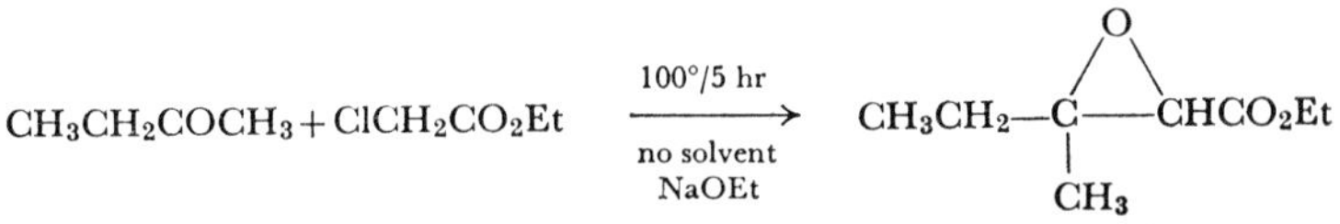

$$CH_3CH_2COCH_3 + ClCH_2CO_2Et \xrightarrow[\substack{\text{no solvent} \\ \text{NaOEt}}]{100°/5 \text{ hr}} CH_3CH_2-\overset{O}{\underset{CH_3}{C}}-CHCO_2Et$$

b.p. 95°/17 mm, 56%

Use of ether as solvent and a nitrogen atmosphere is preferable—work up by washing with cold dil. acid and evaporation of ether.

For many years the reaction was thought to be dependent on carbenes as intermediates, but it now appears that the process resembles aldolization:

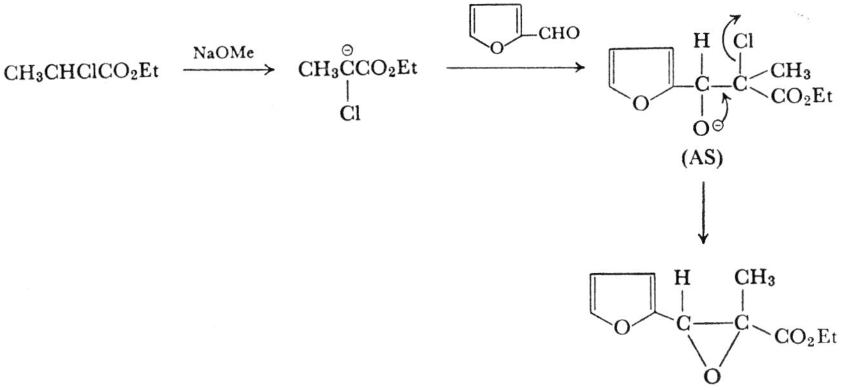

(AS)

50%

A related reaction that affords high yields was used for kinetic studies (see structural formulae at top of p. 107).

Both chlorohydrins (AT) give oxide on further contact—their formation is due to capture of a proton by intermediates of type (AS). This reaction is of first order in aldehyde, phenacyl halide, and in the OH⊖ ion. Removal of proton to form the conjugate base of the phenacyl halide will be too fast to determine the rate; for this is true even for the aldol

106

$$p\text{-NO}_2\text{C}_6\text{H}_4\text{CHO} + \overset{\overset{\text{Cl}}{|}}{\text{CH}_2\text{CO}}-\underset{\underset{\text{OMe}}{}}{\overset{\overset{\text{OMe}}{}}{\boxed{}}}-\text{OMe} \xrightarrow[\text{KOH at }0°]{\text{H}_2\text{O/dioxan}}$$

$$\underset{\underset{\text{H}}{|}}{\overset{\overset{\text{HO}}{|}}{\text{O}_2\text{NC}_6\text{H}_4}-\text{C}}-\underset{\underset{\text{H}}{|}}{\overset{\overset{\text{Cl}}{|}}{\text{C}}}-\text{C}_6\text{H}_2(\text{OMe})_3$$

(AT)

The *meso* form, m.p. 112°, and the racemate, m.p. 171°, were isolated at low conversion.

condensation of acetophenone and benzaldehyde. Hence either step (AU) or step (AV) determines the rate:

$$\underset{\underset{\text{+ Ar'CHO}}{}}{\overset{\overset{\text{H}}{}}{\text{O}\!=\!\!\overset{\ominus}{\text{C}}\!=\!\!\underset{\underset{\text{Ar}}{|}}{\text{C}}\!-\!\text{Cl}}} \overset{\text{(AU)}}{\rightleftharpoons} \underset{\underset{\text{Cl}}{\underset{|}{}}}{\text{ArCOC}}\overset{\overset{\text{H }\;\overset{\ominus}{\text{O}}}{|}}{-\overset{|}{\text{C}}}\!-\!\text{Ar'} \xrightarrow{\text{(AV)}} \text{ArCO}\!-\!\underset{\underset{\text{H}}{|}}{\text{C}}\overset{\overset{\text{O}}{\triangle}}{}\underset{\underset{\text{H}}{|}}{\text{C}}\!-\!\text{Ar'} + \text{Cl}^{\ominus}$$

Ar = —C₆H₂(OMe)₃; Ar' = O₂N—C₆H₄—

If (AV) were slow and rate-determining there would be appreciable amounts of aldehyde and enolate in equilibrium owing to the faster reversal of (AU), and this was shown not to be so because addition of the chlorohydrin Ph.CO.CHCl.CHOH.Ph to base in the presence of the more reactive *p*-nitrobenzaldehyde led only to

$$\text{Ph.CO.}\underset{}{\overset{\overset{\text{H}\quad\text{H}}{|\quad\;|}}{\text{C}\!-\!\!-\!\text{C}}}\!-\!\text{Ph}$$
$$\diagdown_{\text{O}}\diagup$$

with no product detected from interaction of the

$$\underset{\underset{\text{Ph}}{|}}{\overset{\overset{\ominus\;\;\text{H}}{}}{\text{O}\!=\!\!\text{C}\!=\!\!\text{C}}\!-\!\text{Cl}}$$

ion with this nitro aldehyde; therefore the intermolecular step (AU) determines the rate and this is consistent with the effect of substituents. Thus an electron-withdrawing —NO₂ group on the aldehyde accelerates the reaction by encouraging a crossed condensation between the enolate and aldehyde, whereas electron donors such as —OMe and —CH₃ inhibit

107

the crossed reaction and may lead to condensation of two molecules of phenacyl halide:

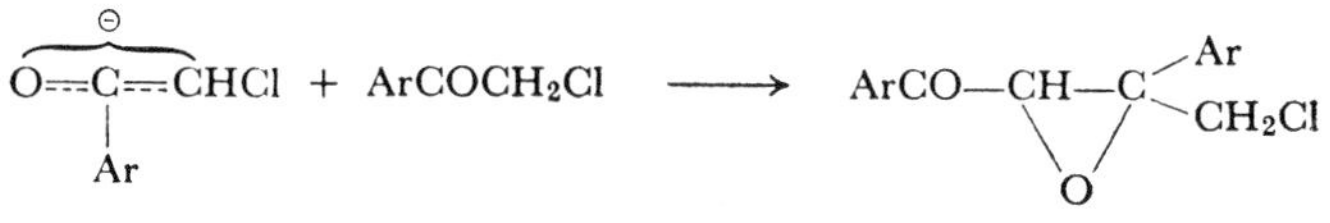

$$\overset{\ominus}{\overbrace{O\!=\!\!=\!C\!=\!\!=\!CHCl}} \; + \; ArCOCH_2Cl \; \longrightarrow \; ArCO\!-\!CH\!-\!C\underset{\diagdown O\diagup}{\overset{\diagup Ar}{\diagdown CH_2Cl}}$$
$$\underset{Ar}{|}$$

Electron donors on the phenacyl halide obstruct this, ensuring a clean reaction in the example (AT) chosen for kinetic study.

The Darzens condensation has been used frequently in the synthesis of natural products, for example in one route to bicyclic monoterpenes:

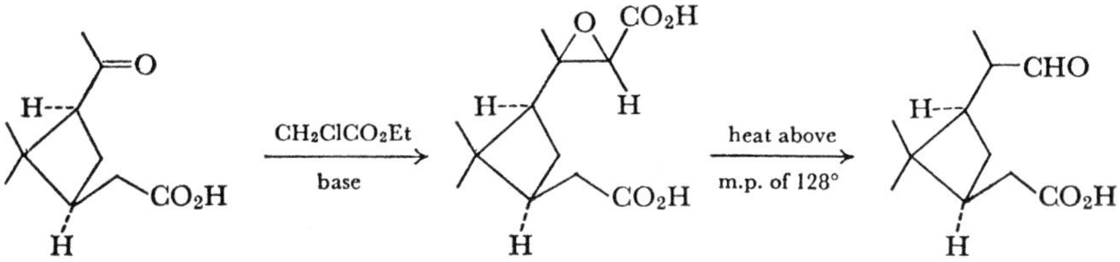

Pinonic acid

whence oxidation of the carbonyl group affords a dicarboxylic acid whose diester now cyclizes in the Dieckmann fashion (p. 133) to the ketone

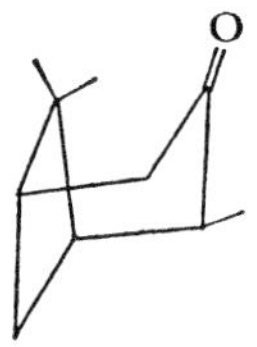

a precursor of the pinenes. For another example, see p. 58.

The Favorsky Rearrangement (1894). This occurs on treatment of an α-haloketone with a strong base:

$$(CH_3)_2.CBr.CO.CH_3 \; \xrightarrow[NaOEt/Et_2O]{} \; (CH_3)_3.C.CO_2Et \quad 61\%$$
(AW)

Dihaloketones rearrange with elimination of hydrogen halide to give the unsaturated acid:

$$CH_3.CCl_2.CO.CH_3 \; \xrightarrow{K_2CO_3/H_2O} \; CH_2\!=\!C(CH_3)\!-\!CO_2H$$

Wholly aqueous solutions are not very satisfactory and solutions of alkali hydroxides (affording acids) or alkoxides (affording esters) in dioxan or alcohol are to be preferred, whilst aromatic hydrocarbons can be used

108

if the solubilities of the reactants make this desirable. Chloroketones are better than bromocompounds which tend to encourage the principal side-reaction, namely the α-epoxyether formation

$$\underset{\overset{|}{\underset{O}{-C-C-}}}{\overset{\uparrow Hal \ \ \overset{\ominus}{\zeta}OR}{}} \longrightarrow \underset{\underset{O}{\diagdown \diagup}}{\overset{OR}{-C-C-}}$$

which results from nucleophilic attack on the carbonyl group. Weaker bases, for example $PhO^{\ominus}$, do not effect rearrangement, in keeping with its accepted mechanism (p. 110) which depends on proton abstraction by a basic nucleophile.

The chief applications are in the preparation of branched-chain and cycloalkane–carboxylic acids, and in ring contraction. A common product is obtained in similar yield whichever α-carbon atom bears the halogen:

$$
\begin{array}{l}
C_3H_7-CHCl-CO-CH_2-CH_3 \\
\text{4-Chloro-3-heptanone}
\end{array}
\searrow
\begin{array}{c}
\xrightarrow[Et_2O]{NaOMe}
\end{array}
\begin{array}{l}
(AX) \\
C_3H_7-CH(CO_2Me)-C_2H_5 \\
\text{Methyl 2-ethylvalerate} \\
65-77\%
\end{array}
$$

$$
\begin{array}{l}
C_4H_9-CO-CHCl-CH_3 \\
\text{2-Chloro-3-heptanone}
\end{array}
\nearrow
$$

This observation excludes a number of suggested mechanisms, for example:

$$
\underset{\underset{\diagdown Hal}{R_2-C}}{\overset{R_1-C=O}{\underset{|}{}}} \xrightarrow[\text{of HHal}]{\alpha\text{-elimination}} \underset{R_2-C:}{\overset{R_1-C=O}{\underset{|}{}}} \longrightarrow
$$

$$
\underset{\underset{\ominus OR}{R_2}}{\overset{R_1}{}} \underset{C=C=O}{\overset{H \diagup OR}{}} \longrightarrow \underset{\underset{R_2}{}}{\overset{R_1}{}}\underset{\diagdown CO_2R}{\overset{\diagup H}{C}}
$$

such a mechanism would lead to the formation of methyl 2-methyl-hexanoate, $C_4H_9-CH(CO_2Me).CH_3$, from the 2-chloroketone in the reaction above (AX). It should be noted that the postulated α-elimination of hydrogen halide is not possible for 3-bromo-3-methyl-2-butanone (AW). One could account for methyl 2-ethylvalerate as the sole product in (AX) and adduce an α-elimination by postulating halogen exchange

$$
\underset{\underset{Hal}{\overset{|}{-C-}}}{} \underset{\overset{O}{\underset{\diagdown C-}{\overset{\|}{C}}}}{}
$$

109

which would make both α-positions equivalent. However this possibility is also excluded by the work of Loftfield, who showed that the ^{14}C-labelled 2-chlorocyclohexanone underwent ring contraction to the ester labelled as shown:

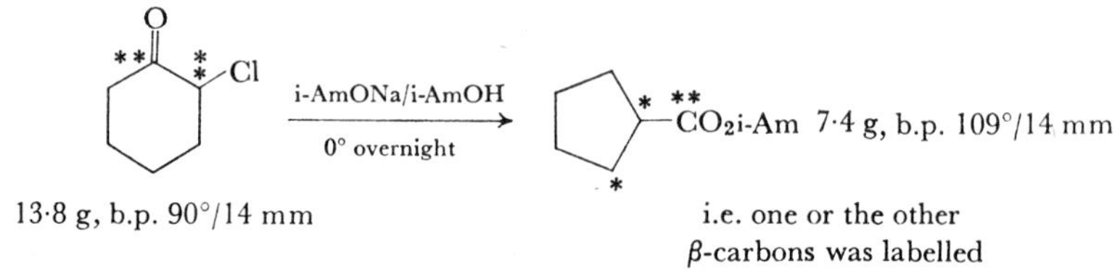

13·8 g, b.p. 90°/14 mm   i.e. one or the other β-carbons was labelled

The labelling pattern in recovered chlorocyclohexanone was unchanged, excluding halogen exchange, and the weighting of labelled carbon in the product was $CO_2H : \alpha\text{-}C :$ both $\beta\text{-}C$ as $2:1:1$. This pattern shows that a symmetrical intermediate is formed:

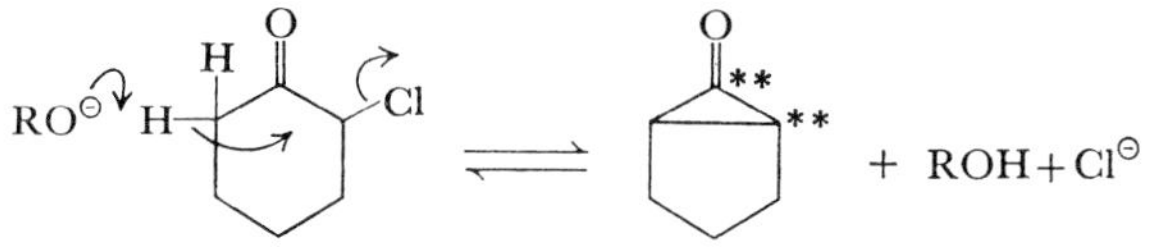

followed by nucleophilic attack:

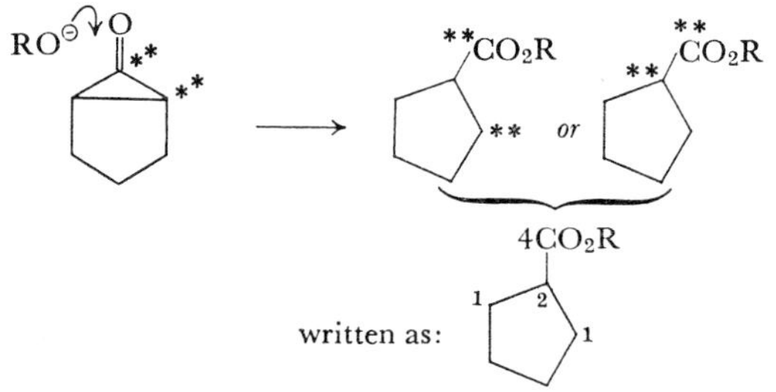

The method of determining the labelled carbons is typical:

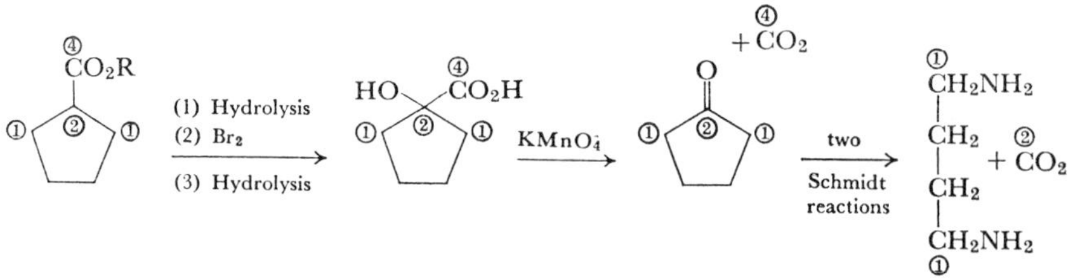

The weighting was as set out above with one-quarter remaining in the tetramethylenediamine, indicated here as equally distributed between

110

terminal carbons because owing to overall symmetry it is not possible to distinguish between the β-carbon atoms of the cyclopentane ring.

It was pointed out by Dewar that it was hard to envisage an S_N2-type transition state for the displacement of chloride ion from 2-chlorocyclohexanone. Thus in (AZ) the carbonyl group and the trigonal carbanion are coplanar and interaction between the π-electrons of the latter and the orbitals of the transannular chlorinated α-carbon atom is unlikely. A zwitterion intermediate is an alternative formulation which is now favoured:

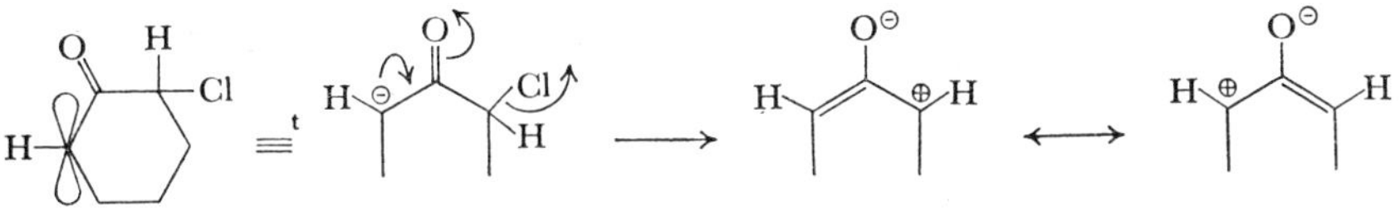

(AZ)　　　　　　　　　　(BA)　　　　　(BB)

where halide ion is expelled to give an intermediate written as (BA) or (BB). The cyclopropane is formed in the next step of the sequence which continues as above (AY).

The formation of a zwitterion accounts for results such as:

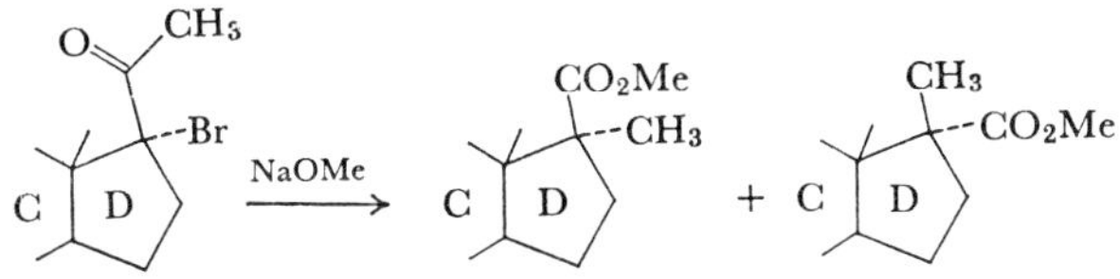

60%　　　40%

for the planar ion

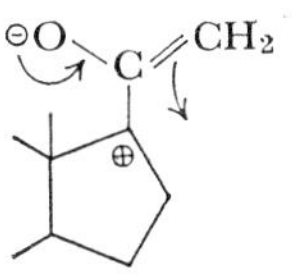

can give two epimeric spiroketones:

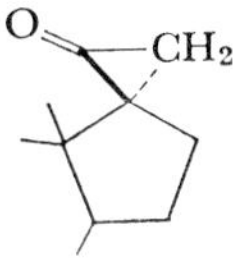

111

and

$$H_2C-C=O$$

(cyclic structure)

which in turn afford the two epimeric products following attack by $MeO^{\ominus}$ ion.

The Wittig Reaction. Since its discovery in 1954 this has become of great importance in the synthesis of olefins from carbonyl compounds. In earlier work an 'ylide (or phosphorane, (BC)) was prepared from a suspension of a phosphonium halide in ether or tetrahydrofuran by reaction with a lithium alkyl:

$$Ph_3P + RCH_2Hal \longrightarrow \underset{\underset{Hal^{\ominus}}{\overset{\oplus}{}}}{Ph_3\overset{\oplus}{P}CH_2R}$$

$$Hal^{\ominus}\begin{bmatrix} \overset{\oplus}{P}-\overset{|}{C}-R \\ Ph_3 \underset{H}{|} \end{bmatrix} \xrightarrow[\substack{-RH \\ -LiHal}]{} Ph_3\overset{\oplus}{P}-\overset{\ominus}{C}H-R$$

$$\text{(with } H^{\swarrow}\!\!\overset{\delta-}{R}\!\!\overset{\delta+}{-Li} \text{ above)}$$

$$\updownarrow \text{(BC)}$$

$$Ph_3P=CHR$$

Triphenylphosphine, m.p. 80°, is a convenient reagent because it is odourless and stable in air in contrast to alkyl phosphines. Triphenyl-alkylphosphonium salts are readily obtained from simple alkyl halides, iodides being the most reactive. For less reactive high-molecular-weight halides heating in solvent (benzene) or at higher temperatures without solvent may be needed: pure phosphonium halides are essential and purification can be effected by recrystallization from tetrahydrofuran. The phosphonium halide yields a red solution of the 'ylide and on addition of the carbonyl compound a betaine (BD) is formed:

$$\underset{\underset{O=C\overset{R_2}{\underset{R_3}{\diagdown}}}{\overset{\ominus}{\nwarrow}}}{\overset{\oplus}{Ar_3P}-CHR_1} \rightleftharpoons \underset{\underset{\underset{R_3}{|}}{O-\underset{|}{C}-R_2}}{\overset{\oplus}{Ar_3P}-CHR_1} \longrightarrow \begin{array}{c} R_1CH=CR_2R_3 \\ + \\ Ar_3\overset{\oplus}{P}-\overset{\ominus}{O} \longleftrightarrow Ar_3P=O \end{array}$$

$$\text{(BD)}$$

this decomposes through a cyclic four-centre transition state to give the olefinic product and triphenylphosphine oxide (Ar=Ph, m.p. 156°). Multiple carbon–carbon bonds which are out of conjugation are unaffected by the reagent, and the new unsaturation is normally formed at room temperature if it becomes conjugated with another in R_2 or R_3

112

(BD). It is sometimes necessary to heat the betaine to complete the reaction; here the 'ylide may be used in a higher boiling solvent like tetrahydrofuran. Olefins will be formed rapidly and essentially irreversibly from phosphoranes with localized negative charge, the rate being determined either by the formation of the betaine (BD) or by its decomposition. The reactivity of the phosphorane and the speed of betaine formation will be increased by substituents on the Ar-group which stabilize a positive charge on the phosphorus atom and increase the contribution of the dipolar form; if delocalization of negative charge is possible over the group R_1 the reactivity of the phosphorane will be reduced. For betaine decomposition the converse applies, for stabilization of electron-deficient phosphorus reduces this rate and the possibility of charge delocalization over the group R_1 increases it through extension of conjugation in the olefinic product. Thus on the one hand the phosphorane (p-MeO—C_6H_4)$_3$P=CH_2 reacts readily with benzaldehyde to form the betaine (BE) which is so stabilized by resonance

$$\left(MeO-\!\!\left\langle\!\!\left\langle\ \right\rangle\!\!\right\rangle\!-\ \right)_3 \overset{\oplus}{P}-CH_2-\underset{\underset{H}{|}}{\overset{Ph}{C}}-\overset{\ominus}{O} \quad \text{(BE)}$$

that it does not decompose, whilst on the other hand the betaine (BF) is formed slowly and decomposes rapidly to give the conjugated ketone:

$$\begin{array}{c} Ph_3P \\ + \\ ClCH_2COCH_3 \end{array} \longrightarrow \underset{Cl^\ominus}{Ph_3\overset{\oplus}{P}CH_2COCH_3} \xrightarrow{Na_2CO_3} Ph_3P{=}CHCOCH_3 \quad m.p.\ 206°$$

$$\Big\updownarrow PhCHO$$

$$PhCH{=}CHCOCH_3 \longleftarrow \underset{O^\ominus-CHPh}{\overset{\oplus}{Ph_3P}-CH-COCH_3}$$

$$\text{Benzalacetone} \qquad\qquad \text{(BF)}$$

An important feature of the reaction is that it is structurally selective and the new unsaturation will take up the position of the parent carbonyl group even when the olefin formed is easily isomerized, e.g.

$$\underset{\underset{Br^\ominus}{\overset{\oplus}{\lfloor\_\rfloor}}}{Ph_3PMe+PhLi} \xrightarrow{Et_2O} Ph_3P{=}CH_2+PhH+LiBr$$
$$\qquad\qquad (BuLi) \qquad\qquad\qquad (BuH)$$

$$Ph_3P{=}CH_2 \ + \ \text{(cyclohexanone)} \longrightarrow \text{(methylenecyclohexane)} \quad b.p.\ 103°,\ 40\%$$

The use of butyl lithium has some advantages over the more stable phenyl lithium because the butane formed does not impede the separation of methylenecyclohexane as does benzene formed from the latter reagent; in both reactions the olefin is formed in about 50 % yield.

The use of lithium alkyls in the preparation of phosphoranes limits the method because of their tendency to react with other functional groups on the starting halide, but other bases such as sodium and lithium alkoxides are suitable provided that the α-hydrogen atom is sufficiently acidic.

$$Ph_3P^{\oplus}\!\!-\!(CH_2)_n\!\!-\!CO_2Et]I^{\ominus} + Me.CO.C_4H_9 \xrightarrow[\text{DMF}]{\text{NaOEt}}$$

$$C_4H_9.C(CH_3)\!\!=\!\!CH\!\!-\!(CH_2)_n\!\!-\!CO_2Et + EtOH + NaI \quad 47\%$$

Dimethylsulphoxide and sodium hydride are an effective combination affording better yields than older procedures:

(*a*) $\quad Ph_3\overset{\oplus}{P}CH_3]\overset{\ominus}{Br} + CH_3SOCH_2\overset{\ominus}{Na}\overset{\oplus}{} \quad\longrightarrow\quad Ph_3P\!\!=\!\!CH_2$ red solution

(*b*) $\quad$ add $\quad$ [Camphor] $\quad\xrightarrow{\text{17 hr at 55°}}\quad$ [2-methylenebornane] $+ Ph_3PO$

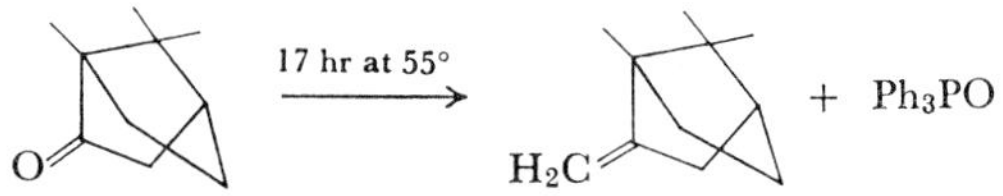

Camphor

In this example, as in some others, the separation of 2-methylenebornane from triphenylphosphine oxide was difficult as the latter was only partially precipitated on pouring into water. Extraction with n-pentane, filtration through alumina, and sublimation were needed to obtain a pure product, m.p. 68–70°, in 73 % yield. The carbonyl group in camphor is highly hindered and a reaction time of about 1 hr at room temperature is generally sufficient for unhindered compounds.

It is advisable to avoid the addition of excess of base in preparing the phosphorane lest it initiates aldolization of the carbonyl component at the second stage, although it must be borne in mind that the carbanion of the phosphorane is a basic centre and can itself induce condensation; this factor has restricted the application of aldehydes in the Wittig reaction. Hauser has shown however that aldehydes can be used with success if the reaction times are kept short. On addition of an aldehyde, the intense colour of the phosphorane is rapidly discharged due to formation of the betaine (BD) and possibly with substantial further reaction to olefin and triphenylphosphine oxide; these end-products are almost completely formed from aldehydes after 30 min at 10°. The rate

114

of conversion is accelerated if the reaction mixture is added to water after the betaine has been precipitated:

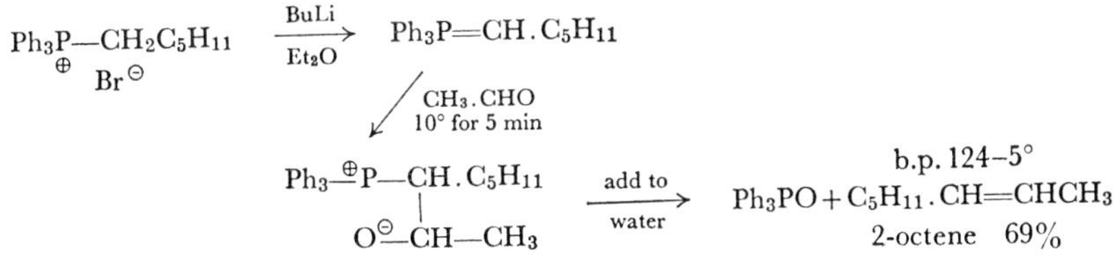

$$Ph_3P—CH_2C_5H_{11} \xrightarrow[\text{Et}_2\text{O}]{\text{BuLi}} Ph_3P{=}CH.C_5H_{11}$$
$$\overset{\oplus}{} Br^{\ominus}$$

$$\diagdown \begin{array}{c} CH_3.CHO \\ 10° \text{ for } 5 \text{ min} \end{array}$$

$$Ph_3\overset{\oplus}{P}—CH.C_5H_{11} \xrightarrow[\text{water}]{\text{add to}} \begin{array}{c} \text{b.p. } 124{-}5° \\ Ph_3PO + C_5H_{11}.CH{=}CHCH_3 \end{array}$$
$$\underset{}{O^{\ominus}{-}CH{-}CH_3} \qquad\qquad 2\text{-octene } 69\%$$

The *cis*-octene was the predominant isomer and this could be the result of decomposition in the polar solvent (cf. p. 117). Terminal olefins are obtained when gaseous formaldehyde or paraform is employed. Unsaturated aldehydes can be used but yields are lower, probably because of their tendency to polymerize in the presence of bases (p. 79).

$$Ph_3P_\oplus{-}CH_2{-}C_5H_{11} \xrightarrow[\text{(2) } CH_2{=}CH{-}CHO]{\text{(1) BuLi}} CH_2{=}CH{-}CH{=}CH{-}C_5H_{11}$$
$$Br^{\ominus} \qquad\qquad \begin{array}{c} 5 \text{ min contact} \end{array} \qquad \begin{array}{c} 1,3\text{-Nonadiene} \\ 34\%, \text{ b.p. } 74°/44 \text{ mm} \end{array}$$

Reaction Stereochemistry. An intermediate betaine can exist in two diastereoisomeric forms (BG and BI) where the four centres involved become coplanar in the transition state leading to the formation of a *cis*-olefin from (BG) in which the residues R_1 and R_2 are eclipsed and to a *trans*-olefin from (BI) in which these groups are less compressed.

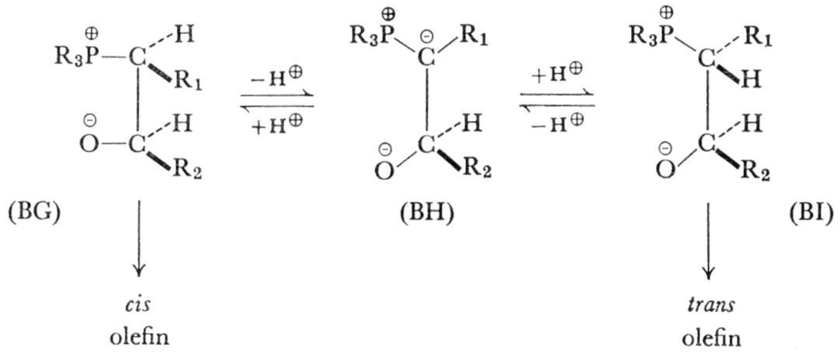

(BG)   (BH)   (BI)

cis olefin   *trans* olefin

Mixtures of *cis* and *trans* products are formed when (BG) and (BI) are equilibrated and this can occur in two ways:

(*a*) When the rate of betaine formation is slow and of a similar order of magnitude to its reversal (k_1 comparable to k_{-1}) and both diastereoisomers revert to the 'ylide:

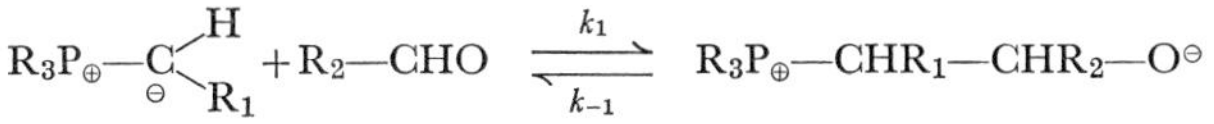

$$R_3P_\oplus{-}\overset{H}{\underset{\ominus}{C}}{\diagdown}R_1 + R_2{-}CHO \underset{k_{-1}}{\overset{k_1}{\rightleftharpoons}} R_3P_\oplus{-}CHR_1{-}CHR_2{-}O^{\ominus}$$

This would be expected for the betaine ((BF), 113).

115

(b) When the olefin is formed slowly from a long-lived betaine which can be interconverted through its conjugate base (BH).

A given structural feature, for example $R_1 = $ aryl, may facilitate both these pathways which may not therefore be distinguishable.

In many instances the overall reaction is fast enough for appreciable amounts of the *cis*-olefin to be formed from the more compressed betaine (BG) by kinetic control; the effect of changing the overall reaction rate is seen in the different mixtures of ethyl tiglate and angelate obtained by the two following procedures:

$$Ph_3P=CHMe + CH_3COCO_2Et$$

68% 32%

Tiglate

Me—C=C—Me / H, CO_2Et

Me—C=C—CO_2Et / H, Me

Angelate

96·5% 3·5%

$$Ph_3P=CMeCO_2Et + CH_3CHO$$

In the first, equilibration is not important because the phosphorane

$$\overset{\oplus}{Ph_3P}-\overset{\overset{\displaystyle Me}{|}}{\underset{\underset{\displaystyle H}{|}}{C}}-\overset{\overset{\displaystyle CH_3}{|}}{\underset{\underset{\displaystyle CO_2Et}{|}}{C}}-O^{\ominus}$$

is very reactive and in the derived betaines the α-hydrogen atom is not very acidic so that the equilibration (BG) → (BH) → (BI) does not occur readily. In the second procedure the phosphorane (BJ) is more stable and the betaine (BK) has no acidic hydrogen α- to the phosphorus atom:

$$CH_3CHO + Ph_3\overset{\oplus}{P}-\overset{\ominus}{C}\overset{CH_3}{\underset{CO_2Et}{\diagup}}$$

(BJ)

$$Ph_3\overset{\oplus}{P}-C\overset{CH_3}{\diagdown CO_2Et} \quad \underset{O-C}{\overset{\ominus}{\diagdown}}\overset{H}{\underset{CH_3}{\diagup}}$$

(BK)

⟶ angelate

Hence the preponderance of tiglate must result from reversal of betaine formation to give the phosphorane (BJ) with negative charge stabilized by the ethoxycarbonyl group, recombination with acetaldehyde leading to an increase in the proportion of the less compressed betaine isomeric with (BK) having a $CH_3 \leftrightarrow CH_3$ interaction rather than $CH_3 \leftrightarrow CO_2Et$.

116

Synthesis of Polyunsaturated Compounds. An important example is the synthesis of the triterpene squalene, the biogenetic precursor of the steroids:

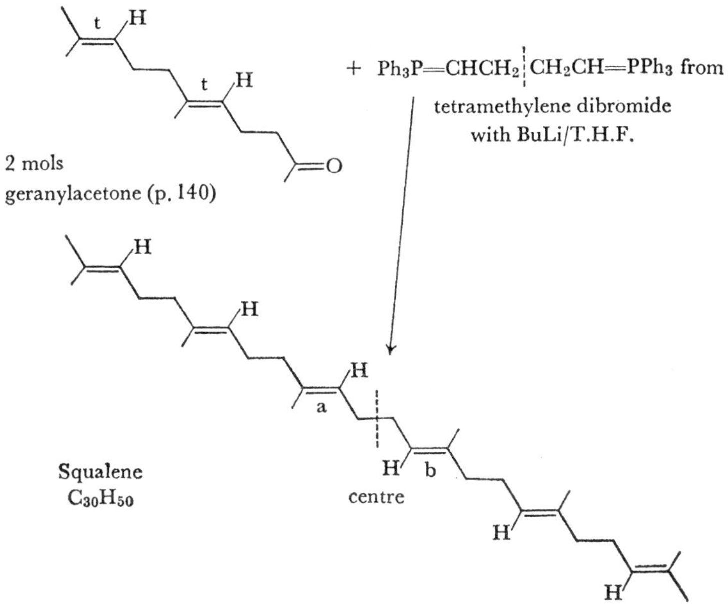

2 mols
geranylacetone (p. 140)

+ $Ph_3P{=}CHCH_2|CH_2CH{=}PPh_3$ from

tetramethylene dibromide
with BuLi/T.H.F.

Squalene
$C_{30}H_{50}$

centre

The natural product has the illustrated all-*trans* structure and was formed in 12·5% yield together with two other isomers having the *cis* configuration at the reaction sites (*a*) and/or (*b*). In this reaction the probabilities of *cis*- and *trans*-olefin formation are comparable because the non-bonded interactions in the diastereoisomeric betaines are similar. If the steric requirements at the two sites are comparable one expects the isomer distribution to be:

$$
\begin{array}{ll}
cis \text{ at } (a) \text{ 50\%} & \nearrow \text{all } cis \text{ 25\%} \\
& \searrow \text{common } cis{-}trans \text{ 50\%} \\
trans \text{ at } (a) \text{ 50\%} & \searrow \text{all } trans \text{ 25\%}
\end{array}
$$

The *cis/trans* ratio is increased in polar solvents, for example dimethylformamide, or in the presence of nucleophilic bases, for example I$^\ominus$, when the electrostatic attraction between phosphorus and oxygen is diminished by solvation or co-ordination of phosphorus with the base.

117

In the betaine (BL) the largest groups will adopt the fully staggered conformation:

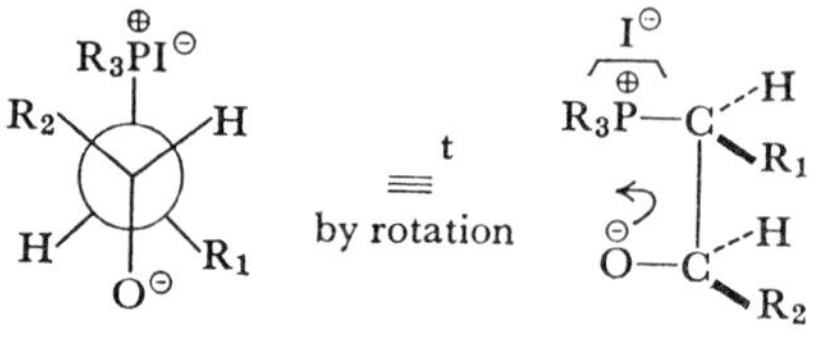

(BL)

and in this preferred configuration a *cis* relation is established between the groups R_1 and R_2 when the four-centred transition state is established. This method of inducing *cis* fusion has been applied to the synthesis of naturally occurring unsaturated acids:

$$CH_3.(CH_2)_3.\overset{t}{CH}=CH-CH\overset{t}{=}CH-CHO + Ph_3\overset{\oplus}{P}-(CH_2)_8-CO_2Et]Br^{\ominus}$$

NaOEt $\downarrow$ I$^{\ominus}$, solvent DMF

$$CH_3.(CH_2)_3-\overset{t}{CH}=CH-CH\overset{t}{=}CH-CH=CH.(CH_2)_7-CO_2Et$$

C

Ethyl α-eleostearate

Reactions of Phosphoranes with other Functional Groups.
The carbonyl component can be further substituted by: —OH, —COR, R—O—R, and by halogen if this is a remote substituent.
Halides.

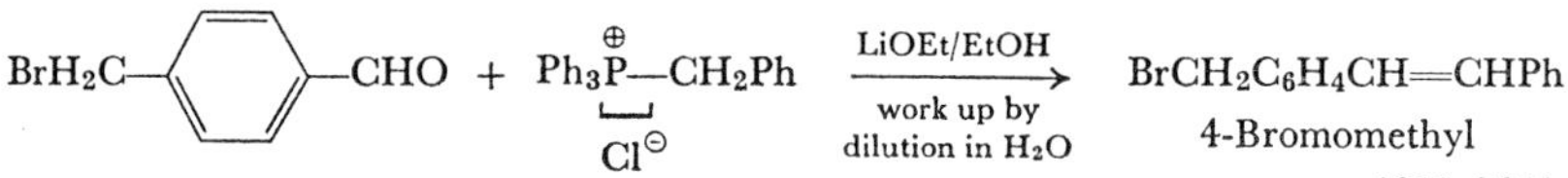

$$BrH_2C-\langle\!\!\langle\;\;\rangle\!\!\rangle-CHO + Ph_3\overset{\oplus}{P}-CH_2Ph \;\;\xrightarrow[\substack{\text{work up by} \\ \text{dilution in } H_2O}]{\text{LiOEt/EtOH}}\;\; BrCH_2C_6H_4CH=CHPh$$
$$Cl^{\ominus}$$

4-Bromomethyl styrene, m.p. 121°, 70%

Cyclic olefins are formed by intramolecular reaction if the substituents are favourably placed:

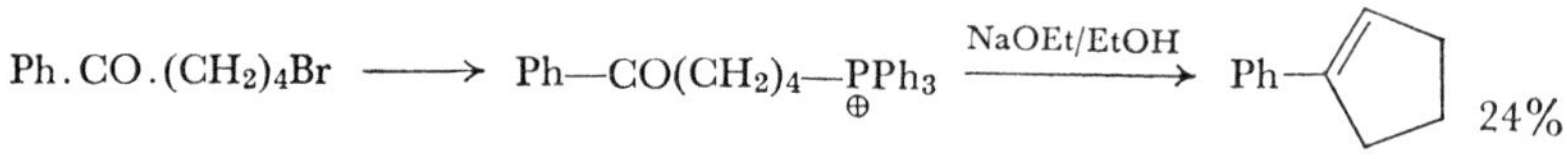

$$Ph.CO.(CH_2)_4Br \longrightarrow Ph-CO(CH_2)_4-\underset{\oplus}{PPh_3} \xrightarrow{\text{NaOEt/EtOH}} Ph-\langle\!\!\rangle$$ 24%

whilst a useful homologation of simple halides is possible with the phosphorane derived from ethyl bromoacetate:

118

$$CH_2Br—CO_2Et + Ph_3P \longrightarrow \overset{\oplus}{Ph_3P}—CH_2CO_2Et \xrightarrow[\text{to } H_2O \text{ soln.}]{\text{1E of NaOH}} Ph_3P{=}CHCO_2Et$$

$$\overset{\ominus}{Br}$$
m.p. 158°

m.p. 117° on
precipitation from
ethyl acetate/
petrol

$$MeI + Ph_3P{=}CHCO_2Et \xrightarrow[\text{Et acetate}]{\text{in}} \overset{\oplus}{Ph_3P}—\overset{\overset{\displaystyle H}{|}}{\underset{\underset{\displaystyle CH_3}{|}}{C}}—CO_2Et$$

$$I^{\ominus}$$
(BM)

Treatment of the precipitated phosphonium salt (BM) with exactly one equivalent of sodium hydroxide in water affords the phosphorane $Ph_3P{=}C(CH_3)CO_2Et$ which decomposes on heating to the steam-volatile ethyl propionate (67% yield); a reaction which is common for basic phosphoranes:

$$\underset{HO—H}{\overset{\oplus}{Ph_3P}—C\overset{CO_2Et}{\underset{CH_3}{\diagdown}}} \longrightarrow Ph_3P—CHCH_3 \longrightarrow Ph_3PO + CH_3CH_2CO_2Et$$

Hence water should be excluded during a Wittig reaction, although phosphoranes that are highly resonance stabilized are unaffected by hot water. A further practical point is that oxygen should also be excluded, for the more reactive phosphoranes decompose to give phosphine oxide and a carbonyl compound, which will in its turn interfere with the synthesis as shown in the first equation below:

$$Ph_3P{=}CHR \xrightarrow{O_2} Ph_3—\overset{\overset{\displaystyle \overset{\ominus}{O}—O}{}}{\underset{\underset{\displaystyle H}{|}}{\overset{\oplus}{P}—C}}—R \longrightarrow Ph_3P{=}O + R—CHO$$

Carboxylic Esters can undergo nucleophilic attack by the phosphorane with the displacement of an alkoxy group; this reaction is particularly facile when the reacting centres are properly disposed for a cyclization of the Dieckmann type (p. 133) to yield cyclic ketones:

$$\overset{\oplus}{3P}—CH_2(CH_2)_5CO_2Et \xrightarrow[\text{t-BuOH}]{\text{KO—t-Bu}} \left[\begin{array}{c} Ph_3.\overset{\oplus}{P} \\ HC\overset{\ominus}{\curvearrowright} \\ H_2C \\ H_2C \end{array} \begin{array}{c} O \\ \diagup C \diagdown \\ CH_2 \\ CH_2 \\ CH_2 \end{array} (OEt \right] \longrightarrow$$

$$I^{\ominus}$$

Ph₃PO 85%
sublimed 200°/0·3 mm
+
Cycloheptanone 90%

$$\xleftarrow[\text{pH 11,150°}]{\text{hydrolyse}}$$

m.p. 208°

52% yield after conc.
and partition $H_2O/CHCl_3$

119

Carbanion Chemistry of Aldehydes and Ketones

Contrast here the reaction of the long-chain phosphonium ester (p. 118) where the cyclization does not compete. Any tendency for keto-esters to undergo intermolecular condensation in this way can be reduced by addition of the keto-ester to the phosphorane:

$$n\text{-}C_3H_7\text{--}(C\equiv C)_2\text{--}CH_2\text{--}CH_2.CH=PPh_3 + OHC\text{--}CH=CH\text{--}CO_2Et$$

$$\downarrow \text{inverse conditions}$$

$$n\text{-}C_3H_7\text{--}(C\equiv C)_2\text{--}CH_2\text{--}CH_2.(CH=CH)_2\text{--}CO_2Et$$

Anacycline

Carbon–Carbon Multiple Bonds are unaffected in the normal course of events (cf. p. 117) but if activated by an adjacent electron-attracting group ($-CO_2R$, $-CO-R$ etc.) addition of a phosphorane may occur as for the Michael reaction (p. 155).

Other 'ylides' of nitrogen, arsenic, antimony, and sulphur are known. Nitrogen 'ylides' are very reactive because there is no possibility of expanding the electron shell by d-orbital resonance to stabilize the carbanion

$$R_3\overset{\oplus}{N}\text{--}\overset{\ominus}{C}H_2 \;\;\nleftrightarrow\;\; R_3N=CH_2,$$

and even relatively unreactive ketones are converted into betaines:

$$Me_4\overset{\oplus}{N}Br^{\ominus} \xrightarrow{R\text{--Li}} Me_3\overset{\oplus}{N}\text{--}CH_2^{\ominus} + RH + LiBr$$

$$Me_3\overset{\oplus}{N}\text{--}\overset{\ominus}{C}H_2 \xrightarrow{Ph_2C=O} Me_3\overset{\oplus}{N}\text{--}CH_2$$
$$O^{\ominus}\text{--}CPh_2 \quad (BN)$$

Betaines of this type (BN) are stable and do not decompose into olefin and amine oxide because the same feature which conferred reactivity on the 'ylide' now prevents the formation of the necessary cyclic transition state. Antimony is different again owing to its stability in the penta-valent state and no 'ylide' is obtained from tetramethylstibonium bromide but a displacement occurs:

$$(CH_3)_4Sb\overset{\delta+}{-}\overset{\delta-}{Br} \longrightarrow Sb(Me)_5 + LiBr$$
$$Me\text{--Li}$$

Dimethylsulphoxonium methylide (BP) is obtained by the action of base on the 'onium' salt (BO):

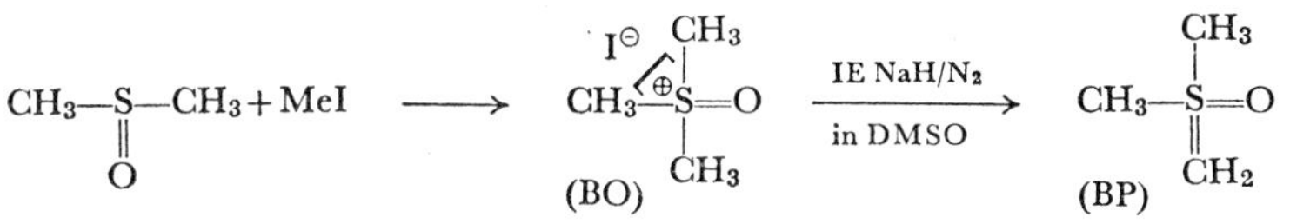

and the related dimethylsulphonium methylide (BR) is derived from trimethylsulphonium iodide (BQ) by the conjugate base of dimethylsulphoxide, itself formed from one equivalent of sodium hydroxide:

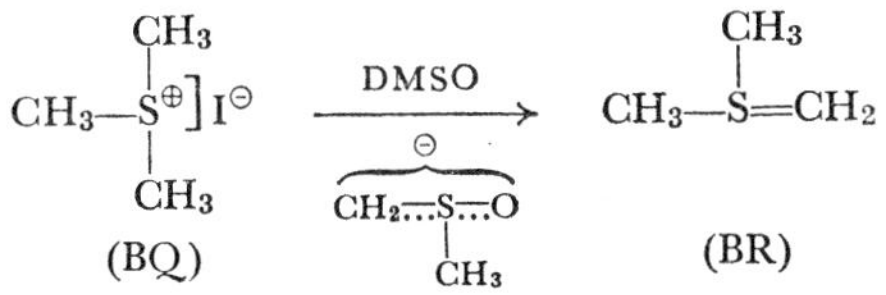

Corey has shown that the sulphoxonium methylide reacts with carbonyl compounds to form epoxides:

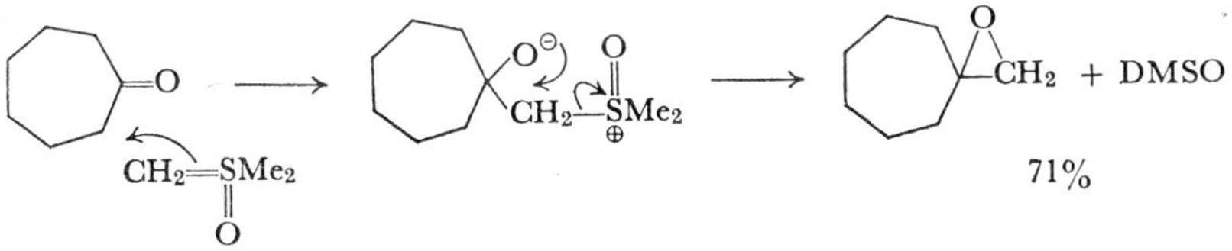

and gives cyclopropane compounds by Michael addition:

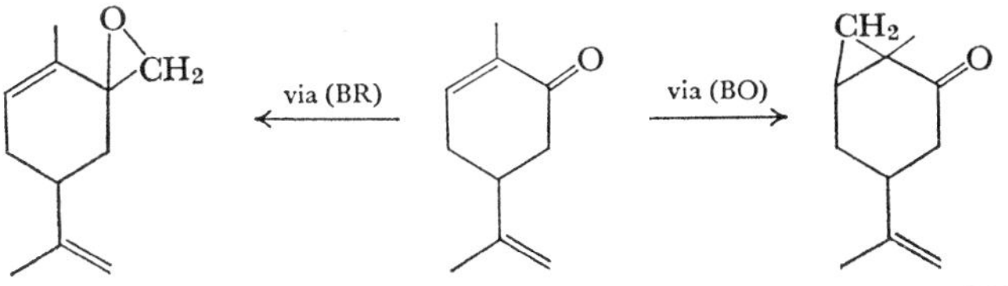

The sulphonium methylide is more specific and reacts with conjugated enones only by 1,2-addition.

Further Reading

TOPICS

M. BALLESTER, *Chem. Rev.*, 1955, **55**, 287 (Darzens condensation).
J. HINE, *Divalent Carbon*. Ronald Press, New York, 1964 (carbenes).
A. LEDWITH, *The Chemistry of Carbenes*. The Royal Institute of Chemistry, Lecture Series 1964, No. 5.

9

Carbanion Chemistry of Aldehydes and Ketones

O. Bayer in, J. Houben and T. Weyl, *Methoden der organischen Chemie*, Vol. 7, p. 89. G. Thieme, Stuttgart, 4th edit., 1954 (Cannizzaro reaction).

W. S. Ide and J. S. Buck, *Org. Reactions*, 1948, **4**, 269.

W. S. Johnson *et al.*, *J. Amer. Chem. Soc.*, 1962, **84**, 2181 (steric control of alkylation).

A. S. Kende, *Org. Reactions*, 1960, **11**, 261 (Favorsky reaction).

J. Mathieu and A. Allais, *Cahiers de Synthese Organique*, Vol. 3, p. 13. Masson et Cie, Paris, 1957.

B. Reichert, *Die Mannich-Reaktion*. Springer, Berlin, 1959.

S. Trippett, *Adv. Org. Chem.*, 1960, **1**, 83; *Quart. Rev.*, 1963 **17**, 406 (Wittig reaction).

H. Wynberg, *Chem. Rev.*, 1960, **60**, 169 (Reimer–Tiemann reaction).

PROBLEMS

1. How would you synthesize:

(a) CH_2OH
    |
    $CH_2—NO_2$ W. E. Noland, *Org. Synth.*, 1961, **41**, 67.

(b) $Ph—(CH=CH)_7—CHO$ J. Schmitt, *Annalen*, 1941, **547**, 280.

(c) $CH_3—CO.CH—CO.CH_3$
               |
    $CH_3—CO—CH—CO.CH_3$ R. G. Charles, *Org. Synth.*, 1959, **39**, 61.

(d)

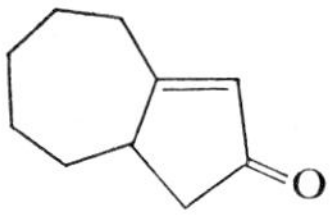

                                      CO_2Me
                                        |
using $CH_3—C(OR)_2—CH_2—NH$

         A. M. Islam and R. A. Raphael, *J. Chem. Soc.*, **1955**, 3151.

(e) $Ph—CH=CH—$

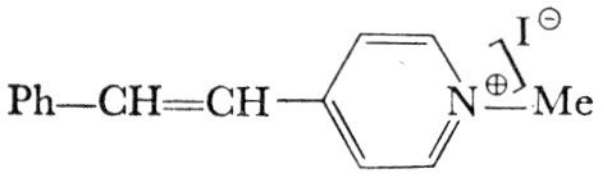

         J. Mathieu and A. Allais, *Cahiers de Synthese Organique*, Vol. 3, p. 48. Masson et Cie, Paris, 1957.

(f) $O_2N—$

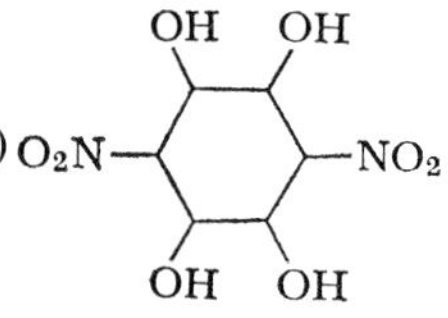

         F. W. Lichtenthaler, *Angew. Chem.*, Intern. Edit., 1964, **3**, 212.

2. Suggest mechanisms for the following reactions:

(a)

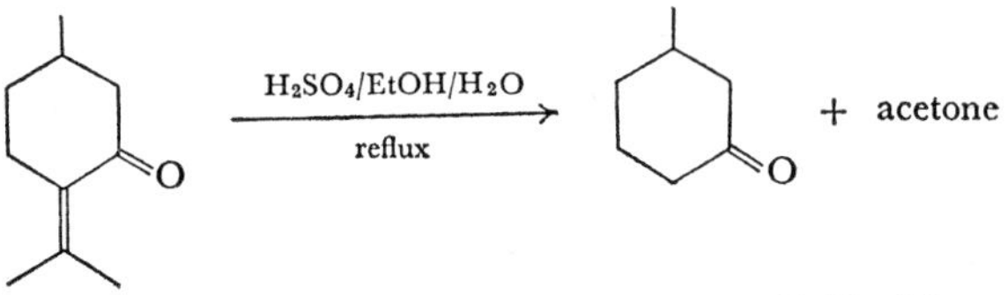

         F. Nerdel, *et al.*, *Annalen*, 1953, **580**, 40.

(*b*)   Ph—C≡C—CO—CH₃ $\xrightarrow{\text{OH}^{\ominus}/\text{H}_2\text{O}}$ Ph—C≡CH + CH₃—CO₂H

(*c*)   2O₂N—C₆H₄—CH₂Cl $\xrightarrow[\text{H}_2\text{O}]{\text{base}}$ O₂N—C₆H₄—CH=CH—C₆H₄—NO₂

M. Ballester, *Chem. Rev.*, 1955, **55**, 287.

(*d*)

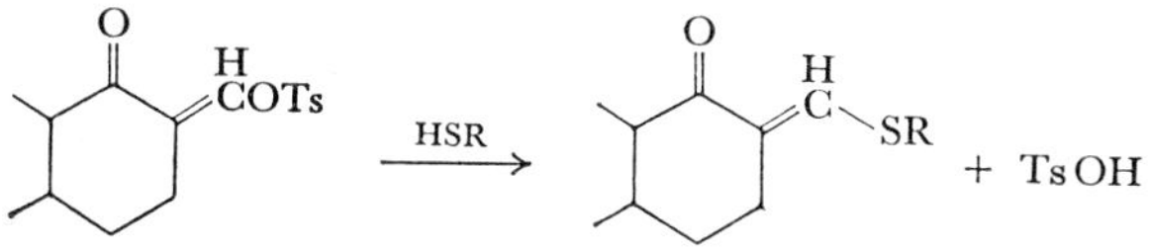

HSR →   + TsOH

(*e*)

$\xrightarrow[-80°]{\text{MeLi}}$ +

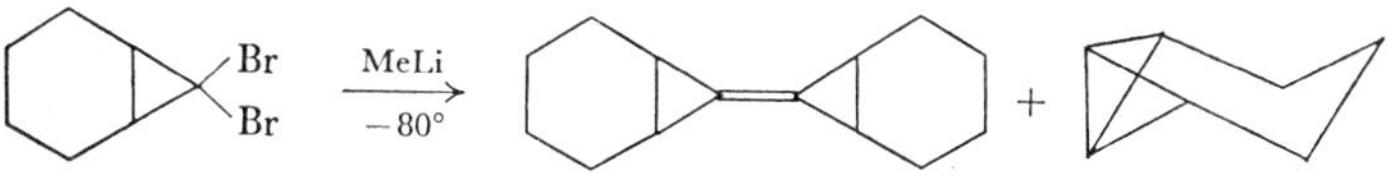

W. R. Moore, H. R. Ward and R. F. Merritt, *J. Amer. Chem. Soc.*, 1961, **83**, 2019.

(*f*)

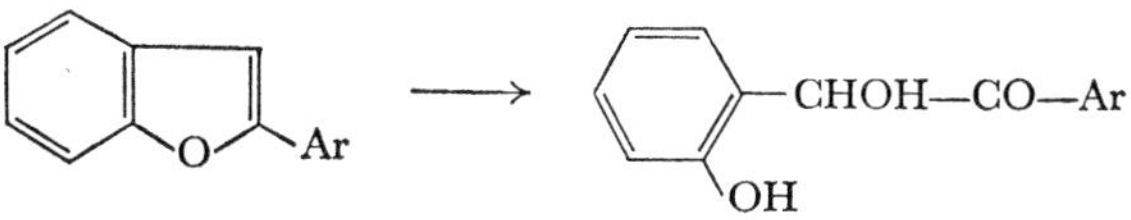

in two stages, one oxidative, the other alkali.

K. Folkers *et al.*, *J. Amer. Chem. Soc.*, 1959, **81**, 4979.

(*g*)

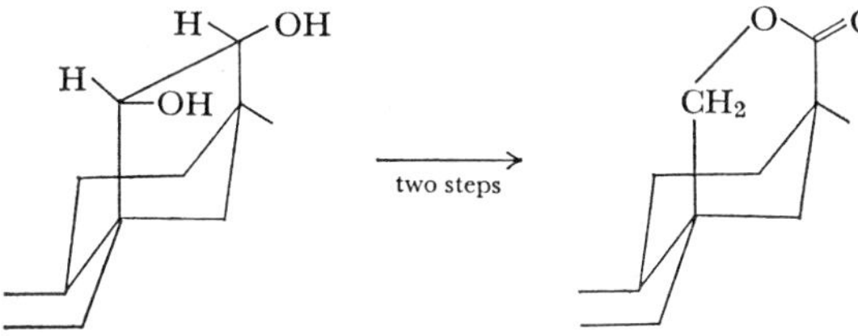

two steps →

A. H. Kapadi and Sukh Dev, *Tetrahedron Letters*, 1964, p. 1178.

3. Outline syntheses of:

(*a*)

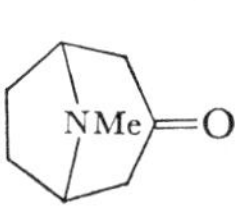

from succindialdehyde and β-ketoglutarate.

R. Robinson, *J. Chem. Soc.*, **1917**, 762.

(*b*)

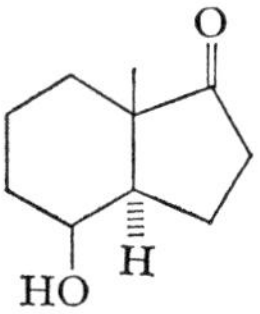

from 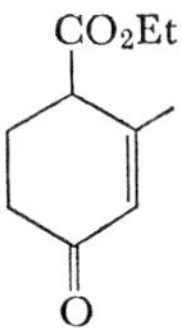   following two Michael additions, one a *net* addition of Cl.CH₂.CH₂—CO₂Et via NaOEt.

H. H. Inhoffen, *Angew. Chem.*, 1958, **70**, 576.
H. H. Inhoffen and E. Prinz, *Chem. Ber.*, 1954, **87**, 684.

(*c*)   NH⊕₃Cl⊖
        |
Ph—CH—CO—CH₂—Ph   from   Ph—C—CH₂—Ph   using t-BuOCl and base.
                              ‖
                              NH

H. E. Baumgarten *et al.*, *J. Amer. Chem. Soc.*, 1960, **82**, 4422.

123

4. Muscarine,

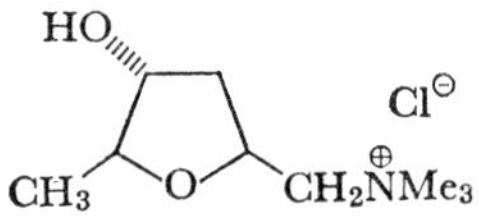

gives a positive iodoform test; account for this.

5. Predict the products of the following reactions:

(a)

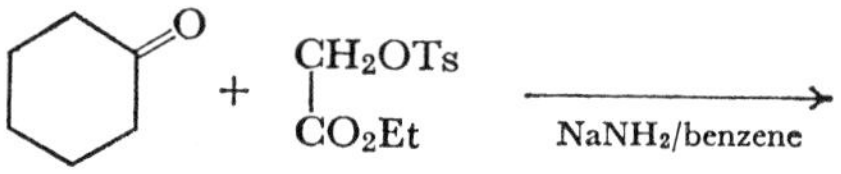

(b)

$$Ph_3P=CH_2 + CH_3CH=CHCO_2Et \longrightarrow$$

S. Trippett, *Quart. Rev.*, 1963, **17**, 428.

(c) $Ph_3P=CHOMe +$

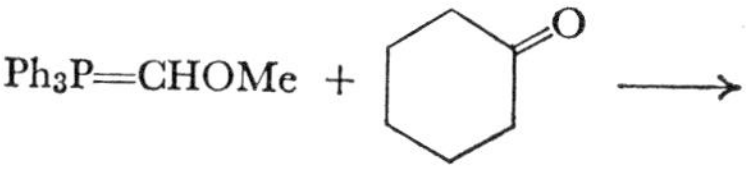

S. G. Levine, *J. Org. Chem.*, 1958, **80**, 6150.

(d)

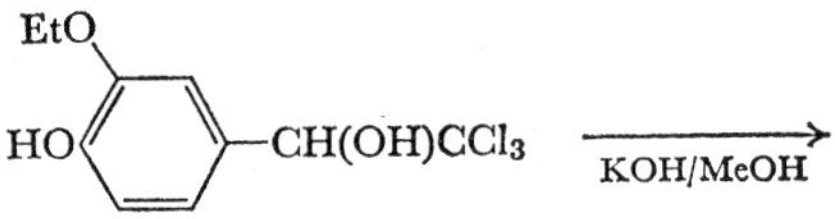

(e) $RCH_2\overset{\oplus}{P}Ph_3 \xrightarrow[PhNO_2]{}$
$Br^{\ominus}$

G. Eglinton and W. McCrae, *Adv. Org. Chem.*, 1963, **4**, 200.

6. Give mechanisms for the following:

(a)

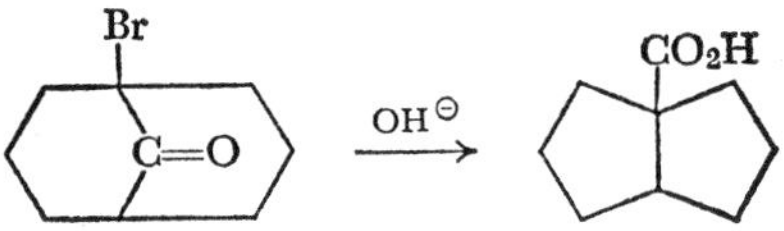

A. C. Cope and E. S. Graham, *J. Amer. Chem. Soc.*, 1951, **73**, 4702.

(b)

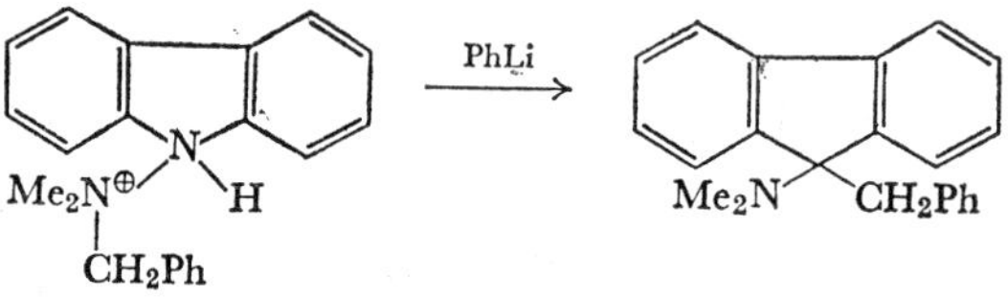

S. Trippett, *Quart. Rev.*, 1963, **17**, 435.

(c)   2PhCHBr—CO—CHBrPh $\xrightarrow{\text{I}^{\ominus}}$

Ph Ph

O=⬡=O

Ph Ph

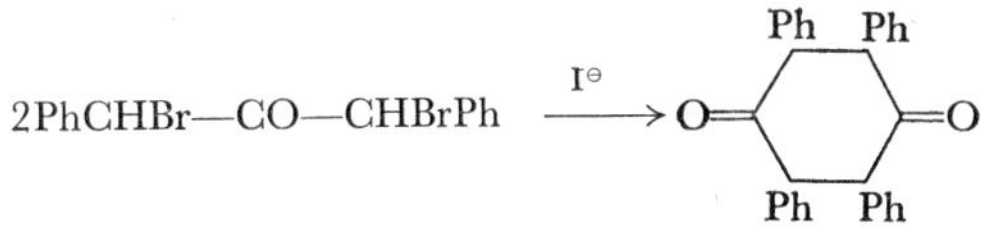

cf. Chapter 6, Problem 7g.

(d)   [structure with Br, AcO⁻ → product with OAc]

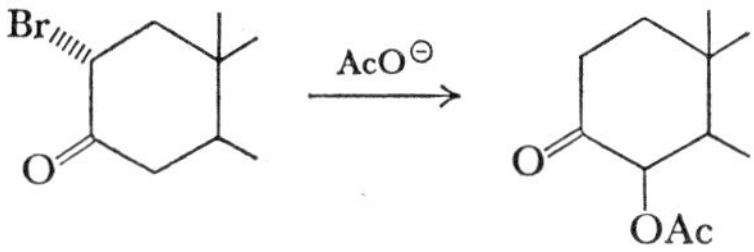

AcO$^{\ominus}$

(e)   PhCH$_2$N(CH$_3$)$_3$ $\xrightarrow[\text{NaNH}_2/\text{NH}_3]{}$ [structure with CH$_3$ and CH$_2$—N(Me)$_2$]
      $\underset{\text{I}^{\ominus}}{\overset{+}{}}$

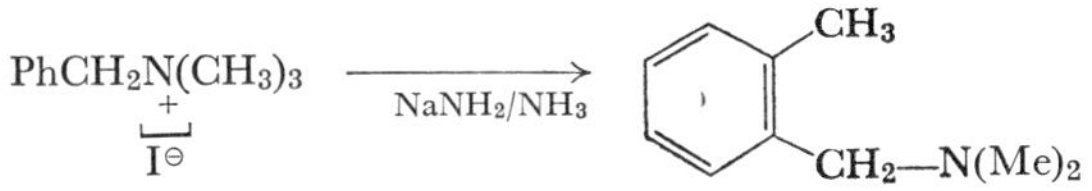

S. W. Kantar and C. R. Hauser, *J. Amer. Chem. Soc.*, 1951, **73**, 4122.

(f)   [structure with O, Br] $\xrightarrow{\text{NaOMe}}$ [structure with CO$_2$Me]

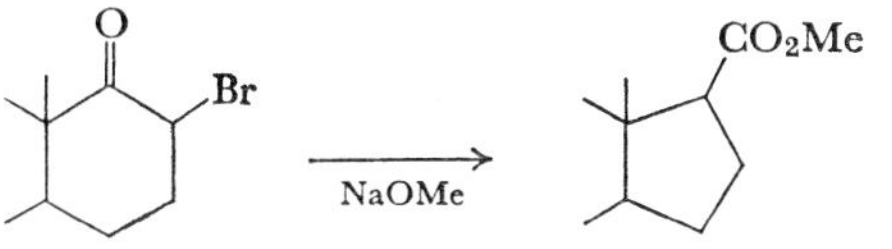

R. B. Loftfield, *J. Amer. Chem. Soc.*, 1951, **73**, 4712.

(g)   [structure with CHCl$_2$, O] $\xrightarrow{\text{OH}^{\ominus}}$ [structure with OH]   +   [structure with CHCl, CHCO$_2$H]

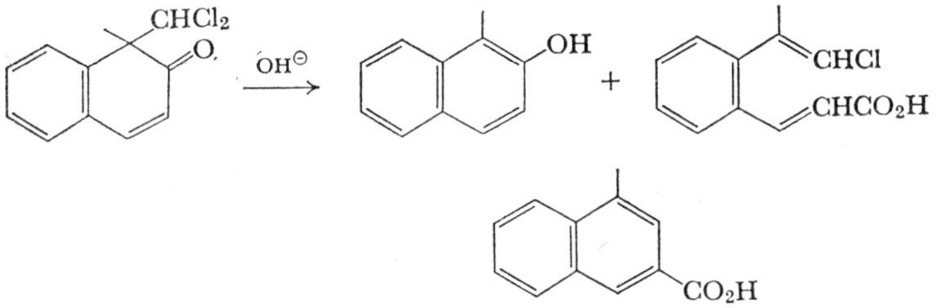

[structure with CO$_2$H]

(h)   Indene as $\xrightarrow{\text{CHCl}_3}$ [structure with Cl]   +   [structure with Cl]
      Na derivative

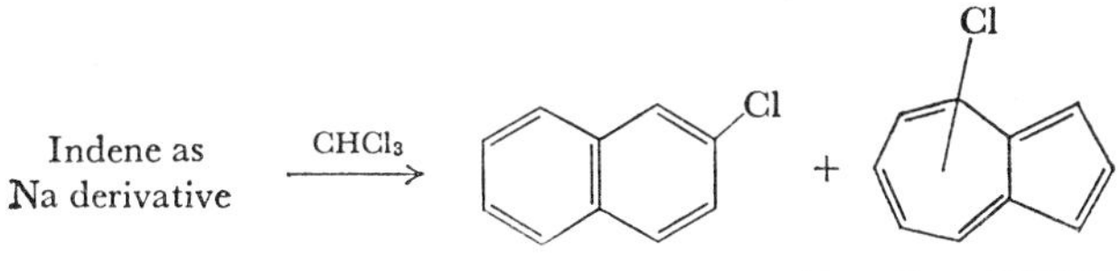

H. Wynberg, *Chem. Rev.*, 1960, **60**, 179, 181.

7. Naphthalene (0·08 mol) was treated with sodium (0·7 g.atom) in ethanol/liquid ammonia and addition of water to the evaporate yielded a product (A), m.p. 42°, having no absorption in the ultraviolet above 200 mμ. (A) afforded a chlorocompound (B), m.p. 84°, on reaction with CHCl$_3$/KOt-Bu and (B) in its turn reacted with Na/NH$_3$ to give (C), which with bromine yielded a product (D; C$_{11}$H$_{14}$Br$_4$), m.p. 129°. (E; C$_{11}$H$_{10}$) was obtained when (D) was treated with KOH/EtOH and had a pronounced ultraviolet absorption at 259 mμ ($\epsilon = 63,000$); its N.M.R. spectrum included olefinic protons at very low field (τ c. 2·8). Assign structures A → E and account for the spectra of the latter. (Hint: contrast Bredt's rule.)

E. Vogel and H. D. Roth, *Angew. Chem.*, Intern. Edit., 1964, **3**, 228.

Chapter 5

CARBANIONS DERIVED FROM CARBOXYLIC ACIDS AND THEIR DERIVATIVES

The Claisen Ester Condensation (1887) follows from attack by the conjugate base of ethyl acetate on another molecule of the ester with the formation of ethyl acetoacetate (equation A). The reaction occurs on warming sodium wire in ethyl acetate which normally contains a small amount of ethanol and this provides the necessary basic catalyst—sodium ethoxide.

$$EtO^{\ominus}+CH_3.CO_2Et \quad \overset{(1)}{\rightleftharpoons} \quad EtOH+\overset{\ominus}{CH_2}-CO_2Et \quad \overset{(2)}{\rightleftharpoons} \quad CH_3-\overset{\overset{O^{\ominus}}{|}}{\underset{\underset{OEt}{|}}{C}}-CH_2-CO_2Et$$

$$CH_3-\overset{}{\underset{\underset{OEt}{|}}{C}}=O$$

(A)

$$\Big\Downarrow {\scriptstyle(3)}$$

$$EtOH+CH_3-CO-\overset{\ominus}{CH}-CO_2Et \quad \underset{EtO^{\ominus}}{\overset{(4)}{\rightleftharpoons}} \quad CH_3-CO.CH_2.CO_2Et$$

The conversion of the β-ketoester into its conjugate base (step 4) is essentially irreversible because this carbanion is highly stabilized by resonance with the adjacent carbonyl and ethoxycarbonyl groups; hence return to starting material via step 3 is inhibited. Working-up entails treatment with dilute acid and separation of the acetoacetate (b.p. 75°/14 mm) from unreacted ethyl acetate by distillation.

Very little condensation occurs with homologous esters in the presence of sodium ethoxide because the inductive effect of the alkyl group in $R{\rightarrow}CH_2-CO_2R$ renders the α-hydrogen atoms less acidic and also destabilizes the anion

$$RCH_2-\overset{\overset{O}{\|}}{C}-\overset{\overset{R}{|}}{\underset{\ominus}{C}}-CO_2R$$

and step 4 is then no longer effective in removing the product from the equilibrium. It should be noted that $EtO^{\ominus}$ ion can give nucleophilic attack and hence if a stronger base is to be used to force the condensation of homologous esters it must be only weakly nucleophilic to avoid

126

displacement of the alkoxy group. Bulky carbanions derived from sodium triphenylmethyl and mesityl magnesium bromide meet these requirements:

$$2(CH_3)_2CH—CH_2—CO_2Et \xrightarrow[\text{(2) dil. acid}]{\substack{\text{(1) } (CH_3)_3C_6H_2MgBr \\ \text{in Et}_2O}}$$

Ethyl isovalerate

$$\overset{\displaystyle CO_2Et \quad CH_3}{(CH_3)_2CH—CH_2—CO.\underset{\displaystyle |}{CH}——\underset{\displaystyle |}{CH}—CH_3}$$

Ethyl α-isovalerylisovalerate
51%, b.p. 133°/32 mm

+ mesitylene, b.p. 75°/32 mm

The condensation should proceed if the conjugate base of the ketoester formed is weaker than the basic catalyst.

Sodium hydride is a very effective condensing agent and is readily available as a stable dispersion in oil;† unlike the hydrides used as reducing agents it does not normally give nucleophilic attack by hydride ion provided α-hydrogen is available on the substrate. The ester is completely converted into its conjugate base at step 1 because of the irreversible evolution of hydrogen:

$$R—CH_2—CO_2R + NaH \longrightarrow R—\underset{\displaystyle \underset{Na}{|}}{CH}—CO_2R + H_2\uparrow$$

and the ketoester is similarly converted irreversibly into its sodio-derivative with the evolution of a second equivalent of hydrogen; measurement of the volume of gas evolved can be used to follow the extent of reaction:

$$2CH_3.CH_2—CO_2Et \xrightarrow[\text{toluene, 95°}]{2NaH} CH_3.CH_2.CO.\overset{\displaystyle CH_3}{\underset{\displaystyle |}{CH}}—CO_2Et$$

95%, b.p. 80°/5 mm

CROSSED CONDENSATIONS

There is no essential difference between the carbanion reactions discussed here and those mentioned in the preceding chapter. We find that crossed condensations between carbonyl compounds and acid derivatives are applicable in synthesis and afford useful yields if one component lacks α-hydrogen:

$$Ph.CO_2Me + C_2H_5.CH_2CO_2Me \xrightarrow[\text{Bu}_2O \; 100°]{NaH \; (0·4 \; mol)} Ph.CO.CH(C_2H_5)—CO_2Me$$

(0·4 mol)   (0·2 mol)   65%

† *Sodium Hydride Dispersions for Organic Syntheses.* Metal Hydrides Inc., Beverly, Mass., 1964.

127

Aldehydes which undergo aldolization are unsuitable for crossed condensations. The self-condensation of ketones may also interfere when crossed reactions are attempted with esters, but the difficulty can then be overcome by formation of the sodio-derivative of the ester followed by addition of a dilute solution of the ketone in an inert solvent; yields are inevitably reduced by some self-condensation of the ester:

$$CH_3(CH_2)_2.CO_2Et + CH_3—CO.CH_2.CH_2.CH_3 \xrightarrow{NaNH_2/Et_2O}$$

$$CH_3.(CH_2)_2—\overset{\overset{O}{\|}}{C}—CH_2—\overset{\overset{O}{\|}}{C}—(CH_2)_2CH_3$$
$$76\%$$

Two equivalents of base are needed because the product is a stronger acid than the starting ketone which is regenerated from its conjugate base by exchange of proton.

$$(CH_3)_3—C—CO_2Me + (CH_3)_3—\overset{\overset{O}{\|}}{C}—CH_3 \xrightarrow{NaH/MeO.CH_2.CH_2.OMe}$$

$$(CH_3)_3C—\overset{\overset{O}{\|}}{C}—CH_2—\overset{\overset{O}{\|}}{C}—C(CH_3)_3$$
$$63\%$$

Enolizable products of crossed reactions of this kind are conveniently separated from solution as the insoluble copper chelates by addition of copper acetate solution. The blue/green chelate regenerates the β-diketone on acidification. This technique is also useful in separating mixtures of alkylation products of β-diketones and β-ketoesters (p. 140).

$$+ CH_3CH_2CO_2Et \xrightarrow[\text{(2) Et}_2\text{O extn. from acid}]{\text{(1) 2NaH at 33°}}$$

$$50\%$$

Esters which cannot compete in this way are more widely used, for example formate for introduction of a protecting group (p. 95). Oxalates are used in the synthesis of α-ketoesters:

$$\xrightarrow[\text{NaOEt}]{(CO_2Et)_2}$$

$$\xrightarrow[\text{>100°}]{\text{Heat}}$$

$$+ CO \quad (B)$$

$$67\%$$

$$PhCH_2CO_2Et + (CO_2Et)_2 \xrightarrow{\text{base}} \overset{PhCH—CO_2Et}{\underset{CO—CO_2Et}{|}} \longrightarrow \overset{PhCH(CO_2Et)_2}{+CO} \quad (C)$$

In favourable circumstances a second intramolecular condensation occurs as illustrated by Komppa's classical approach to the synthesis of bicyclic monoterpenes:

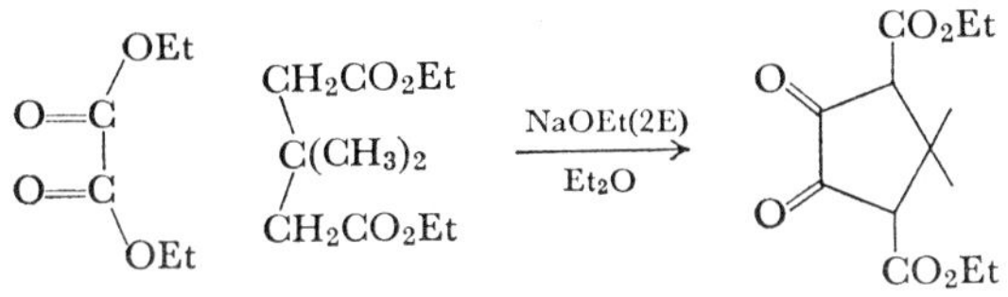

m.p. 98°

α-Ketoesters readily undergo decarbonylation (B and C above) leading overall to a method for the alkoxycarbonylation of ketones:

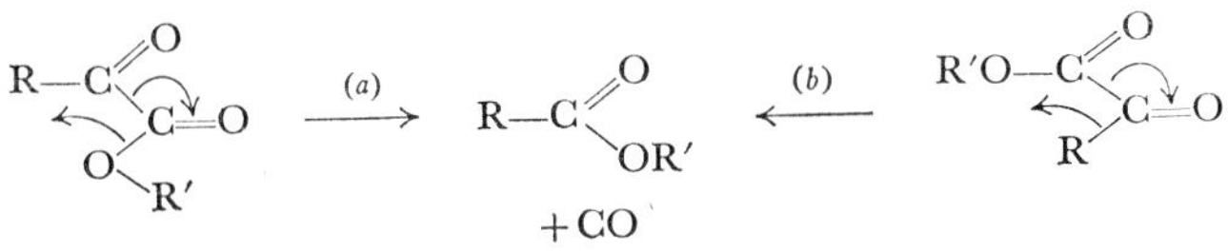

$+CO$

mechanism (b) can operate if the group R is very electron-rich, but for simple compounds mechanism (a) was proved by an isotopic tracer experiment:

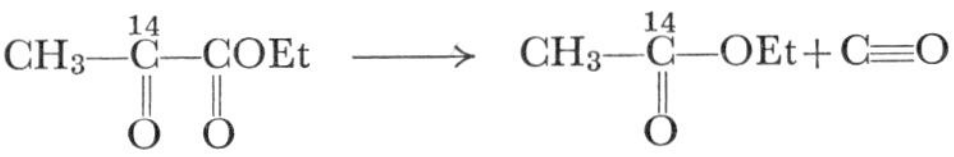

$$CH_3 \overset{14}{-}\underset{\underset{O}{\|}}{C} \overset{}{-} \underset{\underset{O}{\|}}{C} OEt \longrightarrow CH_3 \overset{14}{-}\underset{\underset{O}{\|}}{C} OEt + C\equiv O$$

β-Ketoesters are derivable from a crossed reaction in which halide ion is displaced in preference to alkoxide:

$$R-CO-CH_2-R' \xrightarrow[\text{Br.CH}_2.\text{CO}_2\text{Et}]{\text{LiNH}_2} RCOCHR'-CH_2CO_2Et$$

Primary halides will also react in this way, but in the presence of the strong base the olefin-forming elimination competes seriously when secondary halides are employed and excludes the use of tertiary halides. An important route to γ-ketoacids and others with a greater separation between the functions is the oxidation of alicyclic tertiary alcohols.

The Perkin Reaction (1868). Aldehydes, but not ketones, undergo this base-catalysed aldol-type reaction with acid anhydrides. The reaction is further limited for synthetic work, to aromatic and $\alpha\beta$-unsaturated aldehydes which cannot undergo self-condensation, and to anhydrides of acetic or monoalkyl acetic acids. The products of reaction are β-arylacrylic acids, cinnamic acids being the most important.

$$(CH_3.CH_2.CO)_2O + CH_3CH_2CO_2{}^{\ominus}Na^{\oplus}$$

$$\downarrow$$

$$Na^{\oplus}[CH_3\!-\!\underset{\ominus}{CH}\!-\!CO.O.CO.CH_2CH_3] + CH_3CH_2CO_2H$$

$$Ph\!-\!C\underset{H}{\overset{O}{\diagdown}} \quad \underset{-H^{\oplus}}{\overset{+H^{\oplus}}{\rightleftharpoons}} \quad \left[Ph\!-\!\underset{H}{\overset{OH}{\underset{|}{\overset{|}{C}}}}\!-\!\underset{CH_3}{\overset{H}{\underset{|}{\overset{|}{C}}}}\!-\!CO.O.CO.CH_2CH_3 \right] \quad (D)$$

The condensation is catalysed by the sodium propionate and comes to equilibrium during 24 hr at 130°. On working up by steam distillation of unreacted aldehyde from aqueous alkali followed by acidification, the mixed anhydride (D) undergoes hydrolysis and the aldol—OH group is eliminated to yield dimorphic *trans*-α-methylcinnamic acid:

$$\underset{H}{\overset{Ph}{\diagup}}C\!=\!C\underset{CO_2H}{\overset{CH_3}{\diagdown}} \quad \text{m.p. 74 or 81°, 70\%}$$

Other bases such as sodium carbonate can effect condensation.

The equilibrium in the reaction between aromatic aldehydes and anhydride will lie to the left and the rate of reaction will be slower if an electron donor is present on the benzene ring, for example yields of cinnamic acids obtained from acetic anhydride and *para*-substituted aldehydes under comparable conditions vary as:

Substituent	Percentage yield	
None	50	
Me—	33	with recovery of aldehyde
MeO—	30	in inverse proportion
NO$_2$—	82	

The Azlactone Synthesis (Erlenmeyer, 1893) is closely related to the Perkin reaction and involves condensation between the aldehyde and an α-acylaminoacid. Points of difference are that the azlactone (i.e. lactone ring including nitrogen) synthesis proceeds under milder conditions and may afford high yields where the Perkin reaction fails. It is probable that the first step is the formation of the azlactone:

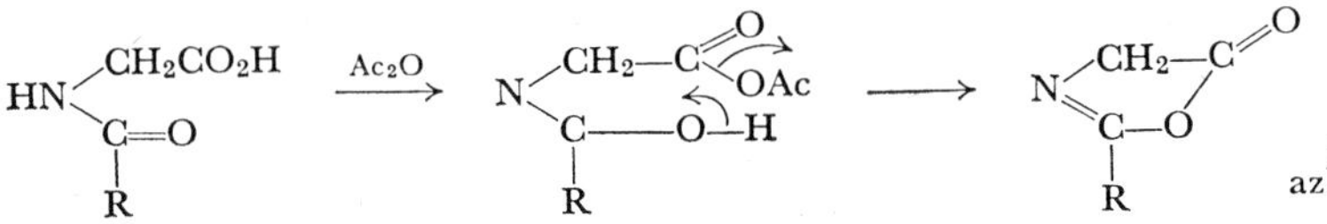

The conjugate base of the azlactone would be more readily formed than that of the acid anhydride, which is the intermediate in the Perkin reaction, because a higher degree of resonance stabilization is possible:

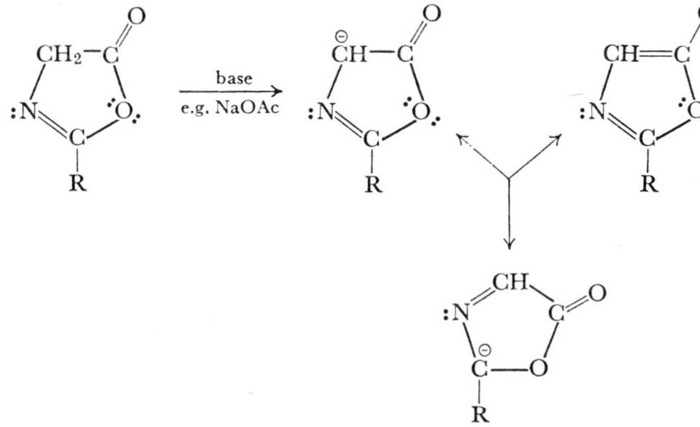

indeed the hybrid of structure (E) with four π-electrons and two un-shared on the ring oxygen would have some aromatic character (cf. the five-ring heterocycles). The condensation step with an aldehyde, for example veratraldehyde, gives good yields of the unsaturated condensation product (F) after heating on a steam bath:

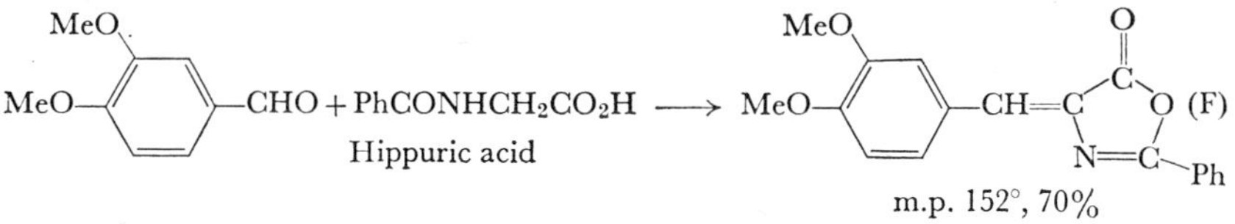

The product 2-phenyl-4-(3′,4′-dimethoxybenzal)-oxazolone is precipitated on diluting the solution with ethanol. Here the elimination of the aldol —OH group is facile since it leads to extensive conjugation and aldolization cannot then be reversed via addition of water (cf. the intermediate D, p. 130, also p. 153) because this cannot exist in the anhydride medium: in consequence of this yields are less dependent on substituents on the nucleus than in the Perkin reaction.

Important applications of azlactones are:
(*a*) Reduction and hydrolysis to α-aminoacids

$$\text{PhCH}=\underset{\underset{\text{Ph}}{\overset{\displaystyle N=C}{\diagdown}}}{\overset{\overset{\displaystyle O}{\overset{\displaystyle \|}{C}}}{\diagup\diagdown}O} \xrightarrow[\text{to soln. in Ac}_2\text{O}]{\text{phosphorus/50\% aq. HI}} \text{PhCH}_2-\underset{\underset{\text{Ph}}{\overset{\displaystyle N=C}{\diagdown}}}{\overset{\overset{\displaystyle O}{\overset{\displaystyle \|}{C}}}{CH}\diagup\diagdown O}$$

hydrolysis

$$\text{PhCH}_2\underset{\underset{\text{NH}_2}{|}}{\text{CH}}-\text{CO}_2\text{H} + \text{PhCO}_2\text{H}$$

Hydrolysis occurs here in the partially aqueous and acidic medium. A good general procedure for the hydrolysis of reduced azlactones is the use of dilute alcoholic alkali; the azlactone reduction can also be effected by sodium/ethanol or by catalytic hydrogenation.

(*b*) Hydrolysis of unsaturated azlactones, preferably in hot alkali, affords α-ketoacids:

$$p\text{-MeO}-\text{C}_6\text{H}_4-\text{CH}=\underset{\underset{\text{Ph}}{\overset{\displaystyle N=C}{\diagdown}}}{\overset{\overset{\displaystyle O}{\overset{\displaystyle \|}{C}}}{\diagup\diagdown}O} \xrightarrow{\text{OH}^\ominus} \begin{array}{l} p\text{-MeO}-\text{C}_6\text{H}_4-\text{CO}-\text{CO}_2\text{H} \quad \text{m.p. } 185° \\ + \text{Ph}-\text{CO}_2\text{H} + \text{NH}_3 \end{array}$$

A small amount of *p*-methoxytoluene is obtained on steam distillation of the alkaline liquors.

(*c*) Peptide linkages can be formed:

(L) Arginine in acetone

$$\text{ArCH}=\underset{\underset{\text{Ac}}{\overset{\displaystyle NH}{|}}}{C}-\text{CO}-\text{NH}-\underset{\underset{\text{CO}_2\text{H}}{|}}{C}(\text{CH}_2)_3\text{NH}-\overset{\overset{\displaystyle NH}{\|}}{C}-\text{NH}_2$$

(2) deacetylation by cold dil. HCl

(1) H₂/Pd

$$p\text{-OHC}_6\text{H}_4-\text{CH}_2\underset{\underset{\text{NH}_2}{|}}{\text{CH}}\text{CO}-\text{NHArg}$$

D-Tyrosyl-L-arginine
and
L-tyrosyl-L-arginine

132

The two diastereoisomers are formed because the hydrogenation is not stereospecific.

Cyclization of Difunctional Compounds. Dicarboxylic esters $RO_2C(CH_2)_nCO_2R$ undergo self-condensation when $n = 1-3$:

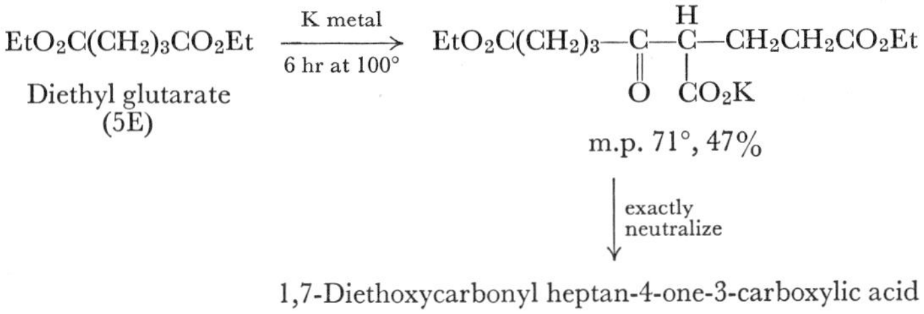

$$EtO_2C(CH_2)_3CO_2Et \xrightarrow[\text{6 hr at 100°}]{\text{K metal}} EtO_2C(CH_2)_3-\overset{\overset{H}{|}}{\underset{\underset{CO_2K}{|}}{C}}-\overset{\overset{}{\|}}{\underset{\underset{O}{\|}}{C}}-CH_2CH_2CO_2Et$$

Diethyl glutarate
(5E)

m.p. 71°, 47%

exactly neutralize

1,7-Diethoxycarbonyl heptan-4-one-3-carboxylic acid

(cf. malonic and succinic esters, pp. 142, 162). When the geometry is favourable intramolecular condensation leads to the formation of a cyclic ketoester (Dieckmann, 1894). This is particularly useful for the formation of the strain-free six-ring, and for five rings, where there is a high probability of the carbanion approaching the ethoxycarbonyl group:

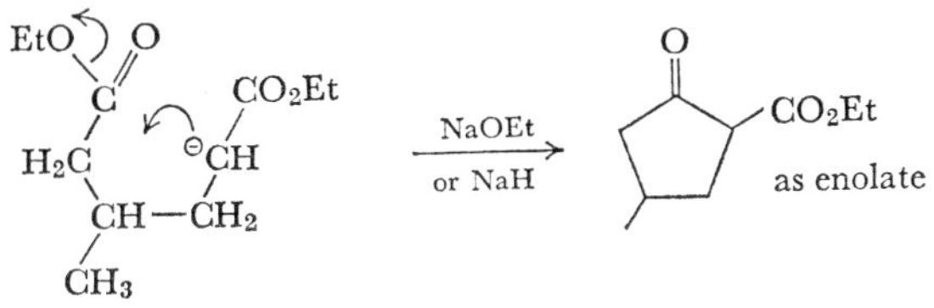

Diethyl β-methyladipate

In the above example the starting material is symmetrical and only one cyclic product is possible, if an unsymmetrical compound is cyclized two position isomers can be formed. Intramolecular reactions are possible whenever a carbanion can approach and displace a stable anion (cf. reactions of haloketones, p. 94):

Ketoesters undergo cyclization:

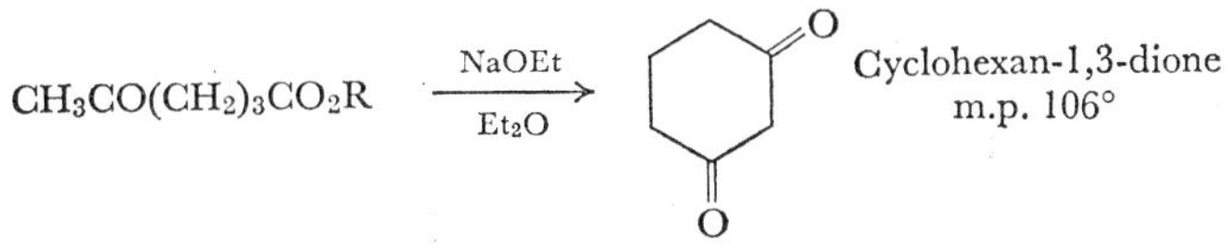

$$CH_3CO(CH_2)_3CO_2R \xrightarrow[\text{Et}_2\text{O}]{\text{NaOEt}}$$

Cyclohexan-1,3-dione
m.p. 106°

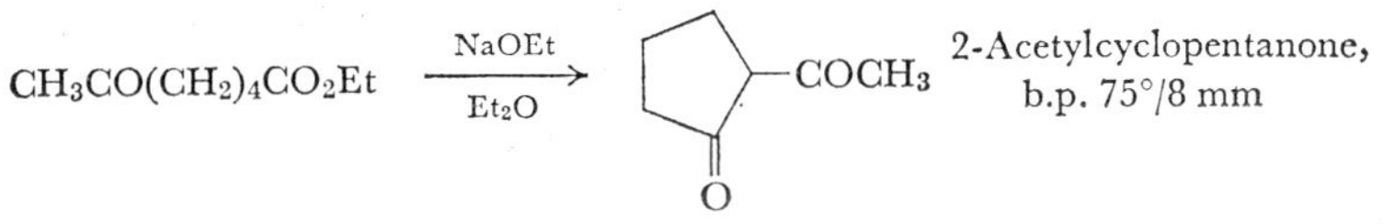

$$CH_3CO(CH_2)_4CO_2Et \xrightarrow[\text{Et}_2\text{O}]{\text{NaOEt}}$$

2-Acetylcyclopentanone,
b.p. 75°/8 mm

133

and the products of Dieckmann cyclizations may themselves be usefully elaborated:

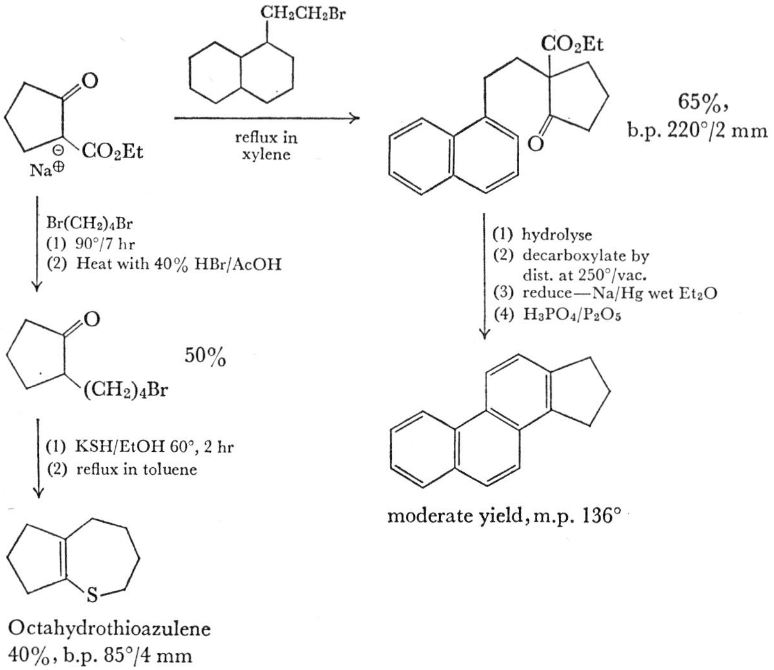
CH₂CH₂Br
O
CO₂Et
Na⊕
reflux in
xylene
CO₂Et
O
65%,
b.p. 220°/2 mm
Br(CH₂)₄Br
(1) 90°/7 hr
(2) Heat with 40% HBr/AcOH
(1) hydrolyse
(2) decarboxylate by
dist. at 250°/vac.
(3) reduce—Na/Hg wet Et₂O
(4) H₃PO₄/P₂O₅
O
50%
(CH₂)₄Br
(1) KSH/EtOH 60°, 2 hr
(2) reflux in toluene
moderate yield, m.p. 136°
S
Octahydrothioazulene
40%, b.p. 85°/4 mm

Poor yields are obtained in the synthesis of cyclic compounds which have strained rings or where the reactive groups are separated by many carbon atoms leading to a low probability of approach of carbanion to the electrophilic centre. An improvement was here effected by Ziegler in his adaptation of the dinitrile cyclization of Thorpe—in very dilute solution collisions between molecules are infrequent and hence intramolecular condensations are favoured even when the probability of approach is low.

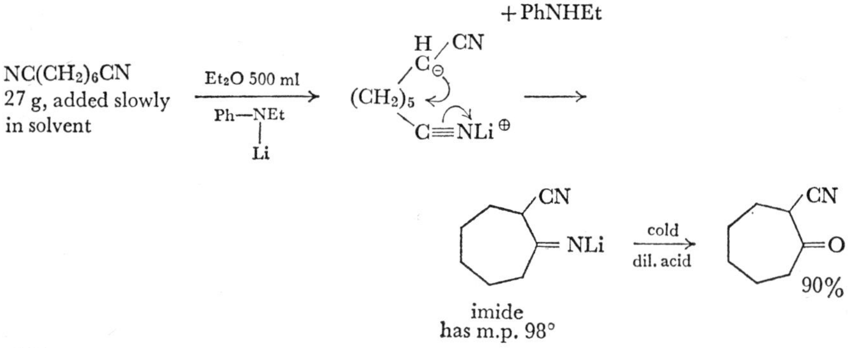
+PhNHEt
NC(CH₂)₆CN
27 g, added slowly
in solvent
Et₂O 500 ml
Ph—NEt
Li
H
CN
C⊖
(CH₂)₅
C≡NLi ⊕
CN
NLi
cold
dil. acid
CN
O
90%
imide
has m.p. 98°

Several hours reflux in 70% sulphuric acid gives ketones by decarboxylation in high yield. The lithium phenylethylamine catalyst was prepared from lithium butyl (40 ml) and ethyl-aniline (93 g) and is effective by exchange of α-hydrogen and does not initiate addition to the —C≡N bond typical of the lithium alkyl itself (p. 36). Overall yields are good for normal rings (C5-7) and large rings (of C > 14) which are essentially free from Pitzer strain and transannular interactions.

The best cyclization procedure, particularly for strained medium-ring compounds (C9-11) is the acyloin condensation developed by Prelog and Stoll. The reaction occurs to a limited extent on the surface of the sodium metal during an ester condensation:

$$2CH_3COOEt \xrightarrow{\;} \underset{\bullet}{2CH_3-C}=O \;\rightleftharpoons\; CH_3.CO.CO.CH_3$$
$$2Na\bullet$$
$$+2EtO^{\ominus}$$

This first reduction step (donation of one electron by sodium) is followed by a second if excess of the metal is present:

$$CH_3-\underset{\bullet}{C}=O+Na\bullet \;\longrightarrow\; CH_3-C\overset{O}{\underset{Na}{\diagdown}} \;(G) \;\rightleftharpoons\; CH_3-\overset{NaO}{\underset{|}{C}}=\overset{ONa}{\underset{|}{C}}-CH_3$$

Acyclic acyloins are obtained by the use of high surface sodium in a refluxing inert solvent under nitrogen, to avoid oxidation by atmospheric oxygen:

Butyroin

$$2Pr-CO_2Et \xrightarrow[Et_2O]{Na} Pr-\underset{NaO}{\overset{|}{C}}=\underset{ONa}{\overset{|}{C}}-Pr \xrightarrow[acid]{dilute} Pr-\underset{O}{\overset{\|}{C}}-\underset{OH}{\overset{|}{CH}}-Pr$$

precipitated as a yellow solid

separated in Et₂O and distilled, b.p. 86°/12 mm, 70%

The esters of dicarboxylic acids undergo an intramolecular coupling to yield an enolate salt of the form:

$$\begin{matrix} \overset{|}{C}O_2Et \\ (CH_2)_n \\ \overset{|}{C}O_2Et \end{matrix} \;\longrightarrow\; (CH_2)_n \begin{matrix} C-ONa \\ \| \\ C-ONa \end{matrix}$$

and this will be preferred to the formation of polymers by intermolecular reaction if the area of metal surface is high, when the ends of the disodio-derivative (G) can pair by sliding on the surface:

135

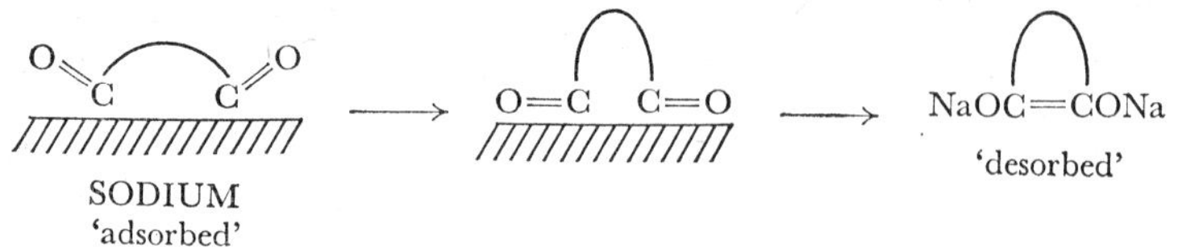

$$O=C \quad C=O \longrightarrow O=C \quad C=O \longrightarrow NaOC=CONa$$

SODIUM
'adsorbed'

'desorbed'

where the essential is a large area of metal surface rather than volume of solution. The yields in the preparation of medium-ring acyloins by reflux in xylene (*c.* 10 hr) are:

Ring size	Product	Percentage yield	m.p./b.p.
8	Suberoin	47	(90°/5 mm)
9	Azeloin	42	42°
10	Sebacoin	65	(100°/1 mm)
11	Cycloundecanol-2-one	71	33°

Large strain-free rings are obtained in high yield by the acyloin condensation and the method is used by the perfumery industry in synthesis of the musks, for example:

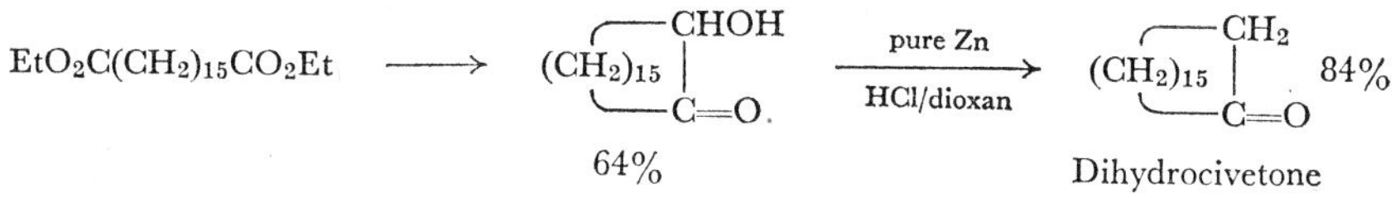

$$EtO_2C(CH_2)_{15}CO_2Et \longrightarrow (CH_2)_{15}\begin{array}{c}CHOH\\|\\C=O\end{array} \xrightarrow[HCl/dioxan]{pure\ Zn} (CH_2)_{15}\begin{array}{c}CH_2\\|\\C=O\end{array} \ 84\%$$

64%

Dihydrocivetone

A dramatic application was Wasserman's synthesis of a catenane with interlocking rings.

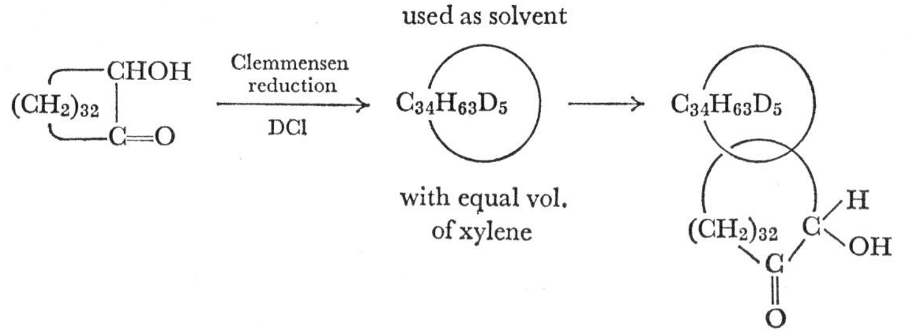

used as solvent

$$(CH_2)_{32}\begin{array}{c}CHOH\\|\\C=O\end{array} \xrightarrow[DCl]{Clemmensen\ reduction} C_{34}H_{63}D_5 \longrightarrow C_{34}H_{63}D_5$$

with equal vol.
of xylene

Incorporation of deuterium showed that the rings were linked in this way because in the infrared spectrum the C–D stretching band was associated with the acyloin fraction after rechromatography. Apart from the reduction to hydrocarbon, here effected by the Clemmensen

136

method, and hydrogenolysis by pure zinc/hydrochloric acid to the ketone, the acyloins can be reduced to *vic* diols by hydrogenation using copper chromite. Oxidation to α-diketones is accomplished by the use of bismuth oxide in acetic acid with removal of the metal produced by filtration.

Normal rings (C5–7) are accessible:

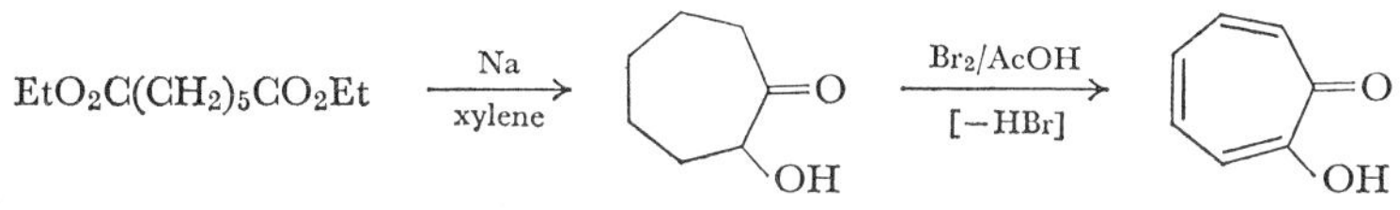

$$EtO_2C(CH_2)_5CO_2Et \xrightarrow[\text{xylene}]{Na}$$

=O, OH

$$\xrightarrow[\text{[−HBr]}]{Br_2/AcOH}$$

=O, OH

Pimeloin, 52%

Tropolone, m.p. 50°

and the starting materials may be alkylated or unsaturated diesters. The formation of alkoxide ion during the cyclization can initiate a competing carbanionoid condensation. Thus when closure of a seven-ring was attempted with a steroid intermediate a Dieckmann reaction occurred:

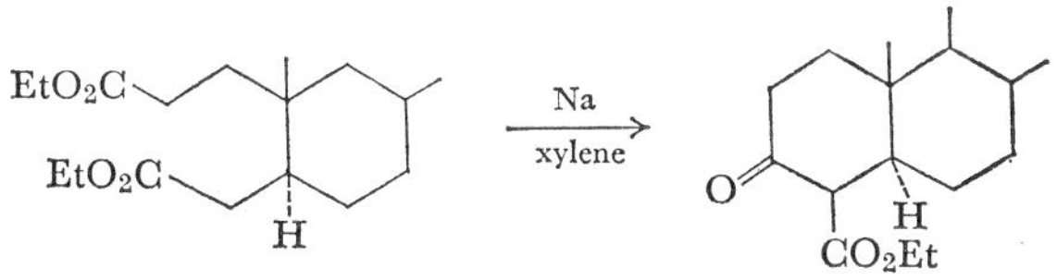

EtO₂C, EtO₂C, H

$$\xrightarrow[\text{xylene}]{Na}$$

O, H, CO₂Et

Sheehan has shown however, that cyclizations often occur more smoothly by treatment of the diester with a solution of sodium in liquid ammonia:

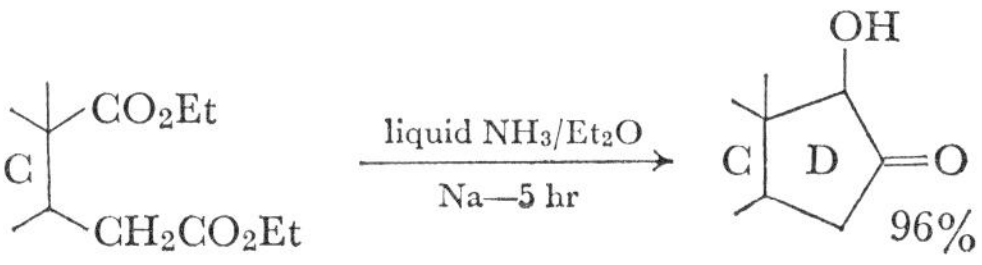

CO₂Et, C, CH₂CO₂Et

$$\xrightarrow[\text{Na—5 hr}]{\text{liquid NH}_3/\text{Et}_2\text{O}}$$

OH, C, D, =O, 96%

Closure of the steroid D ring in this way is the preferred method in that field.

The Alkylation of β-Ketoesters. This was first achieved by Geuther in 1863 who prepared ethyl ethylacetoacetate; another typical example is:

$$CH_3.CO.CH_2.CO_2Et + \text{n-BuBr} \xrightarrow[\text{EtOH}]{\text{NaOEt (5 mols)}} CH_3.CO.CH(\text{n-Bu}).CO_2Et + \text{NaBr} \downarrow$$

5 mols   5·5 mols   neutral soln. on completion
70%, b.p. 115°/16 mm

The active methylene group can be dialkylated but by a two-step synthesis (cf. malonic ester, p. 143). The second alkylation stage is often slow, particularly with alkyl chlorides, and it is advisable to use the strong base, potassium t-butoxide, in t-butanol.

$$CH_3.CO.CH(n\text{-}Bu).CO_2Et \xrightarrow[n\text{-}BuBr]{KO\text{-}t\text{-}Bu} CH_3.CO.C(n\text{-}Bu)_2.CO_2Et$$
$$77\%, \text{b.p. } 148°/18 \text{ mm}$$

The alkylated ketoesters undergo a retro-Claisen condensation which can be a disadvantage, especially in ethanol solution, because it competes with the second alkylation stage:

$$CH_3.CO_2Et + \overset{\ominus}{C}HR.CO_2Et \xrightarrow{EtOH} R.CH_2.CO_2Et + Et\overset{\ominus}{O}$$

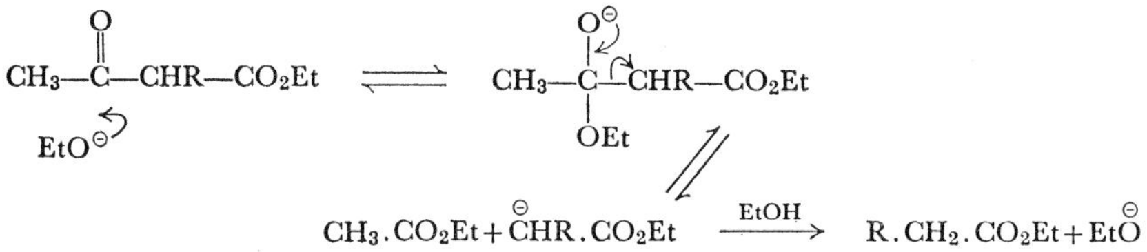

This formation of two acidic fragments, isolated as their esters, is known as 'acid fission'; it intervened in the reaction between ethyl methylacetoacetate and γ-bromopropyl ethyl ether in the presence of ethoxide ion, but a satisfactory result was obtained in an aprotic solvent:

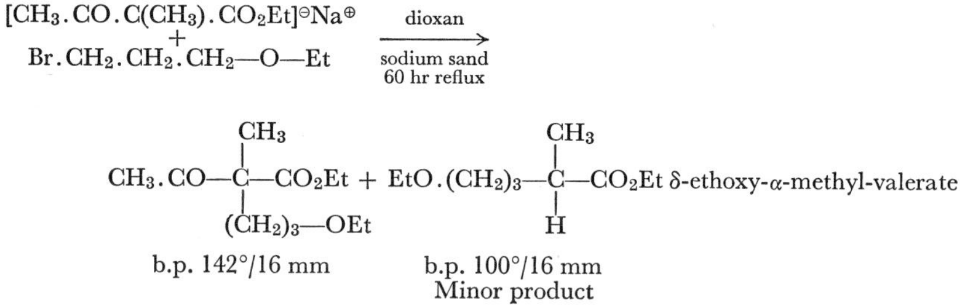

$$[CH_3.CO.C(CH_3).CO_2Et]^{\ominus}Na^{\oplus}$$
$$\overset{+}{Br.CH_2.CH_2.CH_2-O-Et} \xrightarrow[\substack{\text{sodium sand} \\ \text{60 hr reflux}}]{\text{dioxan}}$$

Sodium hydride is a convenient reagent for the preparation of the conjugate base in aprotic solvents, for example, benzene and dioxan.

The 'acid fission' just described has long been used synthetically as an alternative to the malonic ester route (p. 143) to homologues of acetic acid. Ketones are obtained by the alternative method of 'ketonic fission', which occurs when the ketoester is heated in dilute aqueous acid or alkali, or in aqueous-alcoholic alkali:

138

$$\text{CH}_3.\text{CO}.\text{CH(nBu)}.\text{CO}_2\text{Et} \xrightarrow[\text{reflux 5\% NaOH}]{4\ \text{hr}} \left[\text{CH}_3\text{—CO}.\text{CH(nBu)—C} \begin{array}{c} \text{O}^{\ominus} \\ \text{OEt} \\ \text{OH} \end{array} \right]$$

$$\underset{\substack{60\%,\ \text{b.p. }152°}}{\text{CH}_3\text{CO}.\text{CH}_2.\text{nBu}} \xleftarrow[\text{acid}]{\text{cold dilute}} \text{CH}_3.\text{CO}.\text{CH(nBu)—CO}_2^{\ominus}\text{Na}^{\oplus}$$

It is common for low yields of ketones to be obtained in this reaction because attack of the —OH$^{\ominus}$ ions on the other electrophilic centre leads to concomitant 'acid fission', this may sometimes be overcome by the use of the t-butyl acetoacetate which undergoes fission on pyrolysis:

$$\underset{\text{Ketene}}{\text{t-BuOH} + \text{CH}_2\text{=C=O}} \xrightarrow[\text{catalyst}]{\text{NaOAc}} \text{CH}_3.\text{CO}.\text{CH}_2\text{—CO}_2\text{-t-Bu} \quad \text{b.p. 85°/20 mm, 80\%}$$

$$\downarrow \text{2 steps}$$

$$\underset{\substack{84\%}}{\text{CH}_3\text{—CO}.\underset{\substack{| \\ \text{iBu}}}{\overset{\substack{\text{Bu} \\ |}}{\text{CH}}} + \text{CO}_2 +} \underset{\text{H}_3\text{C}}{\overset{\text{H}_3\text{C}}{>}}\text{C=CH}_2 \xleftarrow[\substack{\text{TsOH} \\ \text{catalyst}}]{100°} \text{CH}_3.\text{CO}.\text{C(Bu)(iBu)}.\text{CO}_2\text{-t-Bu}$$

The preparation of ketones from acid chlorides and metal alkyls (p. 35) is another alternative.

The best yields in acid fission are obtained when a catalytic amount of ethoxide ion is used to initiate the retro-Claisen condensation:

$$\underset{\substack{}}{\text{Ph—CH=CH—CH}_2\text{—}\underset{\substack{| \\ \text{H}}}{\overset{\substack{\text{CH}_3\text{—C=O} \\ |}}{\text{C}}}\text{—CO}_2\text{Et}} \xrightarrow[\text{in EtOH}]{\text{EtO}^{\ominus}}$$

$$\text{Ph—CH=CH—CH}_2.\text{CH}_2.\text{CO}_2\text{Et} + \text{CH}_3.\text{CO}_2\text{Et} + \text{EtO}^{\ominus}$$

$$\text{b.p. 115°/1 mm, 92\%}$$

The alkylacetoacetate must be free from acetoacetic ester which would trap ethoxide ion and prevent its functioning; the system must also be anhydrous, for water would also trap the catalyst and the liberated hydroxide ion could initiate some ketonic fission. The δ-ethoxy-α-methyl-valerate formed as a minor product in the reaction mentioned above was probably formed in this way due to the presence of a proton donor, ethylene glycol, in the dioxan used.

Acetoacetic ester has frequently been employed in terpene synthesis, for example:

139

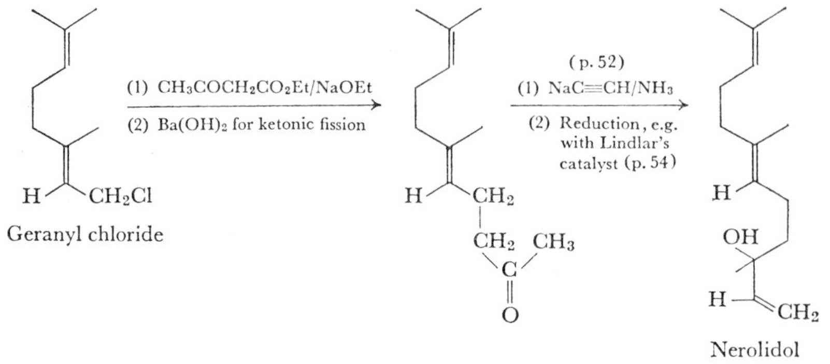

(1) CH₃COCH₂CO₂Et/NaOEt → (2) Ba(OH)₂ for ketonic fission

Geranyl chloride

(p. 52)
(1) NaC≡CH/NH₃ →
(2) Reduction, e.g. with Lindlar's catalyst (p. 54)

Nerolidol

O-alkylation of Ambident Anions competes with the C-alkylation which is normally required, when β-ketoesters and β-diketones are used as intermediates:

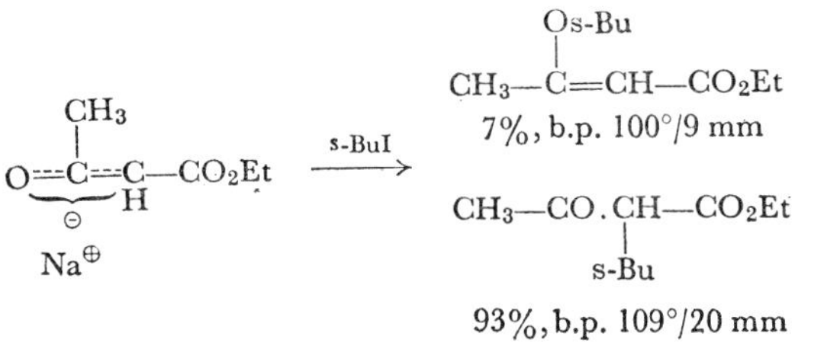

$$CH_3-C=CH-CO_2Et$$
Os-Bu
$$7\%, \text{b.p. } 100°/9 \text{ mm}$$

$$CH_3-CO.CH-CO_2Et \quad (H)$$
s-Bu
$$93\%, \text{b.p. } 109°/20 \text{ mm}$$

The isomers are not separable by distillation, but separation is achieved by gas–liquid chromatography and the products are clearly characterized by their ultraviolet and infrared spectra. The enol-ethers probably have the *trans* configuration and are removed from the mixture by shaking in cold dilute acid for several hours when they are hydrolysed to the original ketoester and the corresponding alcohol. The proportions of the two alkylation products mentioned above (H) are typical of acetoacetic ester; for acetylacetone the proportion of enol-ether can rise above 20 % when secondary alkyl halides are used.

Brändström has summarized some of the factors which influence the course of alkylation. When the enol is particularly stable O-alkylation will result with a reactive electrophile:

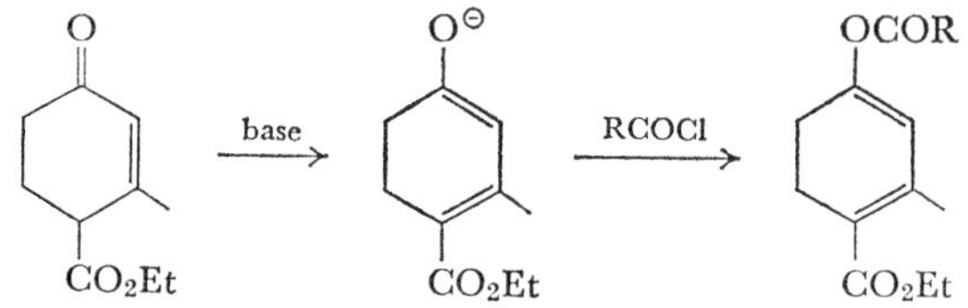

Hagemann's ester

and the phenols exhibit extreme behaviour of this kind where O-alkylation results even when the alkylating agent is of lower reactivity than an acid chloride. It is noteworthy that C-alkylation can predominate even here when the hydroxyl group is hindered:

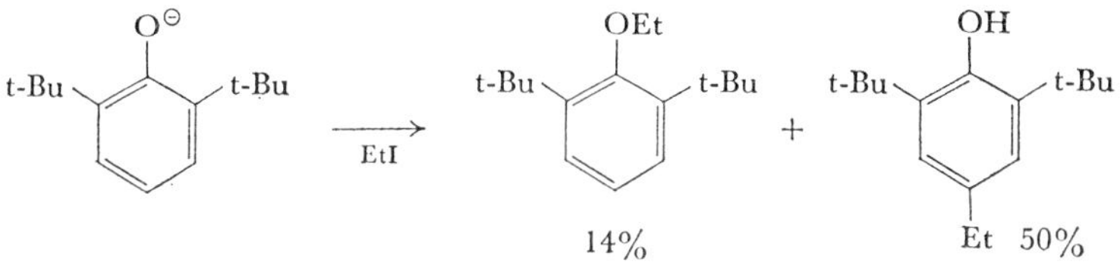

14%   Et 50%

There is significant evidence for the participation of a six-centred transition state (I) in the reaction between alkyl halides and enols of lower stability than phenols leading to C-alkylation:

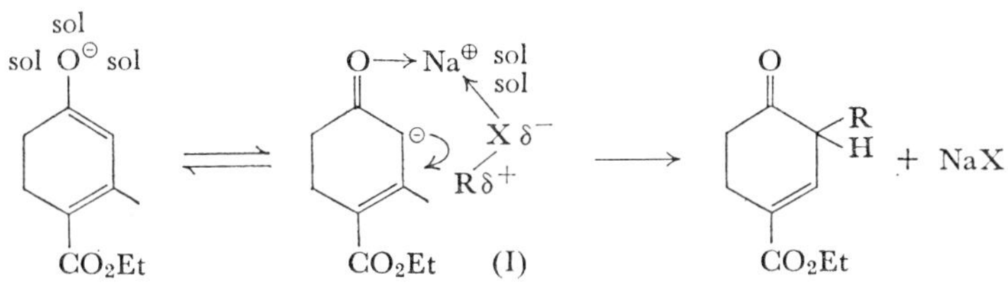

There is no such transition state for O-alkylation and one or more molecules must be displaced from the solvation cage by groups which can co-ordinate with the anion. The transition state for C-alkylation will be more readily established if the enolate anion is originally only weakly solvated, and to achieve this result one works with a concentrated solution containing an excess of the alkyl halide; the greater the co-ordinating power of the halide the better:

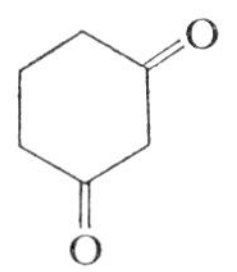

		C-alkyl	O-alkyl
	n-BuBr affords	18%	42%
	n-BuI affords	28%	36%

cyclohexan-1,3-dione

The part played by the metal ion in alkylations is clearly shown by comparing the rates of ethylation of n-butyrophenone in the presence of different alkali metal ions (see structural formulae at top of p. 142).

The rate for the lithium derivative is 75 times that for sodium, which in turn is 100 times faster than the potassium derivative; consistent with more ready co-ordination of the smaller cation and greater assistance

141

$$\text{PhCOC}_3\text{H}_7 \xrightarrow[\text{in Et}_2\text{O}]{\text{LiH, NaH, or KH}} \begin{array}{c} \text{H} \diagdown \diagup \text{Et} \\ \text{C} \\ \text{Ph—C} \diagup\ddots\ \text{Et} \\ \| \quad\ \vdots \\ \text{O} \quad \text{Br} \\ \diagdown\text{M}\diagup \end{array} \longrightarrow \text{PhCOCH(Et)}_2$$

(I′) M = Metal
ion

to breaking the C—Br bond in the transition state. The mechanism shown (I′) should be compared with that postulated for the reaction between Grignard reagents and carbonyl compounds (p. 25).

APPLICATIONS OF MALONIC ACID AND ITS DERIVATIVES

The discussion will be centred round diethyl malonate, $\text{EtO}_2\text{C—CH}_2$ —CO_2Et, and ethyl cyanoacetate, $\text{EtO}_2\text{C—CH}_2\text{—CN}$, whose alkylation reactions are used most often. These compounds are said to contain an 'active' methylene group, because abstraction of a proton by base is facile owing to the resonance stabilization of the resulting anion:

$$\begin{array}{ccc} \underset{\text{EtO}}{\overset{\text{O}}{\diagdown}}\text{C} \overset{\ominus}{\underset{|}{\overset{|}{\text{C}}}}\text{—CN} & \longleftrightarrow & \underset{\text{EtO}}{\overset{\text{O}^{\ominus}}{\diagdown}}\text{C}=\text{C} \diagdown \text{C}\equiv\text{N} \\ \quad\ \text{H} & & \quad\ \text{H} \end{array} \longleftrightarrow \underset{\text{EtO}}{\overset{\text{O}}{\diagdown}}\text{C—C}=\text{C}=\text{N}^{\ominus}$$

The —$\text{C}\equiv\text{N}$ group is more effective in stabilizing negative charge than the —CO_2Et group and cyanocompounds react more readily than esters. A considerable advantage in the use of these compounds is that alkylation only occurs at the methylene group.

It was seen (p. 126) that an alkyl substituent reduces the acidity of acetates and direct alkylation of monocarboxylic esters is not an important method although it is possible in the presence of strong base, for example triphenylmethide, and may be used more in the future with solvents like dimethylsulphoxide (see p. 114).

Malonic Esters are monoalkylated when their sodio-derivatives react with one equivalent of an alkyl halide:

$$\text{EtO}_2\text{C—CH}_2\text{—CO}_2\text{Et} \xrightarrow[\text{EtOH}]{\text{NaOEt(IE)}} \overset{\oplus}{\text{Na}} \begin{pmatrix} & \overset{\text{CO}_2\text{Et}}{\diagup} \\ \overset{\ominus}{\text{C}}\text{—H} \\ & \diagdown\text{CO}_2\text{Et} \end{pmatrix} \longrightarrow$$

$$\begin{array}{c} \quad\quad\quad \overset{\text{CO}_2\text{Et}}{\diagup} \quad +\text{NaBr} \\ \text{Et—C—H} \\ \diagdown\text{CO}_2\text{Et} \quad 90\% \end{array}$$

Diethyl ethylmalonate

If the alkyl halide is too volatile the dialkyl sulphate or alkyl toluene-*p*-sulphonate can be used; the product is isolated after a period of reflux by the evaporation of alcohol, treatment of the residue with dilute acid, and solvent (ether) extraction. The alkylmalonate is a weaker acid than the solvent alcohol and the equilibrium (J) lies to the left:

$$
\begin{array}{ccc}
\text{CO}_2\text{R} & & \text{CO}_2\text{R} \\
| & \xrightarrow{-\text{H}^{\oplus}} & | \\
\text{R—CH} \quad ^{\ominus}\text{OR} & \xleftarrow{+\text{H}^{\oplus}} & \text{R—C}^{\ominus} \quad \text{H—OR} \qquad (J) \\
| & & | \\
\text{CO}_2\text{R} & & \text{CO}_2\text{R}
\end{array}
$$

hence the second alkylation step does not compete with the first and a second, different, alkyl group can be introduced in a separate step:

$$
\begin{array}{ccc}
\text{CO}_2\text{Et} & & \text{CO}_2\text{Et} \\
| & \xrightarrow[\text{in EtOH}]{\text{long reflux}} & | \\
\text{Et—CNa} + \text{iPr—I} & & \text{Et—C—iPr} \quad \text{b.p. } 230\text{–}235°, 46\% \\
| & & | \\
\text{CO}_2\text{Et} & & \text{CO}_2\text{Et}
\end{array}
$$

Diethyl ethyl(isopropyl)malonate

However, if the reaction is carried out in an aprotic solvent, for example benzene, then an appreciable concentration of the monoalkyl anion will exist in solution and substantial dialkylation will occur. Dialkylation also becomes competitive for reactive halides such as benzyl and here the less reactive chlorides are to be preferred to bromides or iodides. The elimination reaction competes with secondary and tertiary halides (cf. p. 129) and reaction between alkoxide and reactive halides leads to ether formation. If a two-step sequence is used then the group introduced first should be that which has the lesser effect on the acidity of the alkyl-malonate, that is, primary halide before secondary. When both groups are primary the larger should be introduced first so as to simplify the fractionation, at this stage, of malonate and alkylmalonate from the unwanted symmetrical dialkylmalonate.

Once alkylated, malonic esters can be converted into a homologous monocarboxylic acid by hydrolysis with decarboxylation in hot aqueous acid:

$$
\begin{array}{l}
\text{CH—(CO}_2\text{Et)}_2 \\
| \\
\text{CH}_2 \qquad \xrightarrow[\text{(2) evaporation}]{\text{(1) 1:1 HCl}} \quad \text{HO}_2\text{C—(CH}_2)_3\text{—CO}_2\text{H} + 2\text{CO}_2 + 2\text{EtOH} \\
| \\
\text{CH—(CO}_2\text{Et)}_2 \qquad\qquad\qquad\qquad\quad \text{Glutaric acid, } 80\%
\end{array}
$$

In many cases the course of hydrolysis may be followed by the solution of the ester and in general solvent extraction would follow on cooling.

143

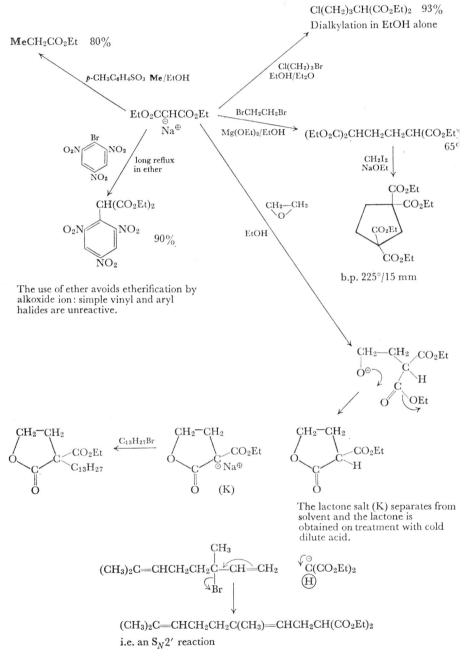

Carbanions Derived from Carboxylic Acids and their Derivatives

The following summary illustrates a number of synthetic routes based on malonic esters:

144

Sodium hydride can be used to produce the carbanion in an inert solvent, whilst alkali metal t-butoxides are effective in t-butanol when the less basic ethoxide fails:

$$i\text{-}Pr\text{---}CH(CO_2Et)_2 \xrightarrow[\text{Na/t-BuOH}]{\text{EtCl}} i\text{-}Pr(Et)C(CO_2Et)_2$$
$$\text{b.p. } 112°/18 \text{ mm,} \qquad \text{(L)}$$
$$60\%$$

Because of the base-catalysed exchange of alkoxy groups it may be necessary to use di-t-butyl malonate in these reactions and this ester is prepared by the acid-catalysed addition of malonic acid to isobutylene:

$$CH_2(CO_2H)_2 + 2CH_2{=}C(CH_3)_2 \xrightarrow[\text{in Et}_2O]{10\% \text{ H}_2\text{SO}_4} CH_2(CO_2\text{-t-Bu})_2$$
$$60\%$$

Cyanoacetic Esters. There is no need to use a stronger base than ethoxide ion in the example above (L) if the malonic ester is replaced by cyanoacetate. Because of the greater inductive effect of the cyano group compared to the ethoxycarbonyl group a monoalkyl cyanoacetate is a stronger acid than the corresponding malonate and stronger also than the solvent ethanol (see p. 143), hence an appreciable concentration of the conjugate base

$$\begin{array}{c} \overset{\displaystyle CN}{\underset{\displaystyle CO_2Et}{|}} \\ R\text{---}\overset{|}{\underset{|}{C}}{}^{\ominus} \end{array}$$

exists in solution and dialkylation occurs more readily. Mixtures of mono- and dialkylcyanoacetates are commonly produced when sodium ethoxide is used as catalyst, which complicates the working up:

$$n\text{-}C_3H_7I + CN.CH_2.CO_2Et \xrightarrow[\text{NaOEt}]{\text{EtOH}} \begin{array}{l} \text{monalkyl compound } 49\% \\ \text{dialkyl compound } 20\% \end{array}$$

Dialkylation tends to increase with the use of more forcing conditions, for example, t-butoxide in t-butanol and to decrease for bulky alkyl groups:

$$i\text{-}C_3H_7I + CN.CH_2.CO_2Et \xrightarrow[\text{NaOEt}]{\text{EtOH}} \begin{array}{l} \text{monalkyl } 63\% \\ \text{dialkyl } 5\% \end{array}$$

145

and the cyanoacetate procedure is therefore preferable when two such groups are to be introduced.

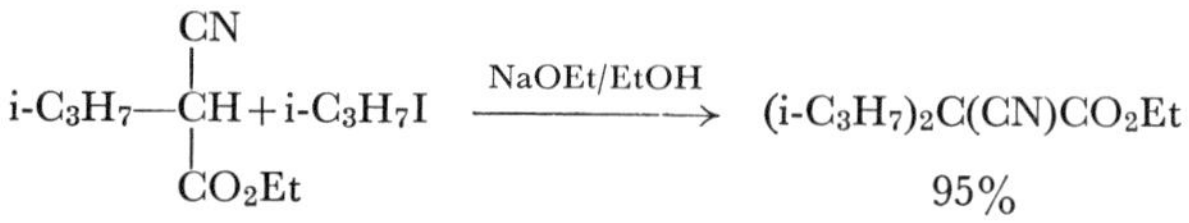

$$\underset{\underset{\text{CO}_2\text{Et}}{|}}{\overset{\overset{\text{CN}}{|}}{\text{i-C}_3\text{H}_7\text{—CH}}} + \text{i-C}_3\text{H}_7\text{I} \xrightarrow{\text{NaOEt/EtOH}} \underset{95\%}{(\text{i-C}_3\text{H}_7)_2\text{C(CN)CO}_2\text{Et}}$$

Di-isopropyl malonic ester can only be obtained in 40% yield with ether as solvent.

The cyanoacetates are hydrolysed with decarboxylation to produce homologous acids and undergo similar reactions to those illustrated above (p. 144) for diethyl malonate. Pyrolysis of a cyanoacetate leads to the synthesis of nitriles:

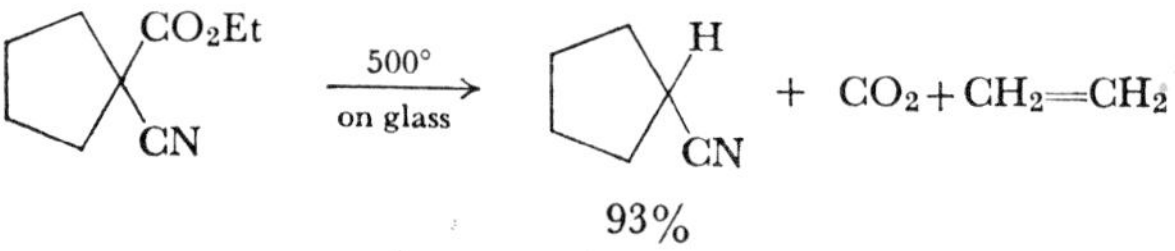

$$\xrightarrow[\text{on glass}]{500°}$$

$$+ \text{CO}_2 + \text{CH}_2\text{=CH}_2$$

93%

t-Butyl esters decompose more readily (at about 300°) to give carbon dioxide and isobutylene (cf. p. 157) and this method of eliding the alkoxycarbonyl group is useful when other easily hydrolysed functions are present in the molecule.

α-Aminoacid synthesis can be accomplished by the nitrosation of malonic ester, cyanoacetic or β-ketoesters, for example:

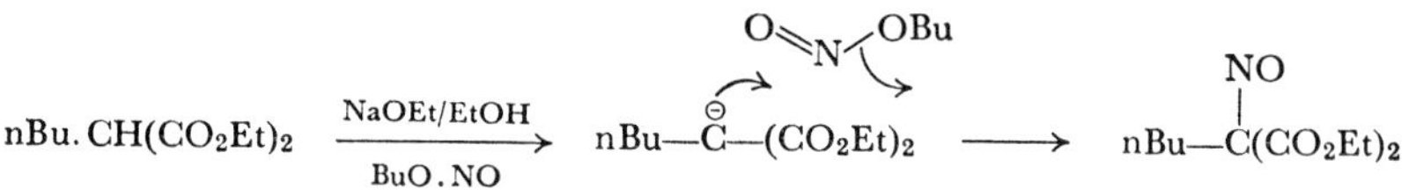

$$\text{nBu.CH(CO}_2\text{Et)}_2 \xrightarrow[\text{BuO.NO}]{\text{NaOEt/EtOH}} \underset{}{\text{nBu—}\overset{\ominus}{\text{C}}\text{—(CO}_2\text{Et)}_2} \longrightarrow \underset{}{\text{nBu—}\overset{\overset{\text{NO}}{|}}{\text{C}}\text{(CO}_2\text{Et)}_2}$$

the nitrosocompound on alkaline hydrolysis and decarboxylation in aqueous acid affords the oximino acid, written as the tautomer (M), in 70% yield; a reduction step follows:

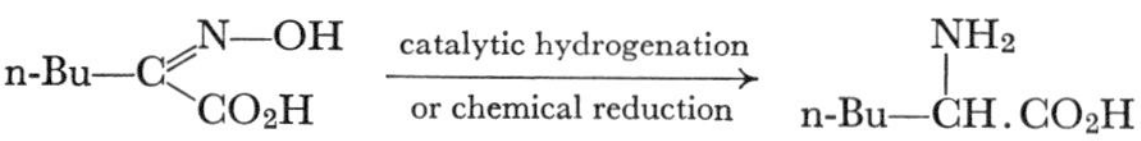

$$\text{n-Bu—C}\underset{\text{CO}_2\text{H}}{\overset{\text{N—OH}}{<}} \xrightarrow[\text{or chemical reduction}]{\text{catalytic hydrogenation}} \underset{}{\text{n-Bu—}\overset{\overset{\text{NH}_2}{|}}{\text{CH}}\text{.CO}_2\text{H}}$$

(M) m.p. 135°

146

Of more importance is the use of acetylamino analogues:

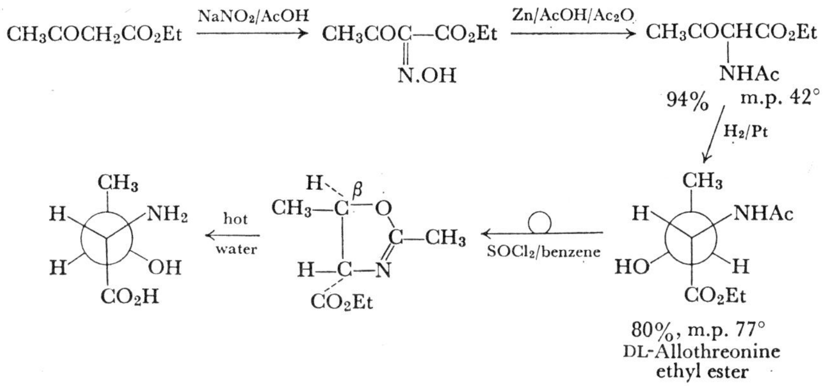
NaNO2/AcOH
Zn/AcOH/Ac2O
CH3COCH2CO2Et
CH3COC—CO2Et
N.OH
CH3COCHCO2Et
NHAc
94%
m.p. 42°
H2/Pt
CH3
H
NHAc
HO
H
CO2Et
80%, m.p. 77°
DL-Allothreonine
ethyl ester
SOCl2/benzene
CH3—C—O
C—CH3
H—C—N
CO2Et
hot
water
NH2
OH
CO2H

The invertion at the β-carbon atom is due to intramolecular attack on the derived chloride, and not to invertion during formation of the chloride:

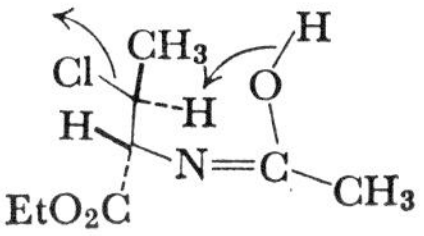
Cl
CH3
H
O
N=C
CH3
EtO2C

Another valuable method is that of C-alkylation of N-acylcyano-acetates discovered by Sörenson in 1903; N-acetylcyanoacetate is widely used:

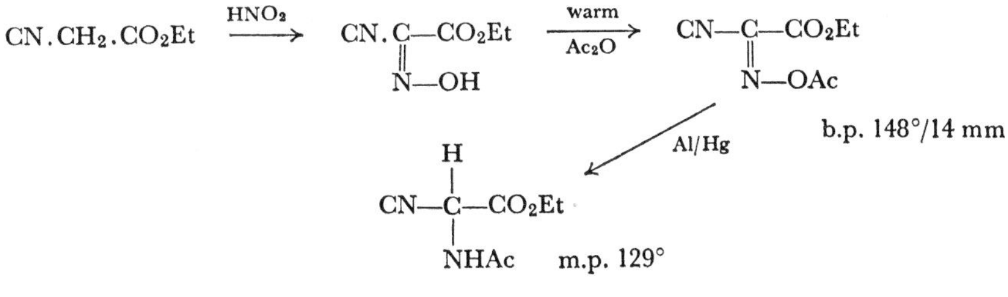
CN.CH2.CO2Et
HNO2
CN.C—CO2Et
N—OH
warm
Ac2O
CN—C—CO2Et
N—OAc
b.p. 148°/14 mm
Al/Hg
H
CN—C—CO2Et
NHAc
m.p. 129°

The acetyl group reduces the nucleophilic character of the nitrogen atom and hence further alkylation is confined to the carbon atom, for an example see structural formulae at top of p. 148.

The product, (DL)-methionine, was isolated after adjusting to pH 6 with acetic acid. When acetylaminomalonate was used in this synthesis a 60% yield was obtained, whilst the cyanoacetate route afforded a 48% yield from the sodio-derivative.

$$HS.CH_2.CH_2.OH \xrightarrow[OH^\ominus]{Me_2SO_4} MeS-CH_2.CH_2.OH \xrightarrow[\text{or HCl}]{SOCl_2} [MeS-CH_2.CH_2-Cl]$$

80%

not isolated

$$+$$

$$NaC \overset{\oplus \ominus}{\underset{}{<}} \overset{CO_2Et}{\underset{CN}{-NHAc}}$$

$$\underset{\underset{H}{|}}{\overset{\overset{NH_2}{|}}{HO_2C-C-CH_2.CH_2-SMe}} \xleftarrow[\text{hydrolysis}]{OH^\ominus} \underset{\underset{CN}{|}}{\overset{\overset{NHAc}{|}}{EtO_2C-C-CH_2.CH_2-SMe}}$$

DL-methionine

m.p. 118°, 60%

The Knoevenagel Condensation is a development of the Perkin reaction (p. 129) where acetate is replaced by a compound containing an active methylene group, when reaction then occurs under much milder conditions. Aliphatic aldehydes can be used because the reaction occurs in the presence of weak bases which do not initiate their self-condensation.

This condensation is used in the synthesis of substituted cinnamic acids from aldehydes and malonic acid in ethanol, containing ammonia or an amine as catalyst. In the Doebner modification pyridine is used as solvent:

Vanillin

+ $CH_2(CO_2H)_2$

(1) 2% piperidine in pyridine, 3 weeks at 20°

(2) dil. acid

m.p. 173°, 80%

substantial decarboxylation occurs in the basic solution. This method is superior to the Claisen condensation and the Reformatsky reaction (p. 37) when a free hydroxyl group is present, but the latter must be used when the carbonyl group has a low reactivity, for example in the synthesis of β,β-disubstituted acrylic acids from ketones.

Cyanoacetic acid, its esters, and malononitrile are more reactive than malonic acid and condense readily with ketones.

$$\underset{Et}{\overset{Et}{>}}C=O + \underset{CO_2H}{\overset{CN}{\underset{}{<}}}CH_2 \xrightarrow[\text{NH}_3 \text{ catalyst}]{\text{acetic acid/benzene}} \underset{Et}{\overset{Et}{>}}C=C\overset{CN}{\underset{CO_2H}{<}} \xrightarrow{150°} \underset{Et}{\overset{Et}{>}}C=CHCN$$

65%

+H_2O removed azeotropically

148

Polystyrene–polyamine resins, converted into their acetates by contact with acetic acid, effectively catalyse the condensation between a wide range of ketones and cyanoacetate or cyanoacetic acid.

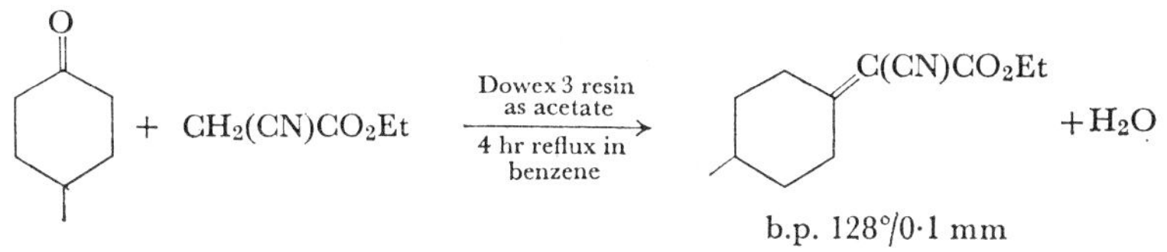

b.p. 128°/0·1 mm
65% complete in 1½ hr

This catalyst gives the following order of reactivity; malononitrile > ethyl cyanoacetate > cyanoacetamide > cyanoacetic acid, whilst ethyl aceto-acetate and ethyl malonate fail to react under these conditions. The alkylidenecyanoacetates are converted into α-ketoacids and amides by epoxidation:

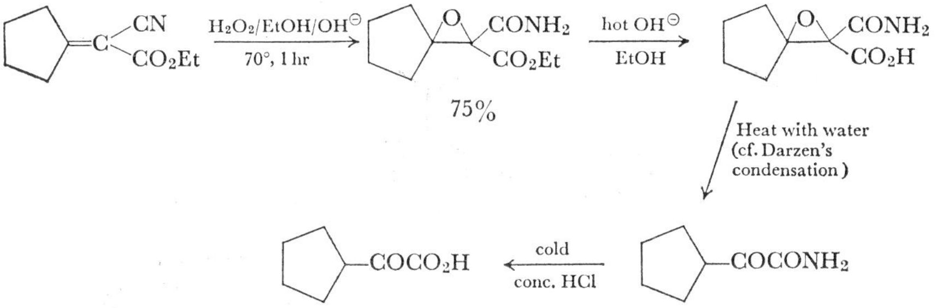

m.p. 54°, 60%

The Reaction Mechanism. Patai and co-workers have shown that the relative rates of the condensation of active methylene compounds with a given aromatic aldehyde in ethanol are:

$CH_2(CN)_2$	$CH_2(CN)CO_2Et$	$CH_2(CN)CONH_2$	$CH_2(CO_2Et)_2$
10,000	1000	10	1

In alcohol, or in alcohol containing a little water, the kinetics are of the second order, which is consistent with S_N2 reaction between the aldehyde and the conjugate base of the methylene compound (see structural formulae at top of p. 150).

The elimination of the $-OH^{\ominus}$ ion may occur in a four-centre transition as shown without protonation of the intermediate (N); certainly all steps following (O) are fast because aldehyde disappears at the same rate as

149

$$\text{H}_2\text{C}{\overset{X}{\underset{Y}{\diagdown}}} \underset{\xleftarrow{\hspace{1cm}}}{\overset{\text{fast}}{\xrightleftharpoons{\hspace{1cm}}}} \text{H}-\overset{\ominus}{\text{C}}{\overset{X}{\underset{Y}{\diagdown}}}$$
(P)

$$\text{ArCHO}+{}^{\ominus}\text{CH(X)Y} \underset{\text{(O)}}{\overset{\text{slow}}{\xrightleftharpoons{\hspace{1cm}}}} \left[\text{Ar}-\overset{\overset{\displaystyle \text{O}^{\ominus}\text{H}}{|}}{\underset{\underset{\displaystyle Y}{|}}{\overset{|}{\underset{|}{\text{C}}}}}-\text{X} \right] \xrightleftharpoons{\hspace{1cm}} \text{Ar}-\text{CH}{=}\text{C}{\overset{X}{\underset{Y}{\diagdown}}}+\text{OH}^{\ominus}$$
(N)

products are formed. The reaction is inhibited by the addition of acid, and in pure water, a stronger acid than ethanol, the reaction is of the first order for the acid dissociation (P) is inhibited, essentially irreversible, and becomes the slowest rate-determining step.

The reaction rate is markedly affected by steric factors and for a hindered aldehyde the forward step (O) will be the slowest. A distinction between the isomeric citrals is possible because the reaction between the hindered *cis*-isomer and cyanoacetic acid has hardly begun in the time required for the *trans*-isomer to react completely:

Citral a

$\xrightarrow[\text{OH}^{\ominus}, \text{ 3 min}]{\text{CNCH}_2\text{CO}_2\text{Et}}$

m.p. 122°, from the acid liquor
The *cis*-isomer, m.p. 94°, is formed slowly.

MICHAEL ADDITION (1887)

Carbon–carbon double bonds in conjunction with electron-attracting groups such as $-\text{CN}$, $-\text{CO}_2\text{R}$, $-\text{CONH}_2$, $-\text{CO}-$, NO_2, $-\text{SO}_2\text{R}$, undergo an extension of condensations of the aldol type which are important synthetically.

The rate of electrophilic addition to olefins is enhanced by substituent alkyl groups, whose inductive effect leads to electron enrichment of the double bond and to stabilization of the intermediate carbonium ion:

$$(\text{CH}_3)_2\text{C}{=}\text{CH}_2 > \text{CH}_3-\text{CH}{=}\text{CH}_2 > \text{CH}_2{=}\text{CH}_2$$

5·5   2·0   (1·0 for reference)

For addition of bromine

The electrophilic addition of bromine to a double bond in conjugation with an electron-attracting group is expected to be relatively slow, but in fact the reverse is true. This indicates that the addition now proceeds by nucleophilic attack by bromine:

$$\underset{\underset{Br}{\overset{\displaystyle Br}{\diagup}}}{-\overset{|}{C}{=}\overset{|}{C}{-}\overset{\displaystyle O}{\overset{\|}{C}}{-}R} \longrightarrow -\overset{|}{\underset{Br}{C}}-\overset{|}{\underset{Br}{C}}-\overset{\displaystyle O}{\overset{\|}{C}}-R$$

where the accumulation of negative charge on the intermediate is facilitated by the carbonyl or similar group. The chemical reduction of conjugated systems can be rationalized in this way, that is, by the nucleophilic addition of an electron to form a stabilized carbanion followed by the donation of a proton by a solvent molecule;

$$Ph-CH{=}CH-Ph \xrightarrow[(+2e)]{Na/EtOH} Ph-\overset{\ominus}{\underset{H}{C}}-\overset{\ominus}{\underset{H}{C}}-Ph \xrightarrow{2H^{\oplus}} Ph-CH_2-CH_2-Ph$$

In synthesis, anions generated by basic catalysts give nucleophilic additions of the same kind:

$$CH_3-CH{=}CH-CO-CH_3 + CH_3.NO_2(10E) \xrightarrow[48 \text{ hr reflux}]{Et_2NH} CH_3-\overset{\displaystyle H}{\underset{\displaystyle CH_2.NO_2}{\overset{|}{\underset{|}{C}}}}-CH_2-CO.CH_3$$

5-Nitro-4-methyl
pentan-2-one
60%, b.p. 112°/14 mm

following nucleophilic attack by the conjugate base the intermediate complex captures a proton from the nitromethane which is also the solvent for the reaction.

$$\underset{B\diagdown H}{-\overset{|}{C}{=}\overset{H}{C}-CO-} \xrightarrow{-H^{\oplus}} \left[-\overset{|}{\underset{B}{C}}-\overset{H}{\underset{\ominus}{C}}-\overset{O}{\overset{\|}{C}}- \longleftrightarrow -\overset{|}{\underset{B}{C}}-CH{=}\overset{O^{\ominus}}{\overset{|}{C}}- \right] \xrightarrow{+BH} \text{product} +B^{\ominus}$$

The base is here truly catalytic in that only trace amounts are needed.

Weak bases are often preferred as catalysts, even though equilibrium is attained slowly, because stronger bases can cause undesirable side-reactions; for example, the base may itself be captured when a reactive acceptor molecule is being used:

$$CH_2{=}CH-CO_2Me \xrightarrow{MeO^{\ominus}/MeOH} MeO-CH_2-CH_2-CO_2Me$$

151

Retroaldolization of the acceptor molecule can also occur on heating:

$$Ph—CH=CH—CO—Ar \xrightarrow[\text{reflux}]{\text{EtO}^{\ominus}/\text{EtOH}} Ph—CHO + ArCO.CH_3$$

A   chalcone

The Michael addition is reversible and the stronger bases encourage reversion particularly at higher temperatures. This is most pronounced when the acceptor is highly alkylated, for the steric requirements and inductive effects of the substituents hinder the forward reaction:

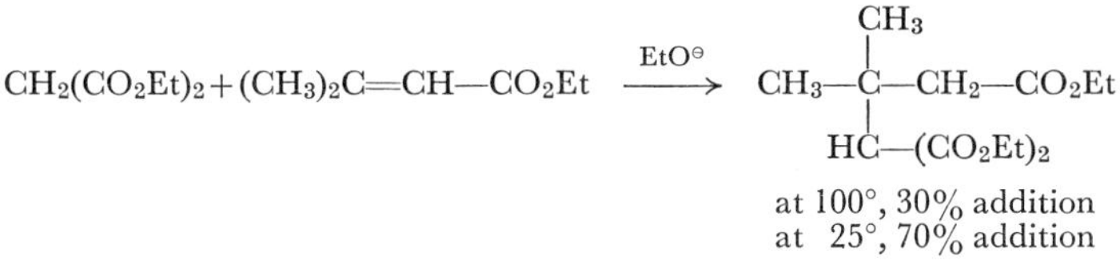

$$CH_2(CO_2Et)_2 + (CH_3)_2C=CH—CO_2Et \xrightarrow{\text{EtO}^{\ominus}} \begin{array}{c} CH_3 \\ | \\ CH_3—C—CH_2—CO_2Et \\ | \\ HC—(CO_2Et)_2 \end{array}$$

at 100°, 30% addition
at 25°, 70% addition

reversion follows the course:

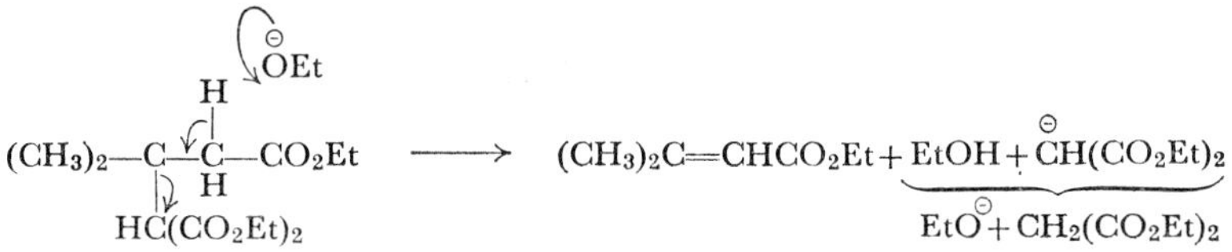

$$\begin{array}{c} H \quad \overset{\ominus}{\underset{}{}}OEt \\ (CH_3)_2—C—C—CO_2Et \\ | \quad H \\ HC(CO_2Et)_2 \end{array} \longrightarrow (CH_3)_2C=CHCO_2Et + \underbrace{EtOH + \overset{\ominus}{C}H(CO_2Et)_2}_{EtO^{\ominus} + CH_2(CO_2Et)_2}$$

and its extent may be limited by using an excess of the more readily available reagent and a catalytic amount of base in the absence of solvent, or in an aprotic solvent: potassium hydroxide in an acetal is a valuable method. These conditions allow a lower concentration of the base which initiates the reversal.

Useful information about structure can follow when the retro-Michael addition is used degradatively:

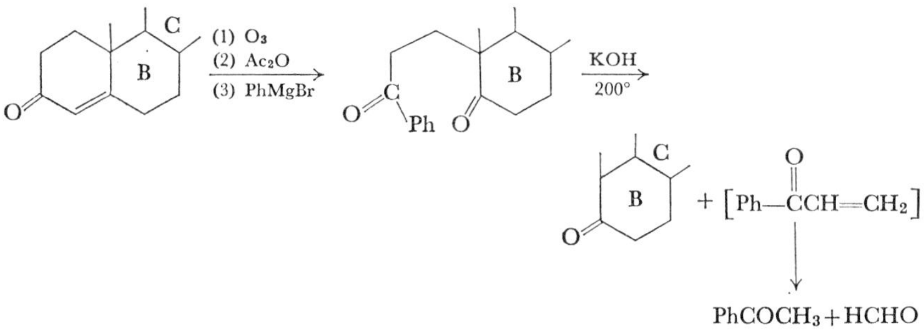

PhCOCH₃ + HCHO

Outgassing of formaldehyde drives this reaction to completion. The products of the Knoevenagel condensation are often very susceptible to the retro-reaction, which can follow an attack by water because the leaving group is a highly stabilized carbanion:

$$Ar-CH=C(CN)_2 \underset{\longleftarrow}{\overset{H_2O}{\longrightarrow}} \overset{\displaystyle Ar-CH-C\overset{\ominus}{\underset{CN}{\diagdown}}{}^{CN}}{\underset{\oplus OH_2}{|}} \rightleftharpoons \overset{H\quad H}{\underset{OH}{Ar-\overset{|}{C}-\overset{|}{C}(CN)_2}}$$

$$\updownarrow$$

$$Ar-CHO + CH_2(CN)_2 \underset{\longleftarrow}{\overset{+H^{\oplus}}{\rightleftharpoons}} \overset{H\quad H}{Ar-\overset{|}{\underset{(\overset{|}{O}{}^{\ominus})}{C}}-\overset{|}{C}(CN)_2}$$

This illustrates the need for the azeotropic removal of water in these reactions (p. 148).

Grignard Reagents have two possible modes of reaction with unsaturated carbonyl compounds: either 1,2-addition (normal) across the carbonyl group or 1,4-addition (conjugated) across the conjugated system, and cyclic six-centred transitions are postulated for both reactions (cf. p. 25).

(Q) for 1,4-addition   (R) for 1,2-addition

These mechanisms are no more than hypothetical because the exact nature of the Grignard is uncertain. Addition of magnesium bromide slightly enhances normal addition and the balance of the two modes is not altered substantially over a wide range of relative concentrations of reagents, although the different molecular compositions of (Q) and (R) do lead one to expect this. Addition of cuprous halides favours conjugate addition, which may be the result of catalysis of this mode rather than suppression of normal addition; this is very likely the result of co-ordination between the cuprous halide and the carbon–carbon double bond which then enters the transition state. Normal addition predominates for aliphatic carbonyl compounds, but conjugate addition becomes more important for aromatic compounds and for metal alkyls which do not normally react with the carbonyl group, for example, dialkylcadmiums.

11   153

The following examples illustrate the features mentioned above:

$$CH_3-CH=CH-CHO + MeMgCl \xrightarrow[\text{treat with NH}_4\text{Cl soln.}]{\text{1 hr in Et}_2\text{O}} CH_3-CH=CH-\overset{\overset{\displaystyle OH}{|}}{\underset{\underset{\displaystyle H}{|}}{C}}-CH_3$$

b.p. 121°, 85%

$CH_3-CH=CH-CO.CH_3 + MeMgBr \longrightarrow$

some reduction of normal addition is afforded by the steric and/or inductive effect of the CH_3 group of the ketone.

$$CH_3-CH=CH-\overset{\overset{\displaystyle CH_3}{|}}{\underset{\underset{\displaystyle OH}{|}}{C}}-CH_3 \quad 72\%$$

$$CH_3-\overset{\overset{\displaystyle CH_3}{|}}{\underset{\underset{\displaystyle H}{|}}{C}}-CH_2-CO.CH_3 \quad 20\%$$

$$CH_3-CH=C-\overset{\overset{\displaystyle O}{\parallel}}{C}-CH_3 \xrightarrow{\text{PhMgBr (1E)}} \left.\begin{array}{l} Ph-\overset{\overset{\displaystyle CH_3}{|}}{C}(OH)-CH=CH.CH_3 \;\; 55\% \\ Ph-\overset{\overset{\displaystyle CH_3}{|}}{C}H-CH_2-CO.CH_3 \quad 20\% \\ Ph-Ph \qquad\qquad\qquad\quad 5\% \end{array}\right\} \begin{array}{l} \text{by GLC} \\ \text{analysis} \end{array}$$

The yield of normal product obtained by inverse addition (Grignard to ketone) was 56%, i.e. independent of relative concentration.

$$Ph-CO.CH=CH(4\text{-MeOC}_6H_4) \xrightarrow{\text{EtMgBr}} Ph-CO-CH_2-\overset{\overset{\displaystyle Et}{|}}{C}H-Ar$$

93%

There is evidence here of a steric and/or an electronic effect.

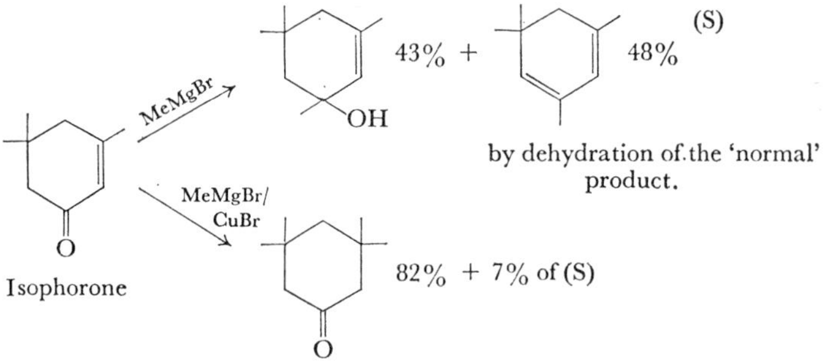

Isophorone

43% + 48% (S)

by dehydration of the 'normal' product.

82% + 7% of (S)

154

The induction of 1,4-addition by a cuprous salt can lead to the introduction of a bridgehead alkyl substituent:

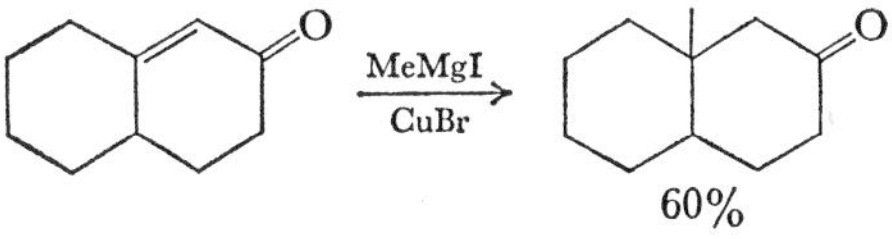

$$\text{60\%}$$

$$Ph_2Cd + Ph—CH\text{=}CH—CO—CH_3 \longrightarrow (Ph)_2CH—CH_2—CO—CH_3$$
in very high yield

Wittig Reagents yield new phosphoranes by Michael addition:

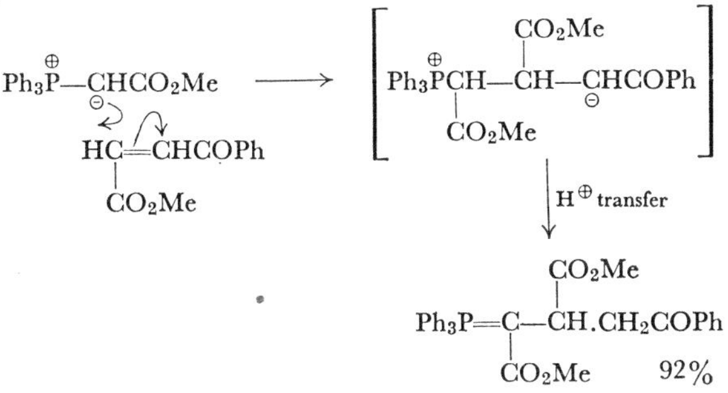

If a stable phosphorane cannot be formed by hydrogen transfer then a nucleophilic displacement may result,

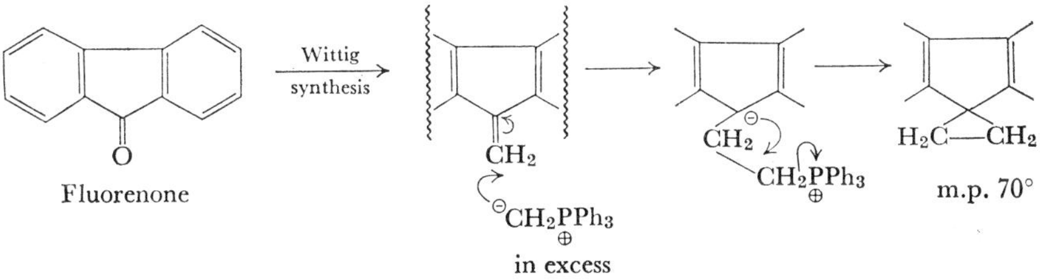

illustrating one consequence of the use of an excess of the Wittig reagent.

Synthesis of Heterocyclic Compounds. The Hantzsch pyridine synthesis (1884) probably involves Michael addition. A simple example is the reaction between formaldehyde, ethyl acetoacetate, and ammonia to give 2,6-dimethyl-3,5-diethoxycarbonyl-1,4-dihydropyridine (T) (see structural formulae at top of p. 156).

155

(1) Acetoacetate and 40% H—CHO/EtNH 40 hr at room temperature.
(2) The oil from (1) dissolved in EtOH and saturated with NH_3.

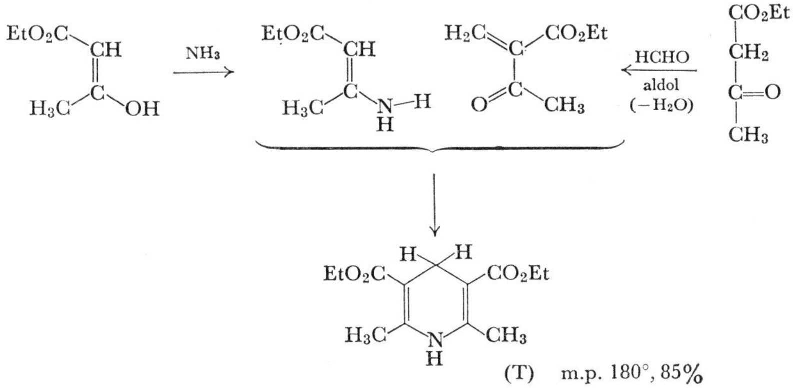

$$\text{(T)} \quad \text{m.p. } 180°, 85\%$$

Alternative starting materials are alkylidene or arylidene-1,3-dicarbonyl compounds and β-amino-$\alpha\beta$-unsaturated esters:

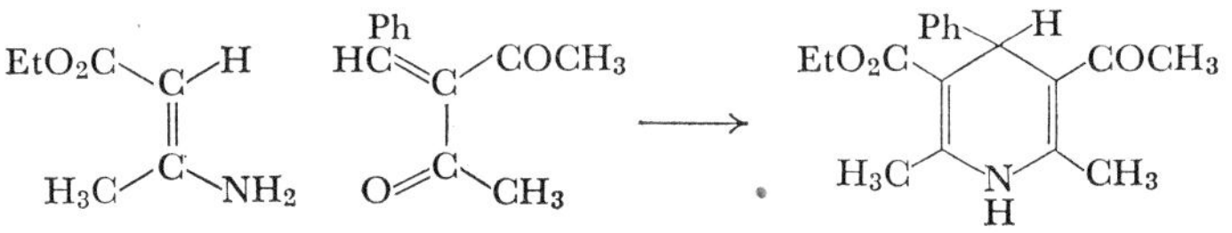

Ethyl β-aminocrotonate

Aminomethylene derivatives of β-diketones and β-ketoesters can also be employed:

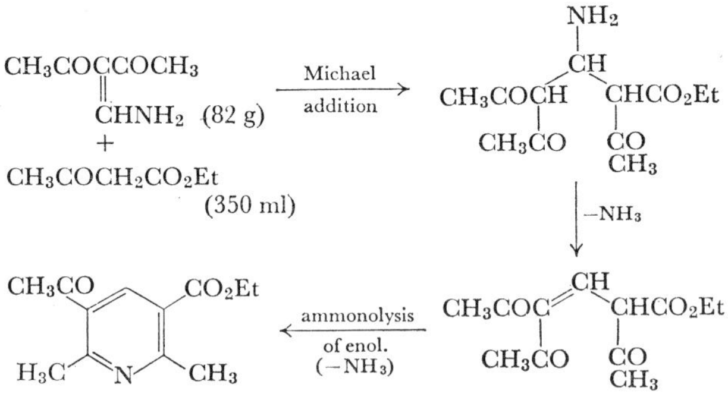

(60 g)

2,6-dimethyl-3-acetyl-
5-ethoxy carbonylpyridine

Hantzsch also devised (1890) a synthesis of pyrroles in which aminocrotonates, formed from acetoacetic ester/NH_3, react with an α-haloketone:

156

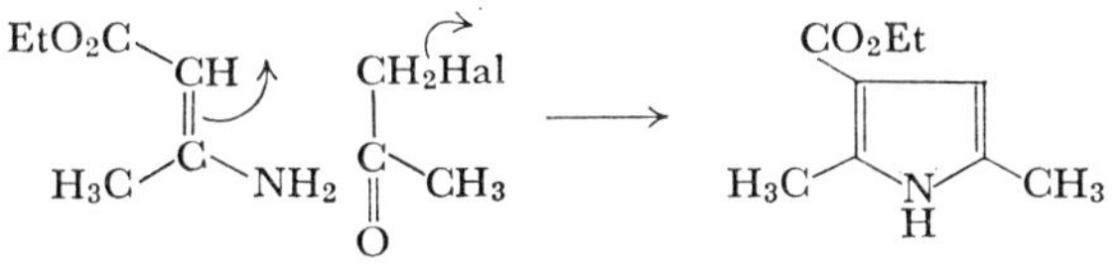

Ethyl 2,5-dimethylpyrrole-
3-carboxylate

there is, however, a competing reaction in which the enol of the ketoester undergoes C-alkylation:

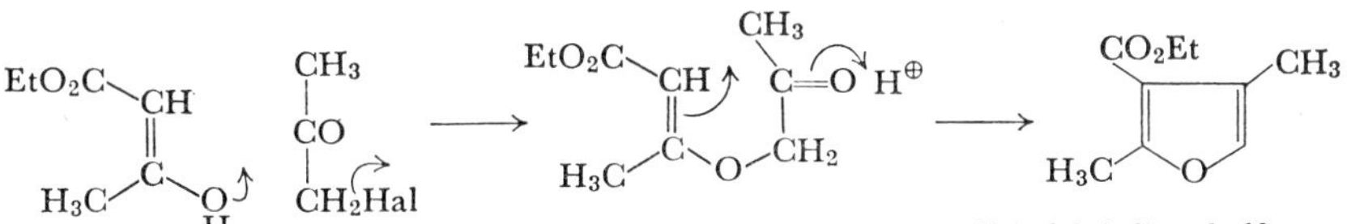

Ethyl 2,4-dimethylfuran-
3-carboxylate

This furan ring-closure is best effected in pyridine as solvent in the absence of ammonia. A general synthesis of pyrroles is that discovered by Knorr in 1886:

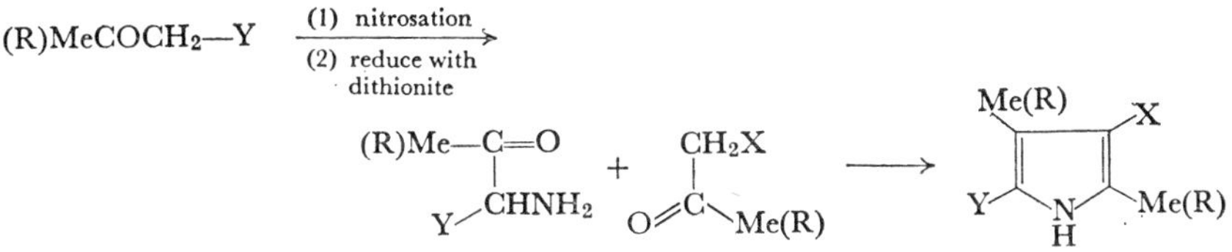

Results are poor when X = alkyl and good when X = R—CO or —CO$_2$R. Y is preferably an activating group, for example —CO$_2$R, whilst R-groups replacing methyl in the above are widely variable; alkyl, aryl, carbonyl, and alkoxycarbonyl.

The ester functions of these products can be used to extend the synthesis or, if they serve only to improve the overall yield, they can be eliminated. t-Butyl esters (p. 139) are useful because the conditions needed to degrade them to the acid (200° and a trace of toluene-*p*-sulphonic acid) also lead to the decarboxylation of pyrrole 2- and 5-carboxylic acids and of pyridine 2- and 4-carboxylic acids.

Reactions of Acrylonitrile. A cyanoethyl group can be introduced into nitroalkanes and carbonyl compounds by the Michael addition of their conjugate bases to acrylonitrile; aldolization only competes seriously when a reactive aldehyde, for example propionaldehyde, is involved. Simple esters and nitriles are unreactive but the reaction is successful for difunctional compounds, $X—CH_2—CO_2R$, where $X = R—CO$, $—CO_2R$, $—CN$, aryl, and $—P(O)(OR)_2$. If more than one α-hydrogen atom is available then polycondensation is likely to occur but formation of the mono-derivative is favoured by an excess of the donor molecule.

$$EtO_2C—CH_2—CN + CH_2\!\!=\!\!CH—CN$$

$\xrightarrow{40°}$ $(CO_2Et)\overset{\displaystyle CN}{\underset{\displaystyle |}{C}}(CH_2CH_2CN)_2$

$\xrightarrow{150°}$ $\overset{\displaystyle CH_2CH_2CN}{\underset{\displaystyle \underset{\displaystyle CN}{|}}{\underset{\displaystyle HC—CO_2Et}{|}}}$ the *relative* rates being nearly equal at this temperature.

MAJOR PRODUCT

$$CH_2.(CO_2Et)_2 + CH_2\!\!=\!\!CH—CN \xrightarrow[65°,\ 4\ hr]{NaOEt/EtOH} H_2C \overset{\displaystyle CO_2Et}{\underset{\displaystyle H_2C}{\overset{\displaystyle |}{\underset{\displaystyle |}{\overset{\displaystyle CH}{\underset{\displaystyle CN}{\overset{\displaystyle |}{\underset{\displaystyle }{CO_2Et}}}}}}}\quad 45\%$$

$$75\ g \qquad\qquad 25\ g$$

$\downarrow$ H$_2$/Raney Ni

$$\left[\ \overset{\displaystyle H}{\underset{\displaystyle H_2C}{\overset{\displaystyle |}{\underset{\displaystyle |}{C}}}}\overset{\displaystyle CO_2Et}{\underset{\displaystyle O}{\overset{\displaystyle |}{\underset{\displaystyle CH_2—NH_2}{C—OEt}}}}\ \right]$$

$\longleftarrow$

ethyl 2-keto pipecolate
m.p. 79°, 57%

$$CH_2(CO_2Et)_2 \xrightarrow[NaOEt\ (0·1\ mol)]{CH_2\!\!=\!\!CH—CN/Et_2O} H—\overset{\displaystyle CO_2Et}{\underset{\displaystyle CO_2Et}{\overset{\displaystyle |}{\underset{\displaystyle |}{C}}}}—CH_2.CH_2—CN$$

1 mol   b.p. 170°

$\downarrow$ reflux in conc. HCl
Et$_2$O extraction

Glutaric acid 70%

Some of the bis-condensation

product $\overset{\displaystyle CO_2Et}{\underset{\displaystyle CO_2Et}{\overset{\displaystyle \diagdown}{\underset{\displaystyle \diagup}{C}}}}(CH_2—CH_2—CN)_2$ separates from Et$_2$O

m.p. 63°

Acrylonitrile and other acceptors in Michael reactions are polymerized by strongly basic catalysts, for example, sodamide/NH$_3$, Grignard reagents, and sodium triphenylmethyl. The order of acceptor reactivity is:

$$CH_2{=}CH{-}CN > CH_3{-}CH{=}CH{-}CN > CH_3{-}CH{=}CH{-}CO_2Me$$

Polyacrylonitrile is formed by 1,2-addition and has the structure

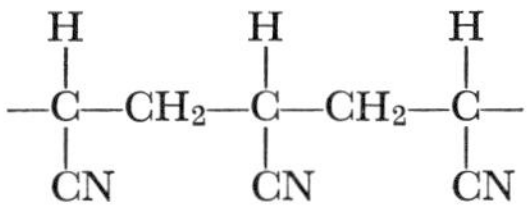

consistent with the infrared spectrum which lacks the absorption of a ketene-imine

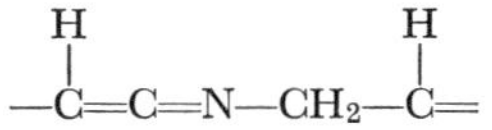

which would result from 1,4-addition. This polymer is hard and heat resistant although it is soluble in very polar solvents such as dimethyl-formamide; it forms oriented fibres by the evaporation of the solvent in air as a solution is squirted through the fine holes of a spinneret. In industrial practice acrylonitrile is polymerized in aqueous media by peroxide catalysts, a method also used for the polymerization of tetra-fluoroethylene

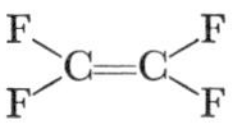

which is also susceptible to attack by nucleophiles. Polytetrafluoro-ethylene is more intractable than polyacrylonitrile and has a very close-packed linear chain which gives it rigidity on heating and the high melting point of 330°.

Robinson's Modification of the Michael Addition. This was intro-duced in 1937 to overcome the loss of reactive unsaturated carbonyl compounds by their base-catalysed polymerization and depends on the slow generation of the acceptor molecule from a Mannich base (p. 89) by elimination, which is followed by addition of the carbanion. This mechanism is not always followed, for direct displacement of the tertiary amine by a unimolecular or a bimolecular mechanism can intervene as in the following reaction where acrylonitrile itself is ineffective:

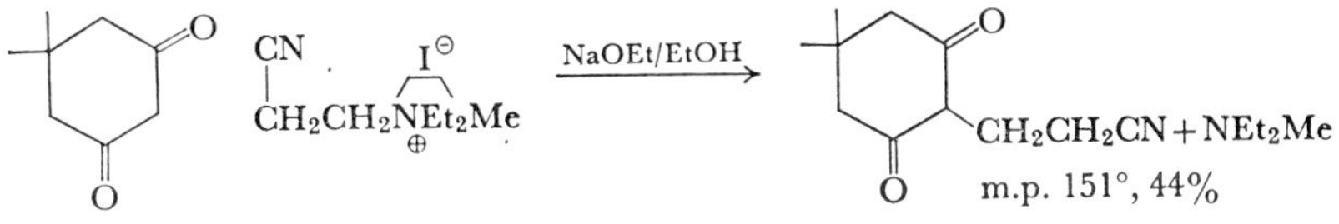

hence in this instance the elimination

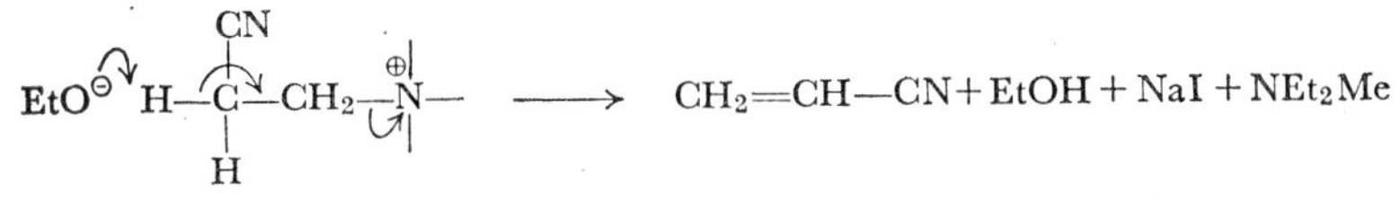

$$EtO^\ominus \curvearrowright H\!-\!\underset{\underset{H}{|}}{\overset{\overset{CN}{|}}{C}}\!-\!CH_2\!-\!\overset{\oplus}{\underset{\downarrow}{N}}\!-\!\longrightarrow\ CH_2\!=\!CH\!-\!CN + EtOH + NaI + NEt_2Me$$

is unimportant. A displacement of this kind must be responsible for
alkylation by quaternary bases which lack β-hydrogen atoms, for
example the synthesis from gramine of the essential aminoacid trypto-
phan:

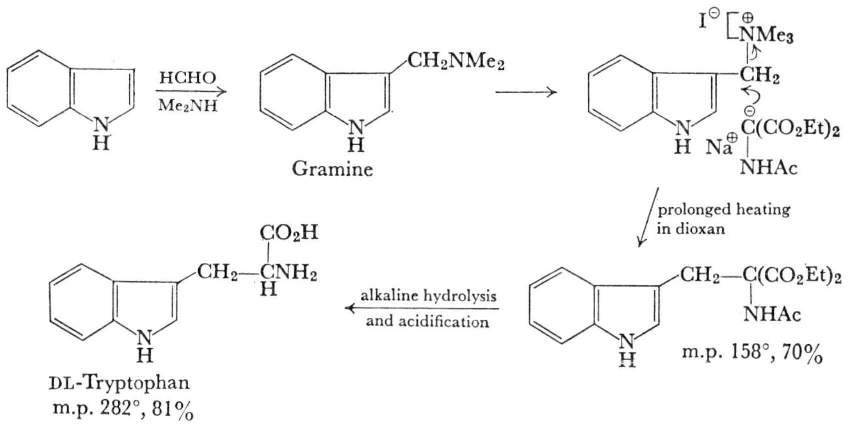

Gramine

DL-Tryptophan
m.p. 282°, 81%

m.p. 158°, 70%

Mannich bases derived from acetone afford a valuable method of
forming cyclohexane rings:

$$CH_3.CO.CH_3 + H.CHO + Et_2NH.HCl \longrightarrow CH_3CO.CH_2.CH_2.NEt_2 \quad 66\%$$
4-Diethylaminobutan-2-one

the methiodide of this base is well crystalline and widely used synthetically:

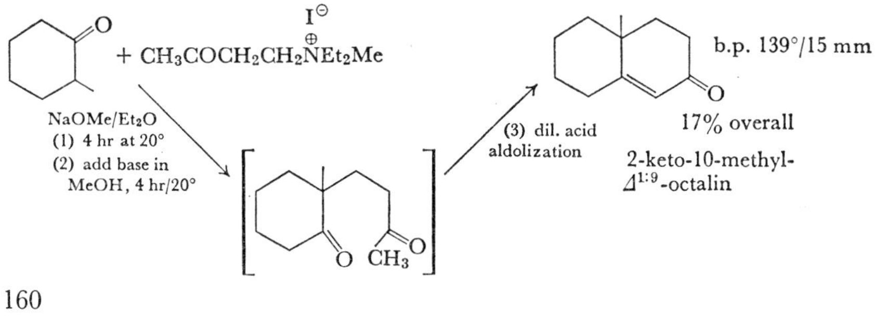

b.p. 139°/15 mm

17% overall

2-keto-10-methyl-
$\varDelta^{1:9}$-octalin

160

The yield rose to 38% when sodamide/Et_2O was used in the first stage, and further improvement followed when a β-ketoester or the formyl derivative of the ketone was employed.

In a synthesis of cyperones, sesquiterpene ketones, McQuillin combined ($+$)dihydrocarvone with diethylmethyl-3-oxopentylammonium iodide and isolated a product with a carbonyl and a hydroxyl group; this was the ketol (U):

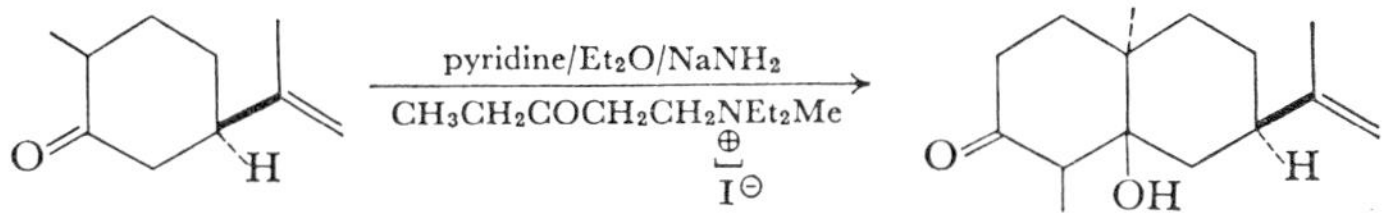

(+) Dihydrocarvone

Ketol (U)
m.p. 106°, $[\alpha]_{5461} + 54°$

($+$)Cyperone (V) and its epimer (W) were also obtained and separated chromatographically.

(V) Cyperone
$[\alpha]_{5461} + 115°$

(W) an epimer
$[\alpha]_{5461} - 353°$

The mechanism is as written:

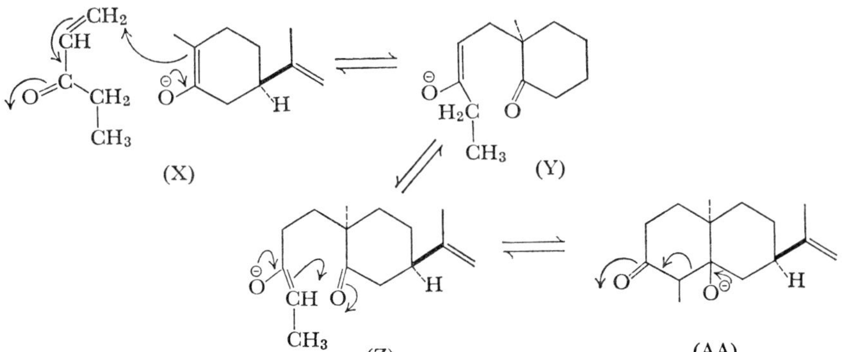

(X)   (Y)

(Z)   (AA)

If the reaction is carried out in ether, without pyridine, it proceeds slowly because the Mannich base is almost insoluble. The combined yield in ether of 30% (20% of ketol) rises to 70% (60% of ketol) when sufficient pyridine is added to dissolve the base, thus overcoming loss of

161

the derived vinyl ketone (X) by polymerization. The ketol (U) with an α-methyl group at the bridgehead affords the C-9 epimer of cyperone on acid-catalysed dehydration and the formation of cyperone in higher relative yield by the slow reaction in the inhomogeneous medium is due to reversal of the cyclization (AA) → (X). A new equilibrium can then be established under thermodynamic control, where the bridgehead methyl group adopts a β configuration.

The Stobbe Condensation (1893). The first step of this reaction is an aldol condensation between an aldehyde or ketone and the conjugate base of a succinate; it is followed by lactonization (AB) and a base-catalysed elimination (AC):

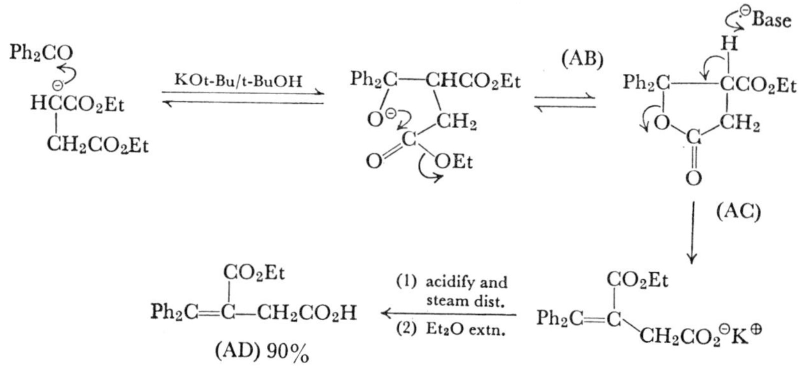

Equilibrium in the final step lies far to the right because the metal carboxylate formed is only weakly nucleophilic and does not initiate reversal by Michael addition, the condensation is therefore slow but effective even for weak electrophiles like benzophenone; aliphatic aldehydes tend to undergo self-condensation. It is of interest that the reaction fails with malonic ester where the sequence would involve the formation of a strained four-membered lactone. Potassium t-butoxide and sodium hydride are good general catalysts.

The reaction products are usually half-esters (as AD) which de-carboxylate under more forcing conditions:

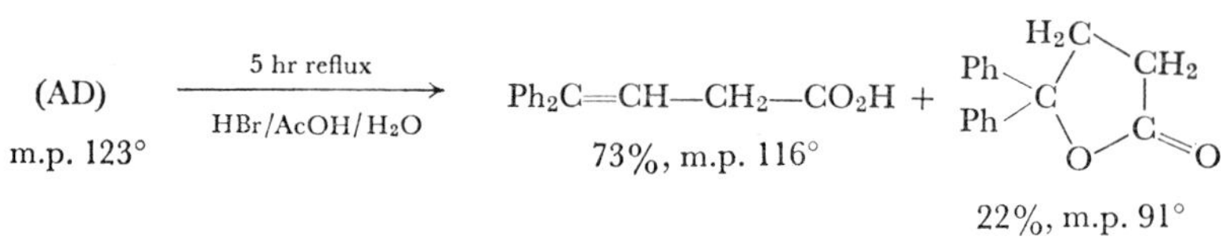

$\alpha\beta$-Unsaturated aromatic acids are readily cyclized to naphthols by Friedel–Crafts procedures:

162

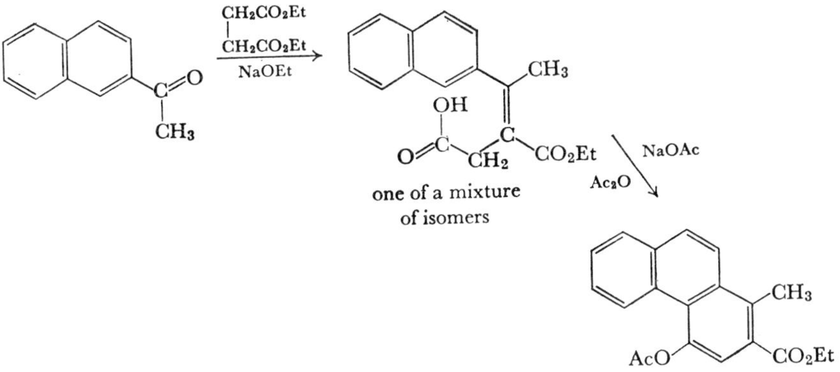

Acetate of ethyl
1-methylphenanthrene-
2-carboxylate, m.p. 128°, 78%

whereas tetralones are obtained following prior hydrogenation of the double bond.

The condensation of a second molecule of the carbonyl compound occurs at the remaining methylene group of the half-ester, but this is sluggish even when strongly basic catalysts are used probably because the existing charge of the carboxylate ion hinders a further proton abstraction. Bis-condensation is best done in two stages with completion of esterification before the second stage is attempted:

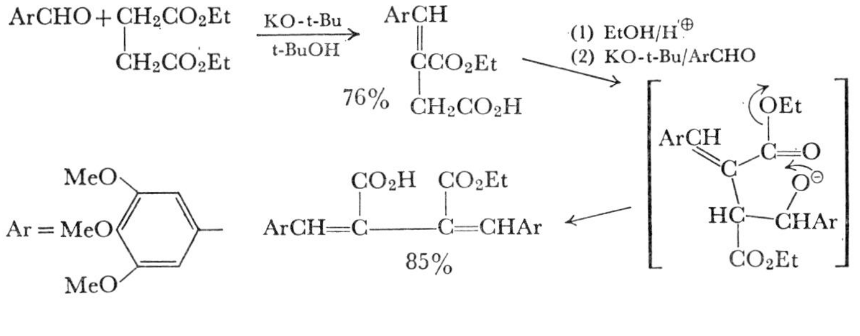

This procedure is applicable to the synthesis of unsymmetrical diaryl-idenesuccinic acids from two different aldehydes.

Further Reading

GENERAL

A. C. COPE, H. L. HOLMES and H. O. HOUSE, *Org. Reactions*, 1957, **9**, 107.
H. HENECKA, *Chemie der β-Dicarbonyl-Verbindungen.* Springer, Berlin, 1950.

163

Carbanions Derived from Carboxylic Acids and their Derivatives

TOPICS

E. D. BERGMANN, D. GINSBURG and R. PAPPO, *Org. Reactions*, 1958, **10**, 179 (Michael reaction).
A. BRÄNDSTRÖM, *Arkiv Kemi*, 1953, **6**, 155 (O- and C-alkylation).
H. E. CARTER, *Org. Reactions*, 1946, **3**, 209 (azlactones).
The Chemistry of Acrylonitrile. American Cyanamid Co., 2nd edit., New York, 1959.
K. T. FINLEY, *Chem. Rev.*, 1964, **64**, 573 (acyloin cyclization).
J. R. JOHNSON, *Org. Reactions*, 1942, **1**, 210 (Perkin condensation).
R. MAYER in *Newer Methods of Preparative Organic Chemistry*, Vol. 2. Interscience, New York, 1963 (cyclopentanonecarboxylate in synthesis).
S. PATAI and Z. RAPPOPORT, *J. Chem. Soc.*, **1962**, 378 (Knoevenagel reaction).
K. ZIEGLER in *Methoden der organischen Chemie*, Vol. 4, part 2, p. 733. G. Thieme, Stuttgart, 4th edit., 1954 (nitrile cyclization).

PROBLEMS

1. How would you synthesize:

(a) from succinate?

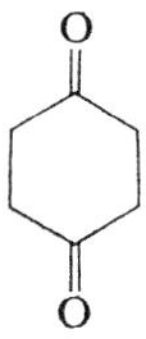

Baeyer, *Ber.*, 1885, **18**, 3454.

(b) =O from acetophenone?

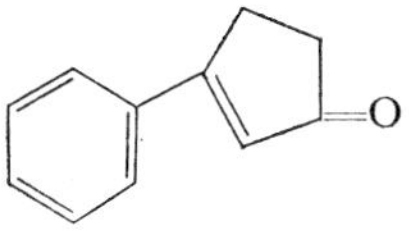

A. L. Wilds, *J. Amer. Chem. Soc.*, 1942, **64**, 1421.

(c) from acetamidomalonic ester and (i) allyl bromide, (ii) bromine?

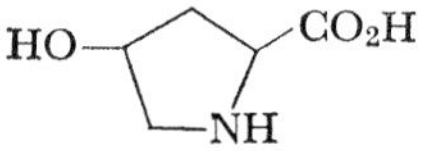

T. Wieland and U. Wintermeyer, *Chem. Ber.*, 1957, **90**, 1721.

(d) Ph— from malonic ester?

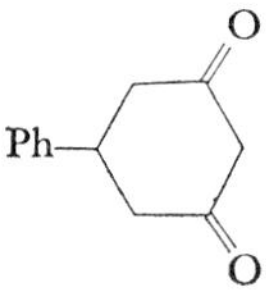

K. W. Rosenmund, H. Herzberg and H. Schutt, *Chem. Ber.*, 1954, **87**, 1265.

(e) from cyclohexanone via Claisen and Reformatsky?

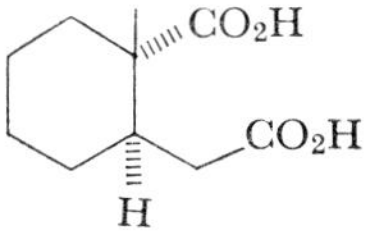

W. E. Bachmann and S. Kushner, *J. Amer. Chem. Soc.*, 1943, **65**, 1963.

(f) $RCO(CH_2)_4CO_2H$ from cyclohexanone?

164

(g) Ph—CH$_2$—CH(NO)CO$_2$H using malonate and then alkyl nitrite?

R. O. Atkinson, C. Ockrent and C. Simons, *Chem. and Ind.*, **1951**, 118.

(h)

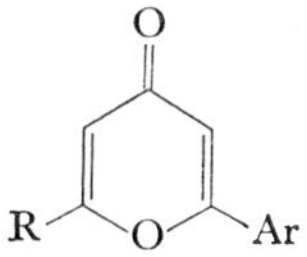

from R—CO.CH$_2$—CO.CH$_3$?

R. J. Light and C. R. Hauser, *J. Org. Chem.*, 1960, **25**, 538, 1110.

2. Write mechanisms for the following reactions:

(a) Ph—CH(CO$_2$Et)$_2$ $\xrightarrow[\text{NaOEt}]{}$ Ph—CH$_2$—CO$_2$Et + (CO$_2$Et)$_2$

H. Henecka, *Chemie der β-Dicarbonyl-Verbindungen*, p. 127. Springer, Berlin, 1950.

(b)

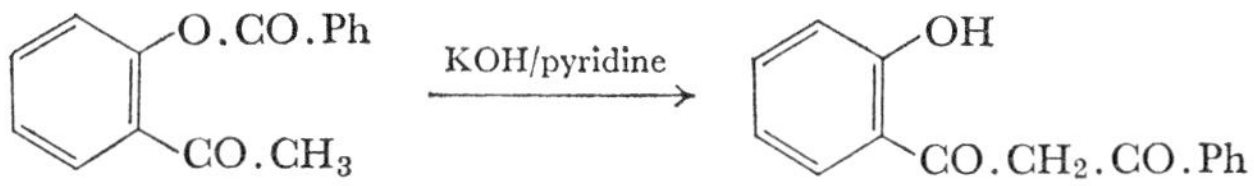

N. V. Nowlan, P. A. Slavin and T. S. Wheeler, *J. Chem. Soc.*, **1950**, 340.

(c)

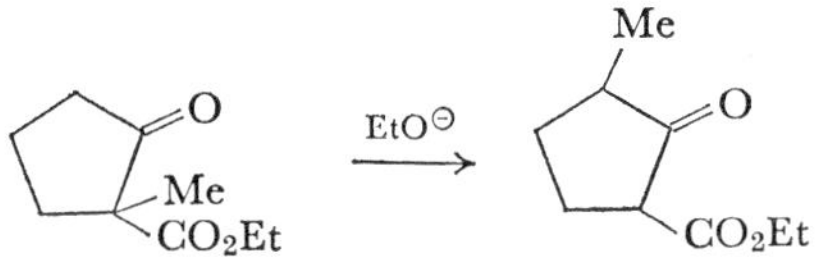

L. Nicole and L. Berlinquet, *Canad. J. Chem.*, 1962, **40**, 353.

(d)

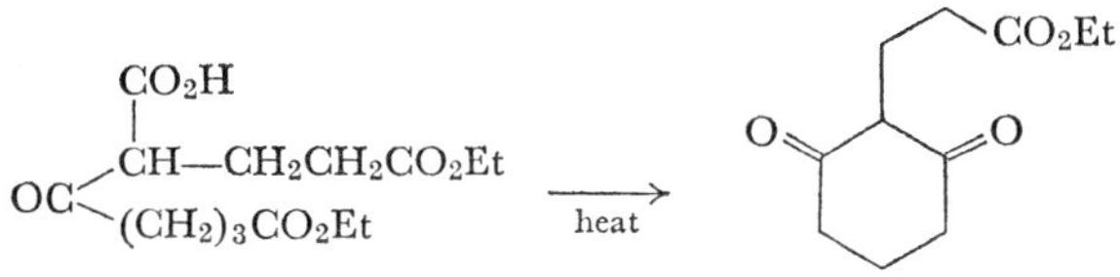

(cf. p. 133)

(e)

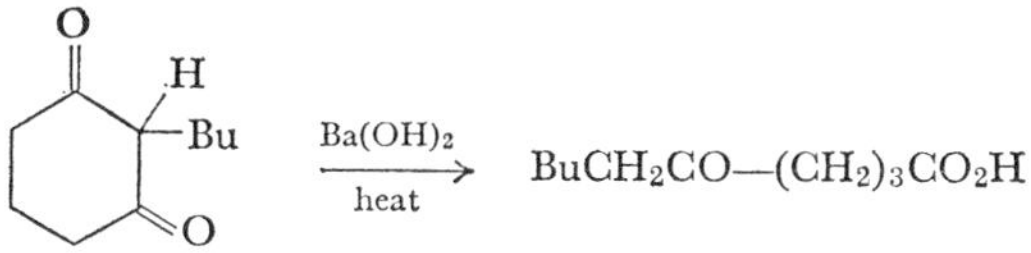

$\xrightarrow[\text{heat}]{\text{Ba(OH)}_2}$ BuCH$_2$CO—(CH$_2$)$_3$CO$_2$H

(f)

$\xrightarrow[\text{H}_3\text{O}^\oplus]{}$ Et$_2$CHCO—(CH$_2$)$_3$CO$_2$H

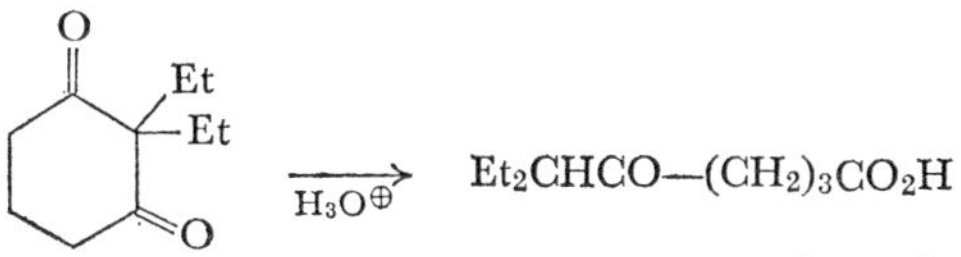

H. Stetter and W. Dierichs, *Chem. Ber.*, 1952, **85**, 61, 1062.

(g)

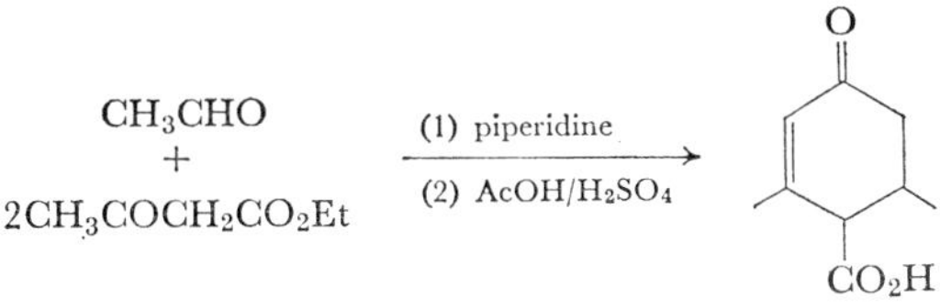

CH$_3$CHO
+
2CH$_3$COCH$_2$CO$_2$Et

$\xrightarrow[\text{(2) AcOH/H}_2\text{SO}_4]{\text{(1) piperidine}}$

Carbanions Derived from Carboxylic Acids and their Derivatives

3. Predict the products of the reactions:

(a)

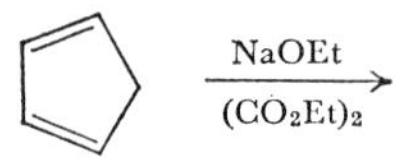

$$\text{(cyclopentadiene)} \xrightarrow[\text{(CO}_2\text{Et)}_2]{\text{NaOEt}}$$

J. Thiele, *Ber.*, 1900, **33**, 671.

(b) t-BuO—COCH$_3$ $\xrightarrow[360°]{}$

C. D. Hurd and F. H. Blunck, *J. Amer. Chem. Soc.*, 1938, **60**, 2419.

(c)

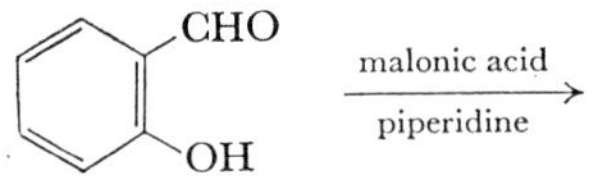

$$\xrightarrow[\text{piperidine}]{\text{malonic acid}}$$

Dutt, *J. Indian Chem. Soc.*, 1925, **1**, 297.

(d)

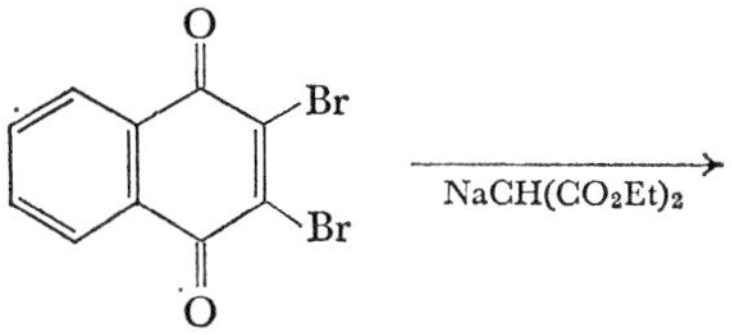

$$\xrightarrow{\text{NaCH(CO}_2\text{Et)}_2}$$

C. Liebermann, *Ber.*, 1899, **32**, 260.

(e)

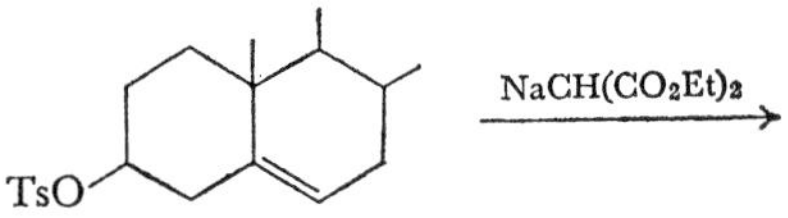

$$\xrightarrow{\text{NaCH(CO}_2\text{Et)}_2}$$

H. Henecka, *Chemie der β-Dicarbonyl-Verbindungen*, p. 113. Springer, Berlin, 1950.

(f) CH$_3$COCH$_2$CO$_2$Bz
  + $\xrightarrow[\text{toluene}]{\text{Mg(OMe)}_2}$
  C$_3$H$_7$COCl

B. R. Baker *et al.*, *J. Org. Chem.*, 1954, **17**, 91.

(g) (EtO)$_2$P(O)CH$_2$R
  + $\xrightarrow{\text{NaH}}$
  CH$_3$COCH$_2$CH$_2$CO$_2$Et

W. S. Wadsworth and W. D. Emmons, *J. Amer. Chem. Soc.*, 1961, **83**, 1733.

(h)

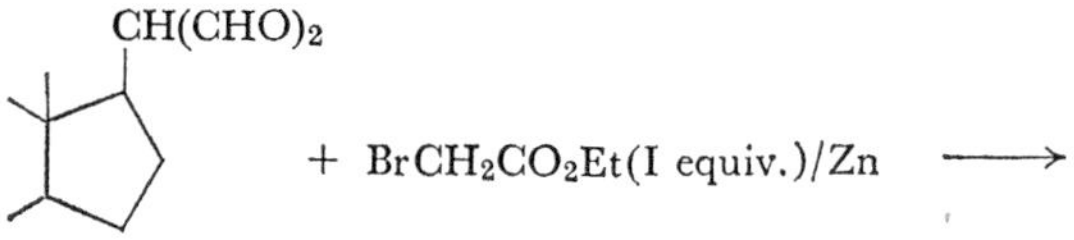

$+$ BrCH$_2$CO$_2$Et(I equiv.)/Zn $\longrightarrow$

D. Bertin, L. Nédélec and J. Mathieu, *Compt. rend.*, 1961, **253**, 1219.

(i)

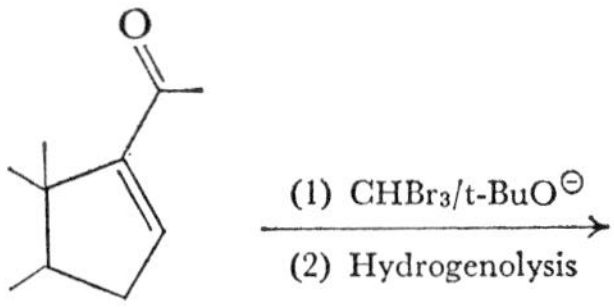

$$\xrightarrow[\text{(2) Hydrogenolysis}]{\text{(1) CHBr}_3/\text{t-BuO}^\ominus}$$

E. Kaspar and R. Wiechert, *Chem. Ber.*, 1958, **91**, 2664.

4. In the synthesis of α-methylcinnamic acid by the Perkin reaction with sodium acetate/propionic anhydride a small amount of cinnamic acid is also obtained; why is this?

Problems

5. Suggest a mechanism for those azlactone syntheses which proceed in acetic anhydride without added base. Benzaldehyde and $PhCONH—CH_2CO_2H$ provide an example.
H. E. Carter, *Org. Reactions*, 1946, **3**, 209.

6. Account for the incorporation of five deuterons in the catenane synthesis (p. 136).

7. Explain the formation of

in substantial yield in addition to the 2,6-dimethyl-3-acetyl-5-ethoxycarbonylpyridine, the anticipated product of the Hantzsch synthesis (p. 156).

8. Account for the reactions:

(a)

R. H. Martin and Sir Robert Robinson, *J. Chem. Soc.*, **1943**, 491.

(b) $Ph_3P=CHCN$
$+$
$EtOCH=C(CN)_2$ $\xrightarrow{base}$ $Ph_3P=C(CN)CH=C(CN)_2$

S. Trippett, *J. Chem. Soc.*, **1962**, 4733.

(c)

L. F. Fieser and M. Fieser, *Current Topics in Organic Chemistry*, 1964, Vol. 1, p. 26.

(d) $CH_2=CHCO_2Me$ (1) piperidine
$+$
CH_2CO_2Me (2a) NaOMe/toluene 110° $\longrightarrow$
$|$
SH

(2b) NaOMe/ether 20° $\longrightarrow$

R. B. Woodward and R. H. Eastman, *J. Amer. Chem. Soc.*, 1944, **66**, 849.

(e)

R. Huisgen, *Chem. Ber.*, 1960, **93**, 65.

9. Suggest a mechanism for the biosynthesis of sparteine

from 2 , 2H.CHO and acetoacetic acid

A. R. Battersby, *Quart. Rev.*, 1961, **15**, 269.

167

Chapter 6

CARBANIONOID REACTIONS
OF AROMATIC SYSTEMS

This kind of behaviour has been seen to occur in the Mannich and Reimer–Tiemann reactions (pp. 89 and 102 respectively) and during alkylation of phenols (p. 141).

The Kolbe–Schmitt Reaction (1860, 1885) is an example of a type of alkylation which occurs when a metal phenolate is heated with solid CO_2 under pressure. The product of this O-carboxylation is unstable under these conditions and phenolic carboxylic acids are formed by C-carboxylation. Salicylic acid is prepared industrially in 80% yield by heating dry sodium phenoxide in carbon dioxide at 150° for several hours and only a trace of *p*-hydroxybenzoic acid is obtained. Use of potassium phenoxide causes a marked change in the product balance and *p*-hydroxybenzoic acid is formed in 44% yield. The two products are worked up by crystallization of the acid salts or by their treatment with dilute mineral acid. The Marassé modification using high temperatures and dry potassium carbonate as the alkali is most generally employed:

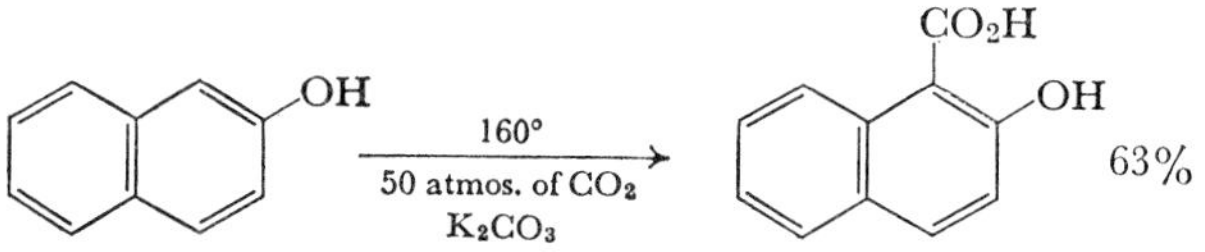

2-Hydroxy-1-napthoic acid

This reaction gives the 2-hydroxy-3-napthoic acid in 78% yield from sodium napthoxide, whilst the potassium salt yields some of this product but mainly the 2-hydroxy-6-napthoic acid (60%), albeit at higher temperatures.

Electron-attracting groups inhibit the reaction but additional —OH and —NH₂ groups promote it:

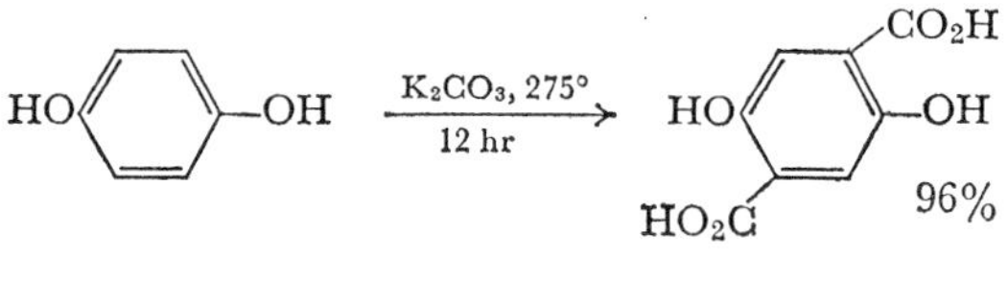

Small amounts of dicarboxylic acids are formed in other reactions under less forcing conditions. An important application is in the synthesis of *p*-aminosalicylic acid used in the treatment of human tuberculosis:

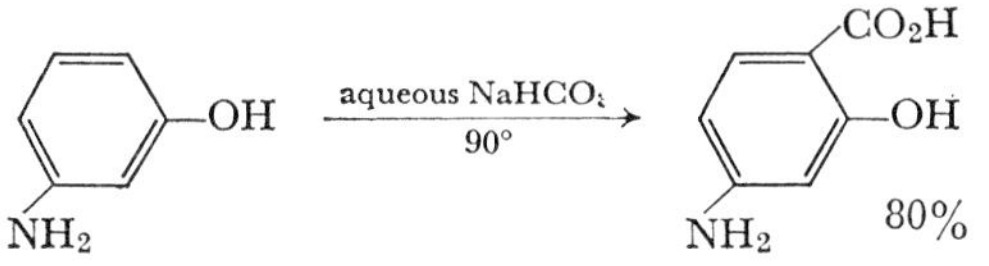

The reaction was thought to proceed through an aryl carbonate:

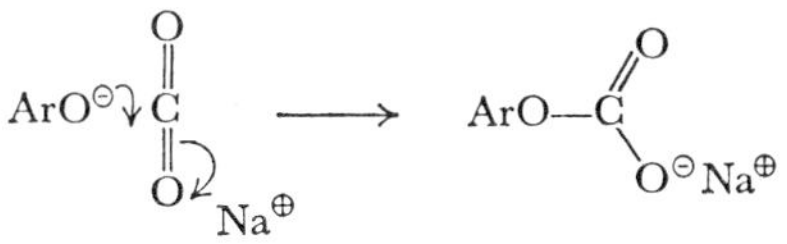

but Lindsey's work indicates that at this stage only a chelate complex is formed, because the product of absorption of carbon dioxide (90% complete at room temperature) reverted to the original reagents merely on addition of solvents, acetone for instance, known to complex with the phenoxide. C-alkylation in a complex of this kind could follow the formation of a π-complex with ultimate transfer of a proton to the phenolic oxygen:

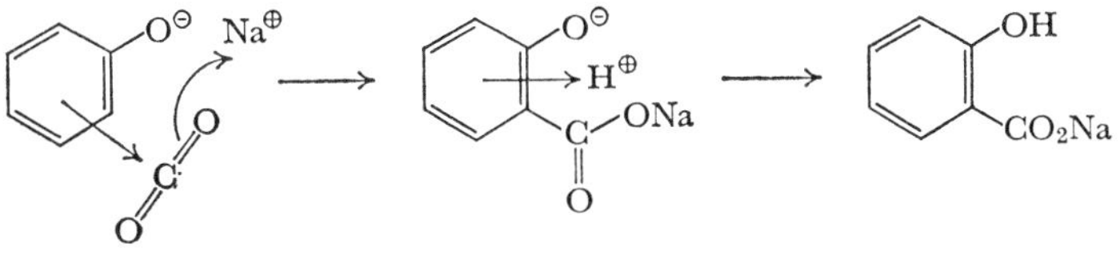

The transfer of the carboxyl group to the *para* position does not occur when the more strongly co-ordinating mono-lithium and sodium salicylates decompose at 250°:

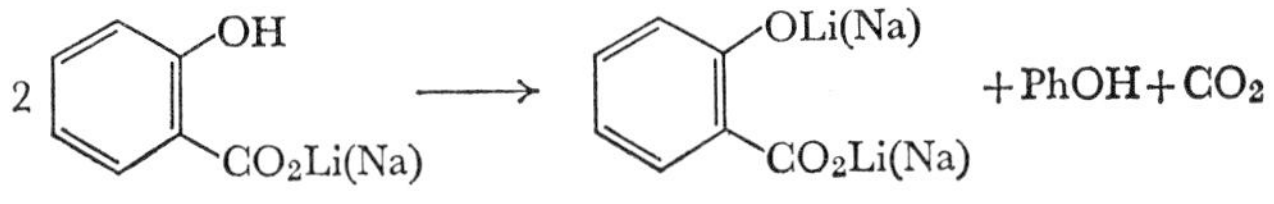

whereas the weaker co-ordinators undergo carboxyl transfer under these conditions:

12

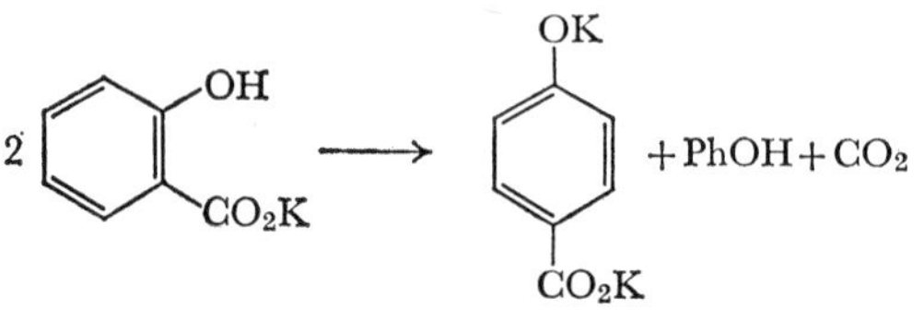

Dipotassium-*p*-hydroxybenzoate

In a related reaction the enolates of aliphatic ketones are carbonated in acceptable yields.

$$CH_3CO(CH_2)_5CH_3 \xrightarrow{NaNH_2/NH_3} \overbrace{CH_2{=}C{=}O}^{\ominus}(C_6H_{13}) \xrightarrow{CO_2} HO_2CCH_2COC_6H_{13}$$

isolated in 48% yield as methyl ester after CH_2N_2

Di- and trihydric phenols can be successfully carbonated in hot aqueous bicarbonate solution, with constant streaming of carbon dioxide to drive the equilibrium to the right:

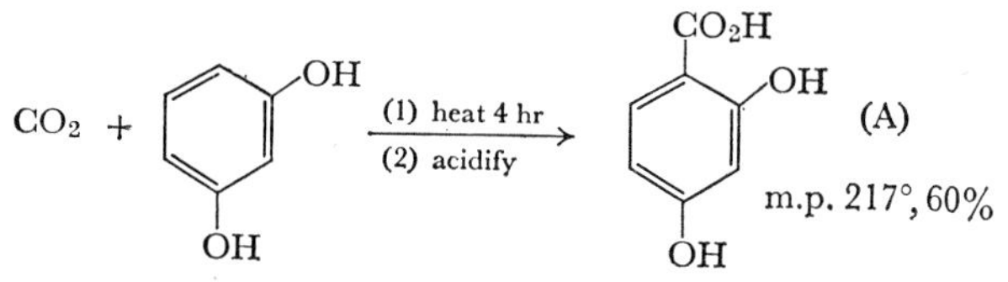

2,4-Dihydroxybenzoic acid

Direct C-alkylation of an enol is a possible mechanism for the reaction of simple phenols in the complex solid-phase reaction and it may well feature in the above reaction (A) in solution:

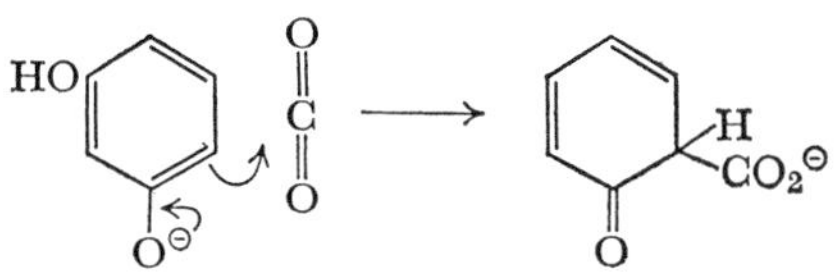

where the aryl carbonate formed by the corresponding C-alkylation would revert to starting materials in the reaction medium.

Decarboxylation. Polyhydric phenolic acids decarboxylate by reversal of the Kolbe synthesis in hot water, and the carboxyl group can therefore be used as a blocking group in the synthesis of isomers inaccessible by direct substitution:

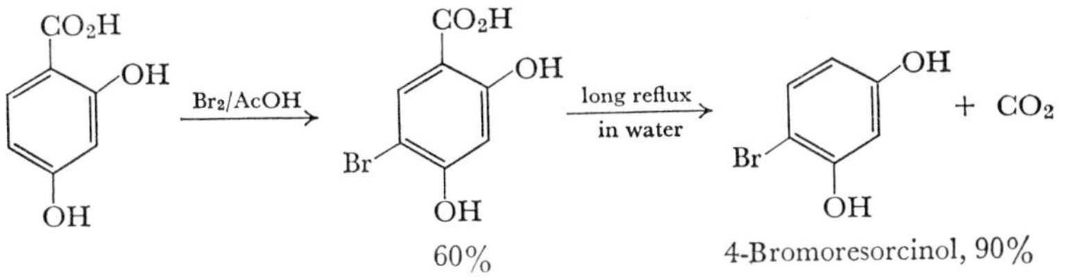

60%   4-Bromoresorcinol, 90%

This is analogous to the desulphonation of sulphonic acids and the reaction is facilitated by the presence of oxysubstituents which stabilize an intermediate complex formed by attack of a proton at the α-carbon atom of the acid:

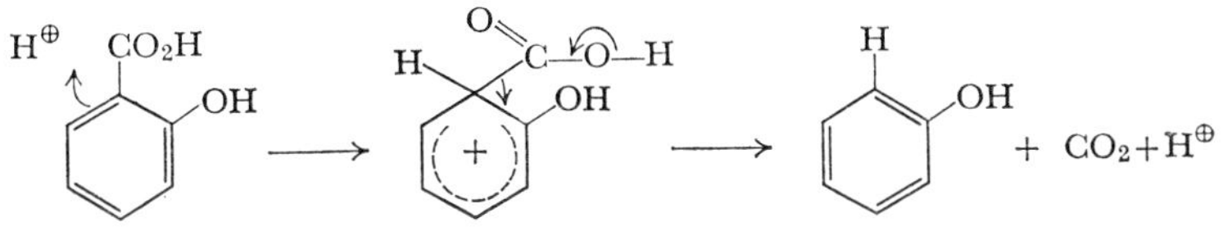

The reaction is bimolecular and dependent on the pH and concentration of the acid.

Many acids are decarboxylated in the form of their anions by a unimolecular process:

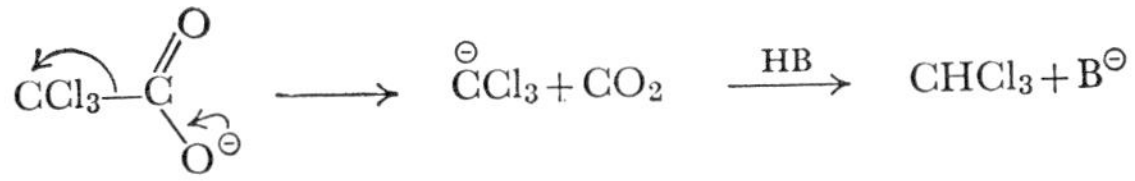

cf. Reimer–Tiemann reaction p. 103. Alternatively a bimolecular process may occur in which the proton interacts with the anion and assists. This mode of decarboxylation occurs frequently when the corresponding carbanion is stabilized, either inductively as in trichloroacetate and in the following example:

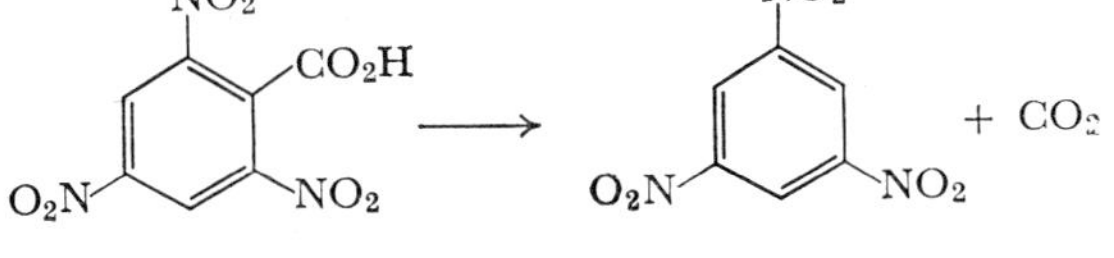

Salts of this acid decarboxate in warm aqueous-ethanol.

171

or by delocalization of charge:

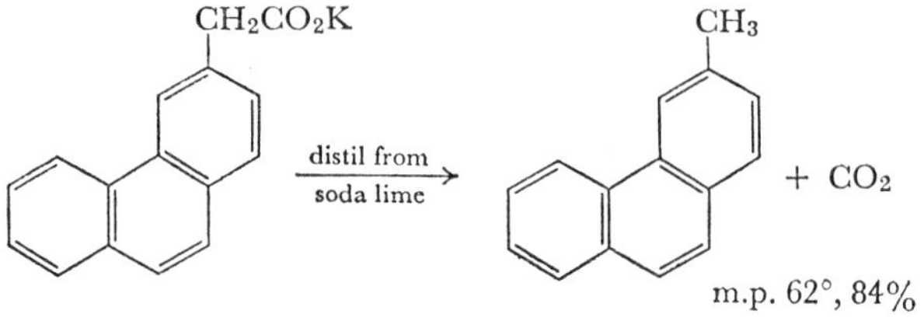

distil from
soda lime

+ CO_2

m.p. 62°, 84%

Cleavage of Carbonyl Compounds. Aldehydes undergo decarbonylation following attack by a nucleophile provided that a sufficiently stabilized intermediate carbanion can be formed. o-Halobenzaldehydes undergo the Cannizzaro reaction (p. 85) in hot concentrated alkali but 2,6-dihalo- and 2,6-dinitrobenzaldehydes react as follows.

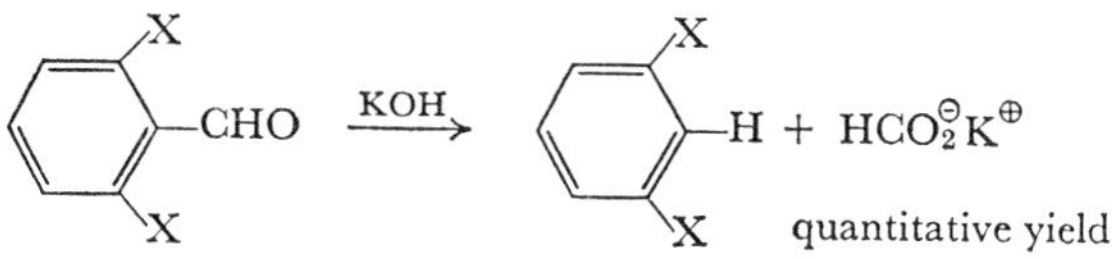

quantitative yield

After hydroxylation of the —CHO group the reaction proceeds as below:

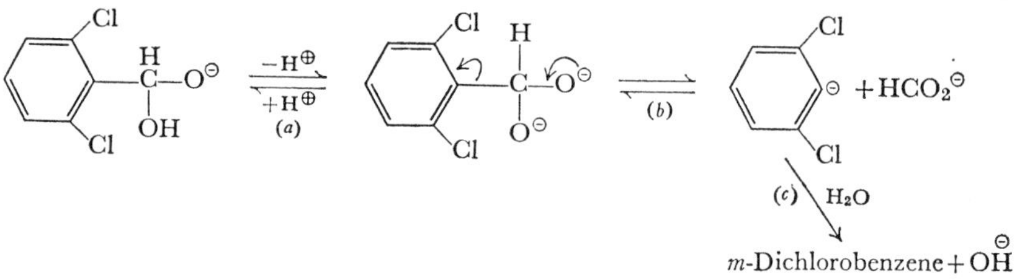

m-Dichlorobenzene + $\overset{\ominus}{O}H$

Since the rate was not reduced when run in D_2O the proton transfers (a) and (c) are fast and the formation of carbanion (b) is therefore the rate-determining step.

A related reaction is that of ketone cleavage:

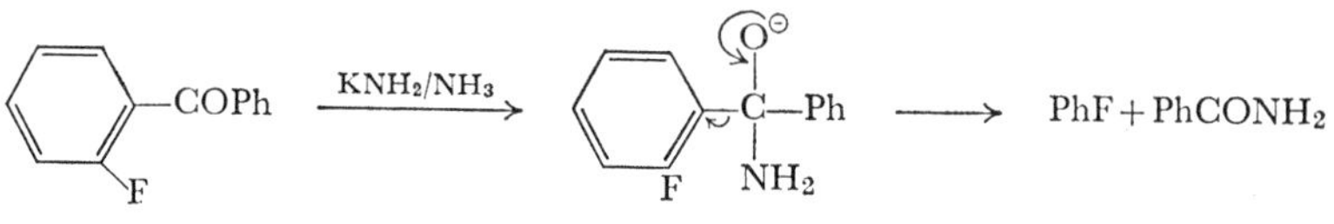

$PhF + PhCONH_2$

(B)

inductive stabilization of the anion by fluorine is apparent because *meta*- and *para*-fluorobenzophenones do not undergo fission. Sodamide

172

does not displace fluorine under these conditions but the fission of
o-chlorobenzophenone leads to aniline and benzamide as the ultimate
products.

Aryne Intermediates were first shown to feature in net substitutions
of halides by Roberts (1953) and Huisgen (1954) and this rationalized a
number of earlier observations of rearrangements attending nucleophilic
substitution, for example:

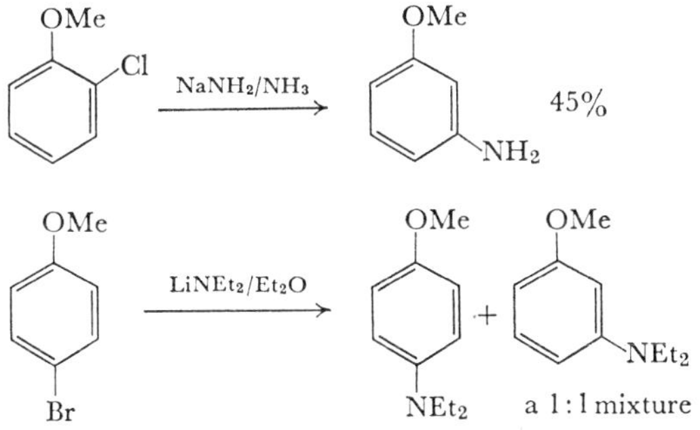

These are called *cine* substitutions because a group enters in a position
other than that vacated by the leaving group. This is the result of the
formation of an aryne, an aromatic nucleus in which one bond acquires
the characteristics of an alkyne:

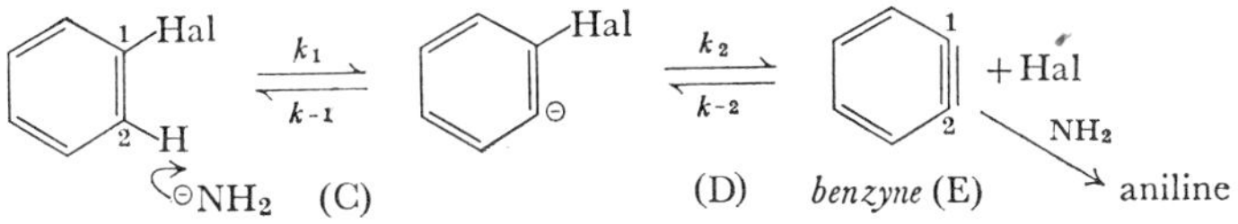

The base-catalysed elimination is of course analogous to the acetylene-
forming elimination of vinyl halides and the rapid reaction of benzyne
with the nucleophilic reagent also finds its counterpart in acetylene
chemistry. Two steps occur in the formation of an aryne. Base removes a
proton (in C) to yield an anion inductively stabilized (cf. B) by the
adjacent halogen atom in the order $F > Cl > Br > I$, which also determines
the relative rates (k_1). In the second step (D), the rate (k_2) is determined by the ease of ejection of halide ion and follows the inverse
order $I > Br > Cl > F$. In fact the fluoride ion is not displaced by $NH^\ominus_2$ in
liquid ammonia although hydrogen exchange occurs by formation of
carbanion and abstraction of proton (deuteron) from the solvent (k_{-1}).
Bromobenzene is the most reactive of the halobenzenes and the rate is
here markedly affected by deuteration at carbons 2 and 6 with little

173

return (k_{-1}) to deuterium-free starting material; features which suggest that for bromobenzene the steps (C) and (D) are concerted. The rapid nucleophilic attack at carbon 1 or carbon 2 of benzyne accounts for the *ortho–meta* and *para–meta* shifts observed in the examples above. In the absence of strong base other mechanisms of *cine* substitution are possible.

Roberts' original proof of this mechanism was by examination of the ammonolysis of ^{14}C-labelled chlorobenzene:

48%

The rearrangement was demonstrated and relative yields of products determined by conversion of the anilines into cyclohexanones by diazotization, hydrolysis to phenols, hydrogenation to cyclohexanols, and their oxidation. Ring expansion by the Schmidt reaction and hydrolysis afforded aminohexanoic acid labelled either at C1 or C2 by *cine* substitution:

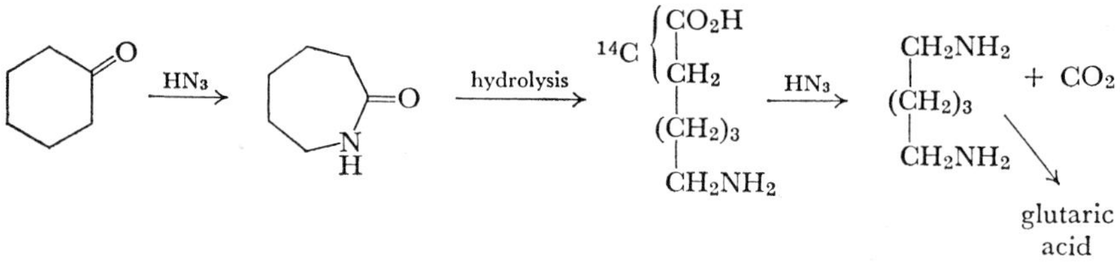

That part of the radioactivity located at C1 (48%) was counted as CO_2 after a further Schmidt reaction, whilst the remainder (52%) was counted in the same way after treatment with nitrous acid and oxidation to glutaric acid.

The structure (E) for benzyne was much criticized on steric grounds for cyclooctyne is the smallest cycloalkyne so far isolated and it has been suggested that the diradical ⟨ ⟩ is a better approximation.

Aryne intermediates are detectable in the reactions of organometallic compounds and their participation in the reaction between fluoro-benzene and lithium phenyl was suggested by Wittig in 1940. It was later shown that these exceptionally reactive intermediates, whatever their detailed structure, could be trapped as their Diels–Alder adducts:

174

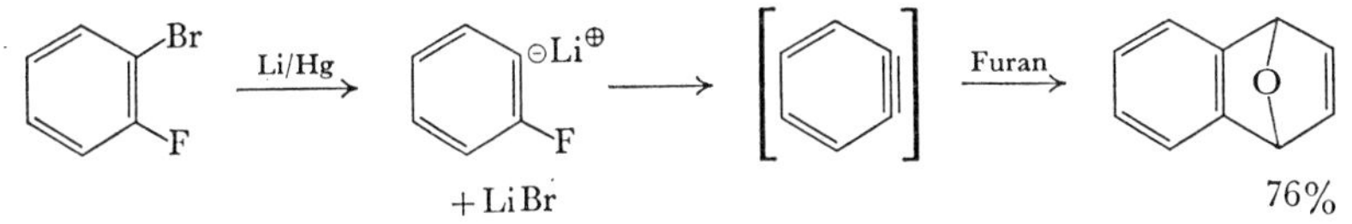

$$+ \text{LiBr} \qquad\qquad\qquad\qquad 76\%$$

A trapping technique has confirmed that benzyne participates in the reaction between halobenzenes and lithium alkyls in ethereal solution:

$$\text{PhHal} + \text{RLi} \longrightarrow \text{PhR} + \text{LiHal}$$

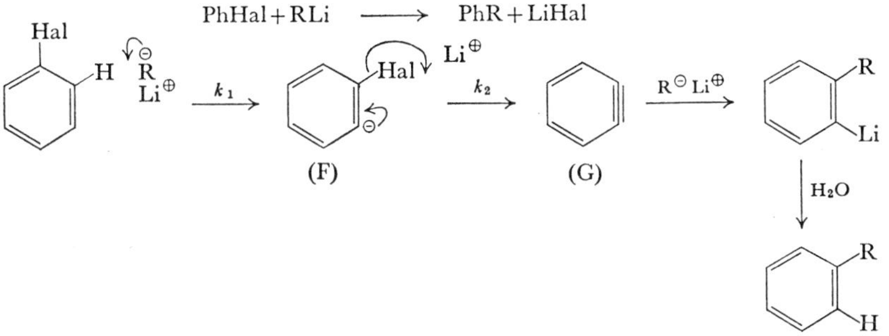

In the aprotic solvent the first step becomes irreversible and determines the rate because fluorobenzene reacts faster by a factor of ten than the other halides, whose reactivity is comparable; hence the acidity of the *ortho*-hydrogen atom is crucial being greatest for fluorobenzene, whilst ejection of halide ion from (F) is fast since assistance by the Li$^\oplus$ ion offsets the differences in C—Hal bond strengths.

Behaviour characteristic of cyclynes has been observed in the reactions of cycloalkenyl halides:

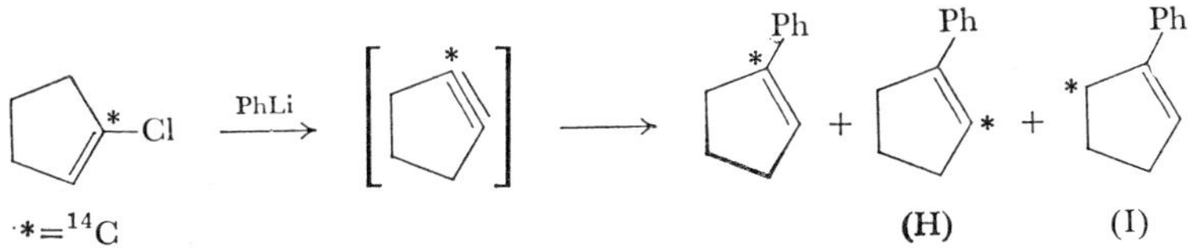

where (I) is derived from (H) by an allylic rearrangement induced by Ph$^\ominus$Li$^\oplus$.

An effective procedure for the synthesis of benzyne, without added catalyst, in a solution free from side-products has been devised by Wittig and Hoffmann. 1,2,3-Benzothiadiazole-1,1-dioxide is prepared:

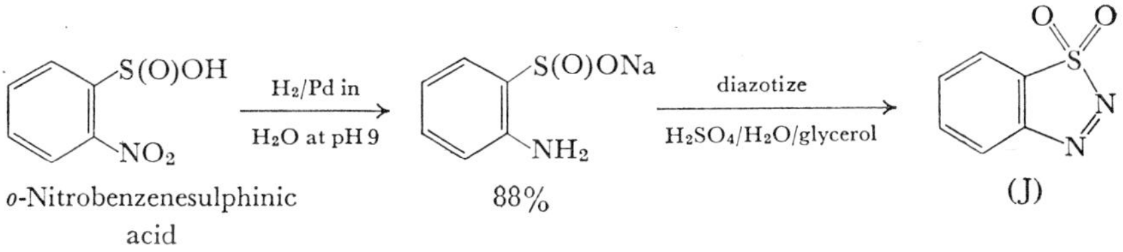

175

The product is extracted from a cold ($c. -5°$) solution with ether, and decomposed above 10° to give benzyne and gaseous side-products:

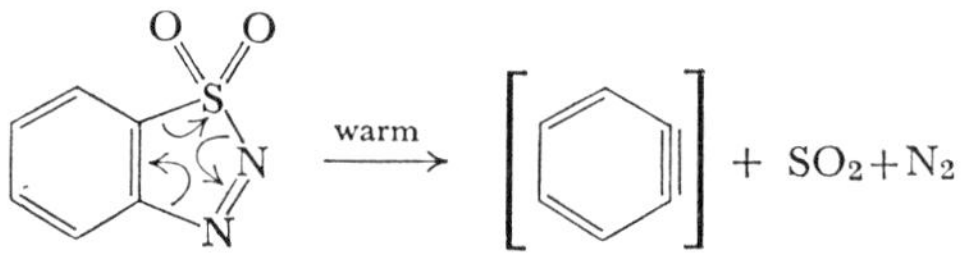

The reversal of the second step of the benzyne-forming elimination above ($G \rightarrow F$) was accomplished by addition of lithium salts to a solution in tetrahydrofuran prepared from the dioxide (J), which on dilution in water afforded a 44% yield of iodobenzene. Smaller amounts of the other halobenzenes were obtained from the corresponding halides.

The potential of the Diels–Alder reaction of arynes for synthesis is illustrated by the following tryptycene preparation. Crude triptycene

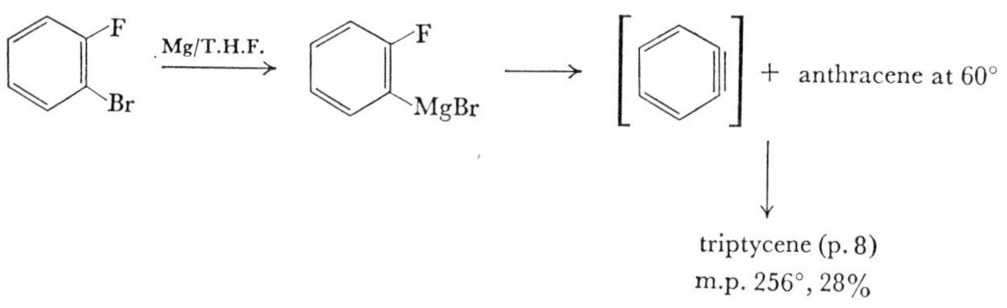

triptycene (p. 8)
m.p. 256°, 28%

was partially separated from anthracene by precipitation of the latter by methanol and separation was completed by precipitating the anthracene-maleic anhydride Diels–Alder adduct from xylene.

Reduction of Carbanions Derived from Aromatic Compounds. This technique was first developed for synthetic use by Birch in 1944 from the earlier work of Wooster (1937). It is a widely held view that in liquid ammonia solutions of alkali and alkaline earth metals the solvated cations are associated with electrons which tunnel through the solvent molecules. Six ammonia molecules are co-ordinated with a sodium ion (K) when molar concentration is exceeded whilst at rather lower concentrations dimer units (L) tend to form:

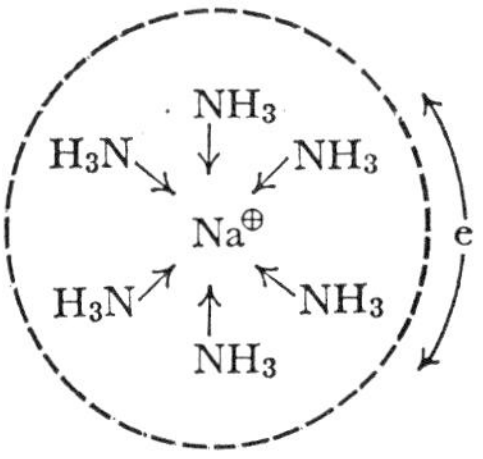

(K) 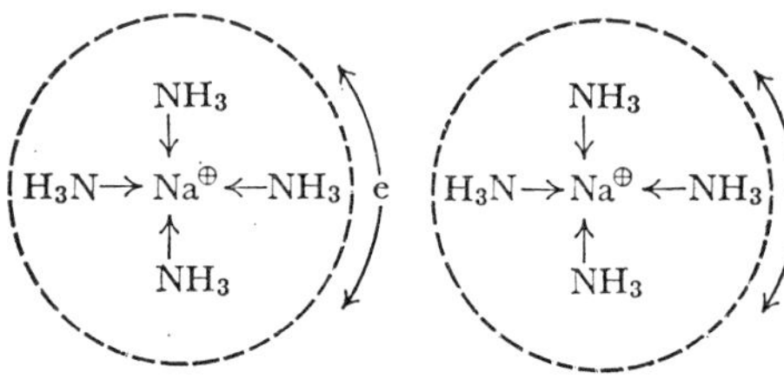   (L)

Solids such as $Ca(NH_3)_6$ have been isolated. The solutions are all deep-blue in colour and have very similar absorption spectra. Reduction occurs by donation of electrons to unsaturated centres followed by protonation of the resulting carbanion, which occurs on reduction by solution of metals in other protic solvents, for example, alcohol and acetic acid. The solvation of electrons does not occur in these more acidic solvents which donate a proton giving solutions of the conjugate base and the metal cation: $Na + ROH \rightarrow Na^{\oplus} + RO^{\ominus} + [H]$ with evolution of hydrogen. Ammonia is such a weak acid as compared to water and the alcohols that this change is very slow; it is greatly accelerated by the addition of a finely divided transition metal, which leads to destruction of the blue colour of the solution of electrons and the formation of sodamide: $Na + NH_3 \rightarrow Na^{\oplus} + NH_2^{\ominus} + [H]$. A soluble salt such as hydrated ferric nitrate is a convenient source of the metal:

$$2Fe(NO_3)_3 . 9H_2O + 36Na + 6NH_3 \longrightarrow 2Fe + 6NaNO_2 + 24NaOH + 6NaNH_2 + 9H_2$$

Strongly basic amide ions are formed when the solvent ammonia donates protons, but owing to its weak acidity this only occurs when the initial electron donation is encouraged by the formation of a resonance-stabilized carbanion:

$$CH_3 - CH = CH - CH = CH - CH_3$$

$$CH_3 - CH = CH - CH_2 - CH_2 - CH_3$$
hex-2-ene, 45%

$$CH_3 - CH_2 - CH = CH - CH_2 - CH_3$$
hex-3-ene, 30%

Formation of paraffins by a second stage of reduction does not proceed because there is no resonance stabilization in the dianion and isolated benzene rings are unaffected. Naphthalene forms a red salt on treatment with two equivalents of sodium in ammonia at $-65°$, at higher temperatures ammonolysis occurs with the production of 1,2- and 1,4-dihydronaphthalene (see structural formulae at top of p. 178). The dianion character of this sodio-derivative (M) has been demonstrated by the addition to its solution in ammonia of isopropyl chloride; the reaction product is readily dehydrogenated to 1,4-diisopropylnaphthalene. When an aromatic residue acquires a negative charge in this way an electronegative fragment may be ejected. Thus aryl halides undergo reduction and since saturated halides are also fissile the technique is sufficiently general to be used for the determination of halogen:

177

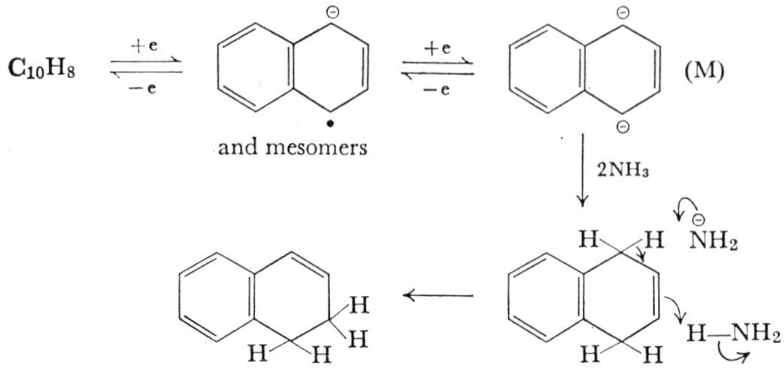

Ammonolysis of the mesomeric dianion (M) affords the 1,4-dihydrocompound which is isomerized by the strongly basic amide ion.

several organic products are possible since reduction competes with Wurtz-type couplings and amination, where arynes participate. Aryl ethers are cleaved in the sense:

$$Ar\text{—}OR + 2e \longrightarrow ArO^{\ominus} + R^{\ominus} \longrightarrow ArOH + RH$$

affording the stable phenoxide ion.

The reduction of benzene derivatives, as distinct from ether cleavage and halogen fission, occurs if an alcohol is added to the system:

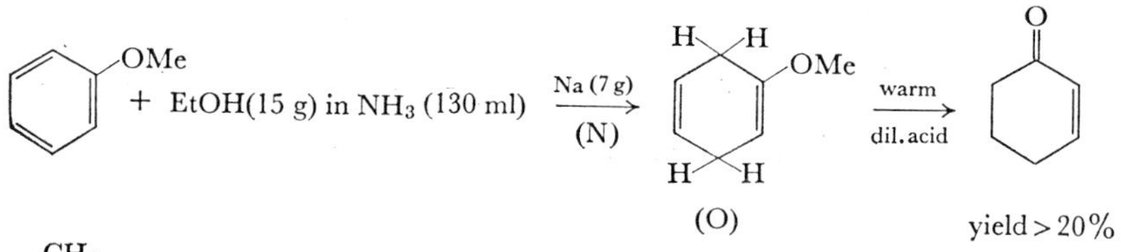

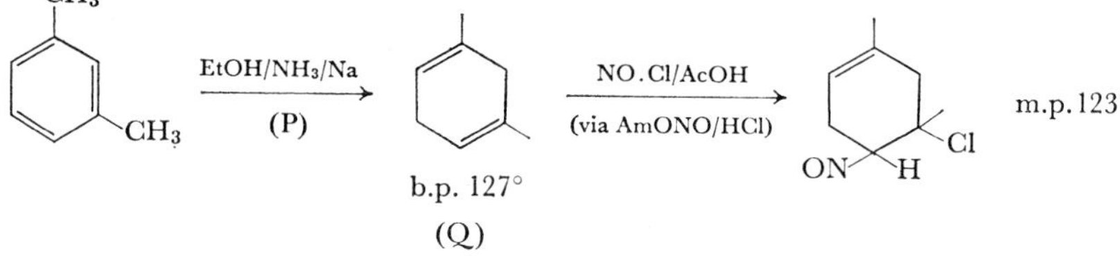

It is evident that reduction to alicyclic products follows the addition of the stronger acid in these reactions (N, P), for the enol ether (O) is easily hydrolysed to the conjugated enone and the olefin (Q) undergoes the typical addition of nitrosyl chloride. The products (O, Q) are rather unstable and are best separated from residual aromatic compounds by GLC when their very different spectra emerge. Treatment of (Q) with sodamide causes isomerization to the stable conjugated diene,

178

which is of course itself reduced by Na/NH_3. It is evident that an excess of the metal should be avoided because this induces the fission reaction already mentioned and base-catalysed isomerization follows on accumulation of sodamide. This latter side-reaction is more probable in commercial ammonia which contains traces of iron, which also destroy the alcohol by accelerating the otherwise slow reaction:

$$\text{Metal} + \text{R—OH} \longrightarrow \text{Metal—OR} + [\text{H}]$$

making the reduction less efficient. The following working procedure minimizes these side-effects:

(*a*) distillation of ammonia from the cylinder rather than pouring the liquid;
(*b*) addition of the metal to a solution of the substrate;
(*c*) use of an excess of alcohol which also buffers the system $NH_2^\ominus + ROH \rightarrow NH_3 + RO^\ominus$.

Lithium, although more expensive than sodium, has a number of advantages; its reduction potential is higher and it is more soluble in ammonia, hence more co-solvent, for example tetrahydrofuran, can be added to increase the concentration of the substrate.

This extremely valuable conversion of aromatic precursors into the less stable 1,4-dienes does not always follow the course indicated above for naphthalene. A dianion derived from benzene and analogous with

(M) would have the structure $\ominus$⟨ ⟩$\ominus$ which is not resonance stabilized

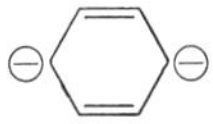

and would therefore be a stronger base than (M), easily reduced by ammonia alone without addition of an alcohol. Since this is contrary to observation a two-step mechanism is preferred for the reduction:

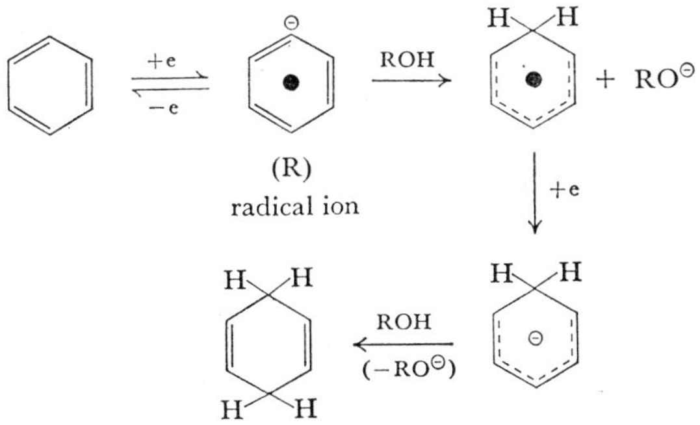

(R)
radical ion

The first step involves loss of aromatic character and is reversible and lies to the left, but the further additions of two protons and the second

179

electron are fast, irreversible, and under kinetic control. Protons are therefore added to those ring positions at which the highest electron density appears, and the mode can be predicted in most instances by applying two rules:

(1) In the radical ion (R) the greatest electron density will be developed *meta* to the most strongly *ortho–para* directing group, for *ortho-* and *para*-located negative charges are destabilized.

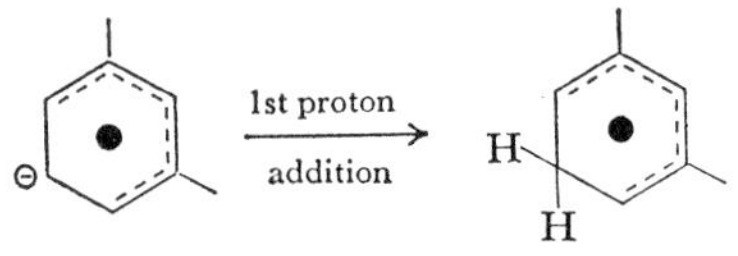

(2) Following the addition of a second electron the greatest electron density is expected at the central carbon of the dienate anion (S)

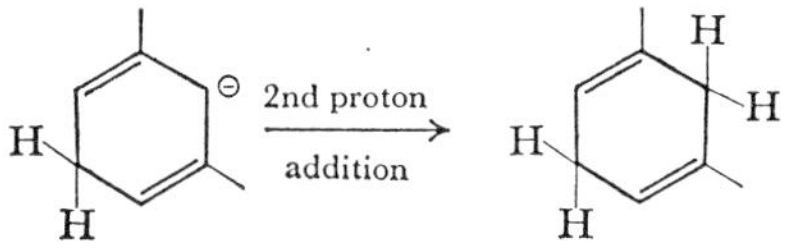

(S)

The carboxyl group activates the benzene ring and sodium benzoate is reduced in the absence of alcohol which was however included in the following reaction:

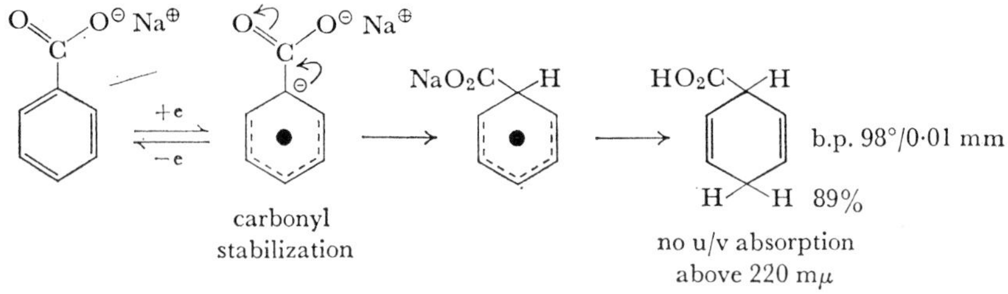

Three equivalents of sodium and alcohol were used and the basic anions neutralized by the addition of ammonium chloride.

$$EtO^{\ominus} + NH_4Cl \longrightarrow EtOH + NH_3 + Cl^{\ominus}$$

$$NH_2^{\ominus} + NH_4Cl \longrightarrow 2NH_3 + Cl^{\ominus}$$

Further Reading

TOPICS

B. R. BROWN, *Quart. Rev.*, 1951, **5**, 131 (decarboxylation).
J. F. BUNNETT, *Quart. Rev.*, 1958, **12**, 1 (nucleophilic aromatic substitution).
H. HEANEY, *Chem. Rev.*, 1962, **62**, 81 (aryne chemistry).
A. S. LINDSEY and H. JESKEY, *Chem. Rev.*, 1957, **57**, 584 (Kolbe–Schmitt reaction).
J. MARCH, *J. Chem. Educ.*, 1963, **40**, 212 (decarboxylation).
H. SMITH, *Organic Reactions in Liquid Ammonia*. Interscience, New York, 1963.
M. C. R. SYMONS, *Quart. Rev.*, 1959, **13**, 99 (metal solutions, physical aspects).
G. WITTIG, *Angew. Chem.*, Intern. Edit., 1962, **1**, 415 (cyclynes).

PROBLEMS

1. Account for the formation of products in the reactions:

(a)

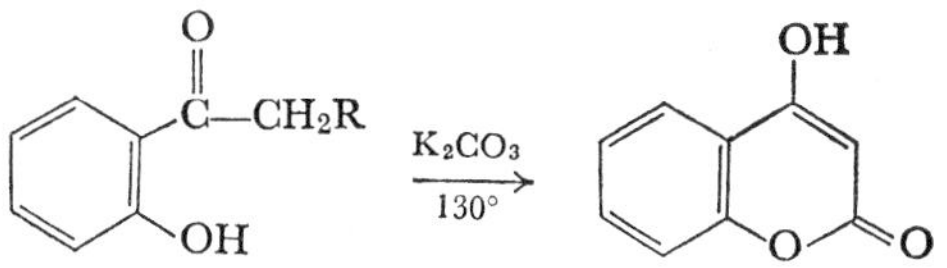

P. da Re and E. Sandri, *Chem. Ber.*, 1960, **93**, 1085.

(b)

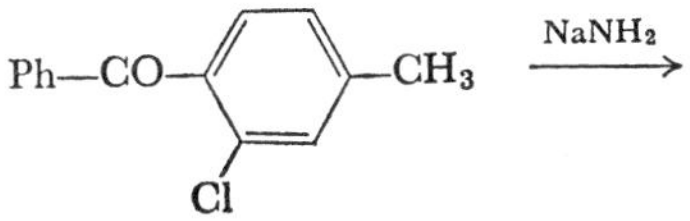

$Ph-CO-\underset{Cl}{\text{C}_6H_3}-CH_3 \xrightarrow{NaNH_2} PhCONH_2 + o\text{-}, m\text{-}, \text{and } p\text{-toluidine}$

(c)

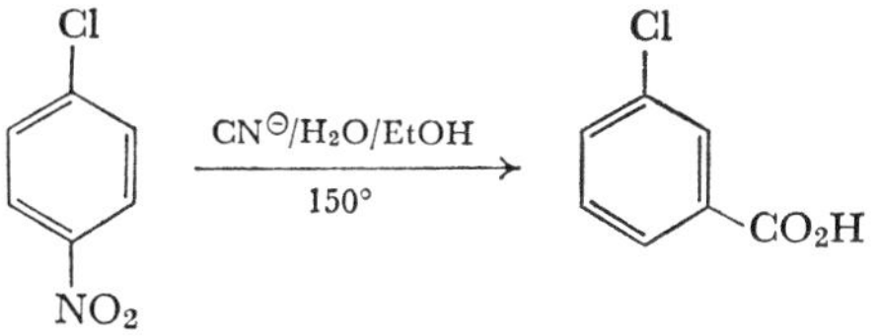

J. F. Bunnett and M. M. Rauput, *J. Org. Chem.*, 1956, **21**, 944.

2. Account for the rate order:

Fluorobenzene	2-Fluoronaphthalene	9-Fluorophenanthrene
9·4	50	77

in the formation of the arynes by reaction with PhLi.

3. Give a mechanism for:

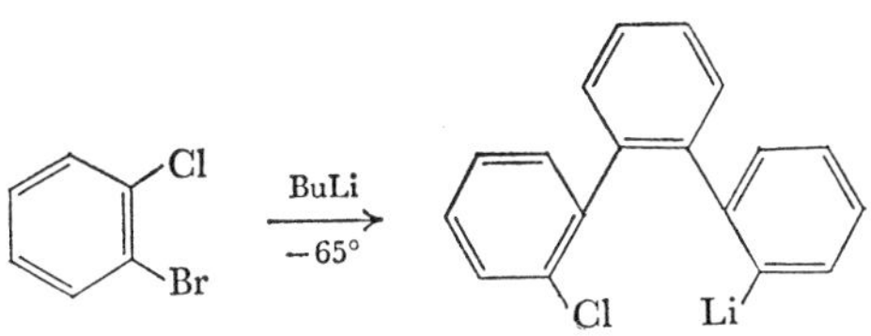

H. Gilman and R. D. Gorsich, *J. Amer. Chem. Soc.*, 1956, **78**, 2217.

What product would be formed ultimately at higher temperatures?

Carbanionoid Reactions of Aromatic Systems

4. Account for the formation of the following reaction products:

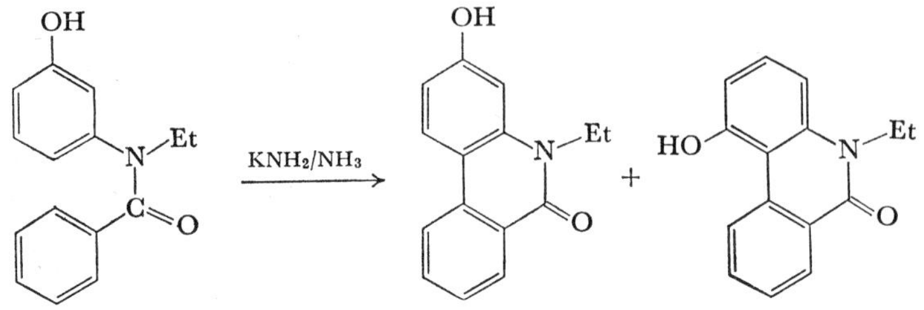

OH (structure) + KNH₂/NH₃ → products

$$\xrightarrow{KNH_2/NH_3}$$

D. H. Hey, J. A. Leonard, C. W. Rees, *J. Chem. Soc.*, **1963**, 5266.

5. Predict the mode of 1,4-addition of hydrogen in the Birch reduction of:

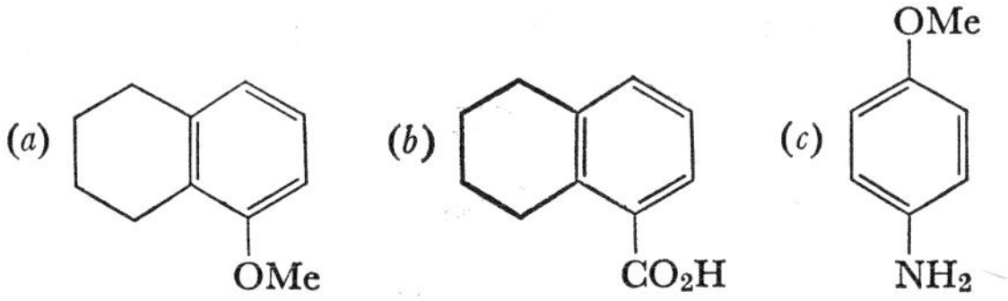

(a) (tetralin with OMe) (b) (tetralin with CO₂H) (c) (benzene with OMe and NH₂)

(c) E. A. Braude, A. A. Webb and M. U. S. Sultanbawa, *J. Chem. Soc.*, **1958**, 3328.

6. Suggest mechanisms for the following reactions:

(a)   Ph—O—P(O)(OEt)₂ $\xrightarrow{\text{Li/NH}_3/\text{EtOH}}$ benzene

G. W. Kenner and N. R. Williams, *J. Chem. Soc.*, **1955**, 522.

(b) (1-methoxynaphthalene) $\xrightarrow{\text{Na/NH}_3/\text{EtOH}}$ naphthalene

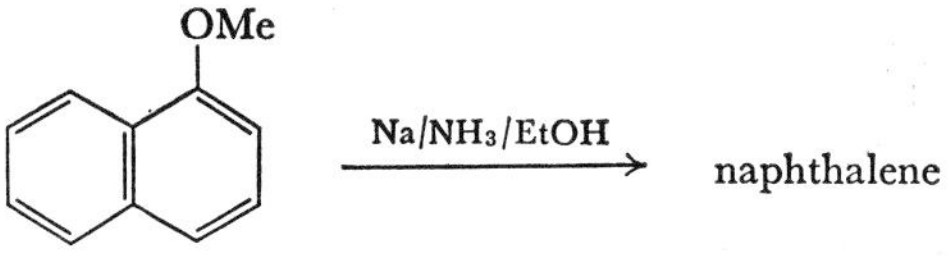

(c) (1,2,3-trimethoxybenzene) $\xrightarrow{\text{Na/NH}_3/\text{EtOH}}$ (product)

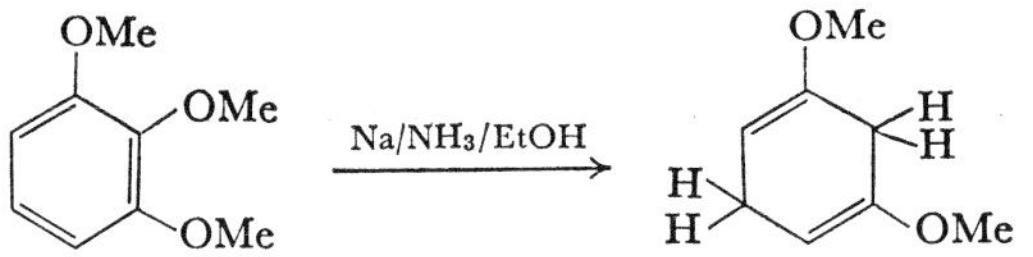

A. J. Birch, *J. Chem. Soc.*, **1947**, 102.

(d) (steroid structure, AcO, MeO) $\xrightarrow[\text{(2) Dil. acid}]{\text{(1) Li/NH}_3/\text{EtOH}}$ (product)

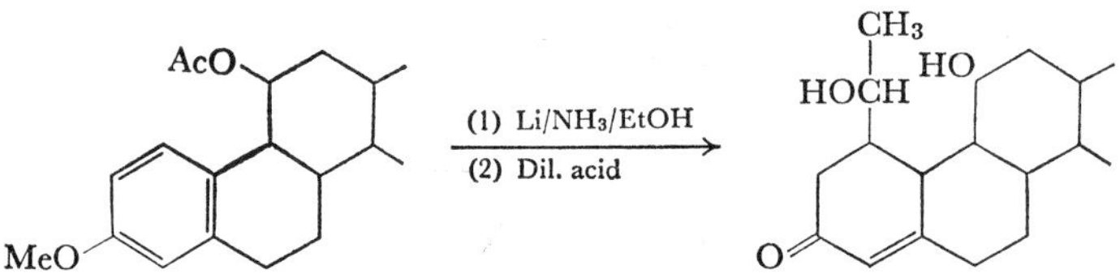

B. J. Mayerlein and J. A. Hogg, *J. Amer. Chem. Soc.*, 1958, **80**, 2220.

(e)   PhO—⟨benzene⟩—OMe $\xrightarrow[\text{(2) Dil. acid}]{\text{(1) Na/NH}_3}$ benzene + HO—⟨benzene⟩—OMe

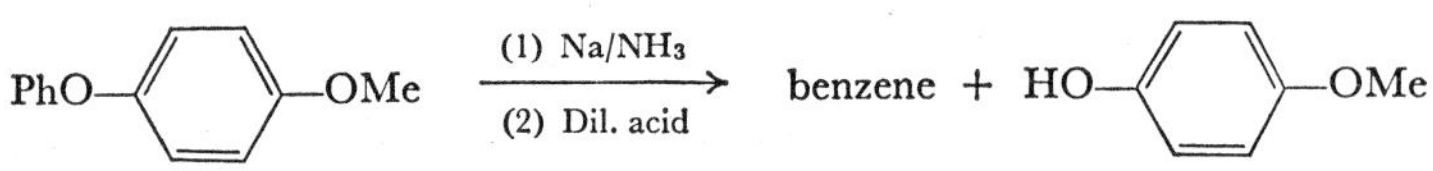

P. A. Sartoretto and F. J. Sowa, *J. Amer. Chem. Soc.*, 1937, **59**, 605.

182

(f)

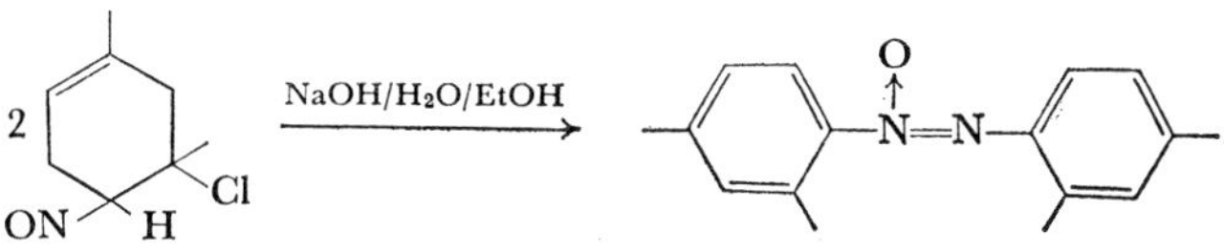

A. J. Birch, *J. Chem. Soc.*, **1944**, 431–432.

(g)

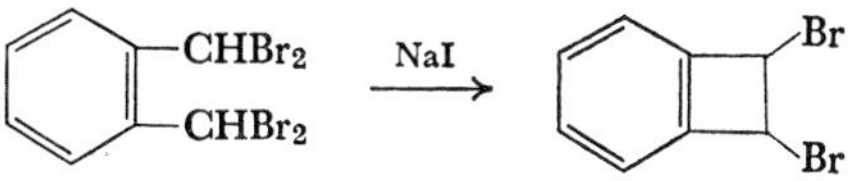

M. P. Cava and D. R. P. Napier, *J. Amer. Chem. Soc.*, 1956, **78**, 500.
How would you synthesize the parent hydrocarbon of this product using an aryne intermediate?

J. F. Bunnett and J. A. Skorcz, *J. Org. Chem.*, 1962, **27**, 3837.

CHAPTER 7

DIAZOCOMPOUNDS

Diazomethane (CH_2N_2) is a toxic yellow gas with boiling point $-23°$. It is represented as a resonance hybrid:

$$\overset{\ominus}{C}H_2-\overset{\oplus}{N}\equiv N\colon \qquad \overset{\ominus}{C}H_2-\overset{\oplus}{N}=\ddot{N}\colon$$

(A)

$$CH_2=\overset{..}{N}=\ddot{N}\colon$$
$$\overset{\oplus}{}\overset{\ominus}{}$$

Three important precursors for diazomethane are N-nitroso-N-methyl-urea (B), N-nitroso-N-methylurethan (C), and N-nitroso-N-methyl-toluene-p-sulphonamide (D) which are prepared as follows:

$$\begin{array}{c} CH_3\overset{\oplus}{N}H_3]Cl^{\ominus} \\ + \\ O=\overset{}{C}(NH_2)_2 \end{array} \xrightarrow[\text{water}]{\text{boil in}} \begin{array}{c} CH_3NHCONH_2 \\ + \\ NH_4Cl \end{array} \xrightarrow[\text{NaNO}_2]{\text{dil. H}_2SO_4/0°} \begin{array}{c} CH_3\overset{|}{N}CONH_2 \\ \overset{|}{N}O \end{array} \qquad (B)$$

70%, precipitated as an unstable yellow solid

$$\begin{array}{c} EtOCOCl \\ + \\ CH_3NH_2/H_2O \end{array} \longrightarrow \underset{\text{b.p. }60°/13\text{ mm}}{EtOCONHCH_3} \xrightarrow[\text{under Et}_2O]{\text{NaNO}_2/\text{HNO}_3} \begin{array}{c} EtO \\ \diagdown C=O \\ \overset{|}{C}H_3N-NO \end{array} \qquad (C)$$

decomp. on dist.

$$\begin{array}{c} CH_3C_6H_4SO_2Cl \\ + \\ 2CH_3NH_2 \end{array} \xrightarrow[\text{H}_2O]{\text{in}} \underset{\text{m.p. }78°}{CH_3C_6H_4SO_2NHCH_3} \xrightarrow[\substack{\text{in cold}\\\text{dil. acid}}]{\text{nitrosate}} \begin{array}{c} O \\ \| \\ CH_3C_6H_4-\overset{}{S}-N-NO \\ \| \quad | \\ O \quad CH_3 \end{array} \quad (D)$$

m.p. 60°, 90%

These react with alkali and diazomethane is formed by displacement of the alkoxycarbonyl or equivalent function with decomposition of the anion formed:

184

$$:N=O \quad OH^{\ominus} \qquad :N=O \quad OH$$
$$CH_3-\overset{..}{N}-\overset{|}{C}-NH_2 \quad \rightleftharpoons \quad CH_3-\overset{|}{\underset{..}{N}}\!-\!\!-\overset{|}{C}-N\dot{H}_2$$
$$\overset{||}{O} \qquad\qquad\qquad\qquad \overset{|}{O^{\ominus}}$$

$$\left[\begin{array}{c} H \\ | \\ H-\overset{|}{\underset{\ominus}{C}}-\overset{..}{N}=N-OH \end{array}\right] \rightleftharpoons \left[CH_3-\overset{..}{N}:^{\ominus} \atop N=O \right] + \left[\begin{array}{c} O \\ \parallel \\ C-NH_2 \\ | \\ OH \end{array}\right]$$

$$\downarrow \qquad\qquad\qquad\qquad\qquad\qquad \downarrow OH^{\ominus}$$

$$\overset{\ominus}{:}CH_2-\overset{\oplus}{N}\equiv N: + OH^{\ominus} \qquad\qquad -CNO^{\ominus} + H_2O$$

N-nitroso-*N*-methylurea is used for the *ex situ* preparation of diazomethane which is trapped as a solution in diethyl ether or methylene chloride when it outgases from aqueous alkali. The urethane (C) is a useful *in situ* source with an alcohol as solvent and an alkali carbonate as base. The nitrososulphonylamide (D) is a particularly stable precursor and is commercially available. The solvent can be changed to benzene, dioxan, or tetrahydrofuran by their addition with simultaneous distillation of ether; the solutions once prepared should be used immediately as they have been known to explode on keeping. Homologous diazoalkanes are made in the same way from *N*-alkyl derivatives (of B, C, D) but their lower stability has restricted their application. In contrast to the homologues the carbanionoid centre (cf. A) is stabilized by the α-substitution of $-CO_2R$, $-Ar$, and $-CO-$ groups; ethyl diazoacetate is an important intermediate obtained by nitrosation of glycine ethyl ester:

$$CH_2-CO_2Et \quad \xrightarrow{\;OH^{\ominus}\;} \quad \overset{H}{\underset{N_2^{\oplus}}{\overset{|}{\underset{|}{C}}}}-CO_2Et$$
$$\overset{|}{NH.NO}$$

Reactions with Acids. Carboxylic acids, enols, and phenols are alkylated:

$$CH_3-CO-CH_2-CO_2Et \quad \xrightarrow{CH_2N_2/Et_2O} \quad CH_3-\overset{OCH_3}{\underset{}{\overset{|}{C}}}=CH-CO_2Et + N_2$$

Ethyl β-methoxycrotonate,
b.p. 188°/725 mm

This reaction is not a measure of the enol in equilibrium because this is displaced as alkylation occurs. Following protonation of the diazocompound:

13

$$CH_2\overset{\oplus}{-}N\equiv N \longrightarrow CH_3-\underset{\oplus}{N}\equiv N$$
$$\overset{\ominus}{\underset{H^{\oplus}}{\downarrow}}$$

the methyl group readily undergoes nucleophilic attack by the conjugate base; for example:

$$R-\overset{O}{\overset{\parallel}{C}}-O^{\ominus} CH_3-\underset{\oplus}{N}\equiv N \longrightarrow R-CO_2CH_3 + N_2$$

Weakly acidic phenols react slowly and steric hindrance can prevent reaction. Reactivity is reduced by intramolecular hydrogen bonding particularly when the very stable six-ring chelates are formed; inter-molecular interactions with polar solvents are also inhibitory.

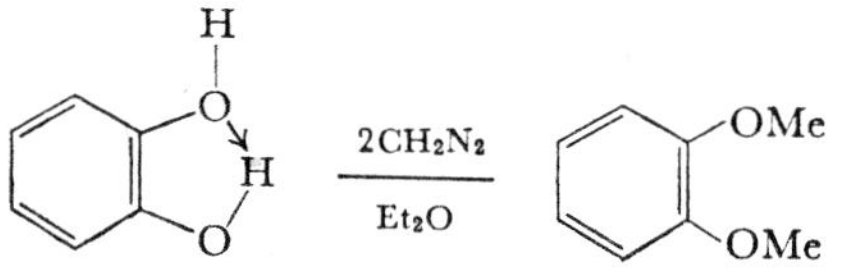

5-ring chelate

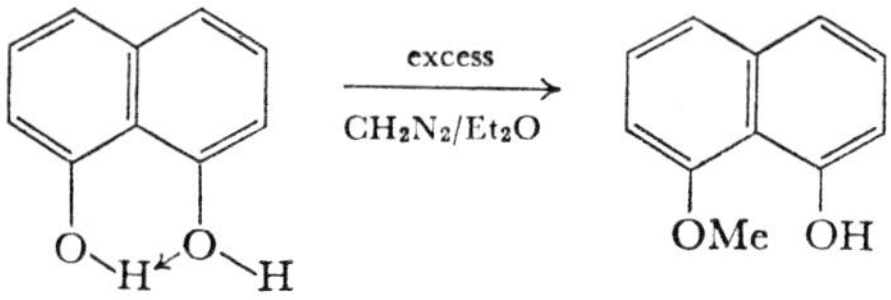

6-ring chelate

In Nature methylation is effected by a similar transfer from an 'onium' salt of methionine:

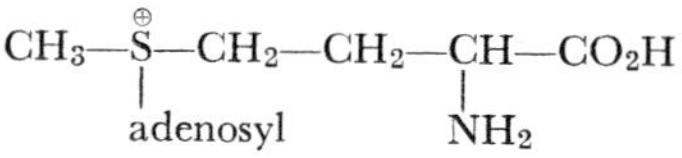

$$CH_3-\overset{\oplus}{S}-CH_2-CH_2-CH-CO_2H$$
$$\underset{adenosyl}{|} \qquad \underset{NH_2}{|}$$

Simple alcohols are not sufficiently acidic to react with diazomethane under the above conditions but will do so in the presence of an acid catalyst. Most Brönsted acids are inapplicable because they themselves consume the reagent in a reaction of the type: $HCl + CH_2N_2 \rightarrow CH_3Cl + N_2$ but fluoboric acid is effective since B—F bond fission is so difficult:

$$(CH_3)_3-C-OH \xrightarrow[\substack{\text{trace of } HBF_4 \\ \text{completed at room temp.}}]{CH_2N_2 (1\cdot5E)/CH_2Cl_2, -5^\circ} (CH_3)_3C-OMe$$
$$45\%$$

Primary and secondary alcohols give better yields.

186

Lewis acids can be used and the alkylation extended to $-\overset{\mid}{N}-H$ groups:

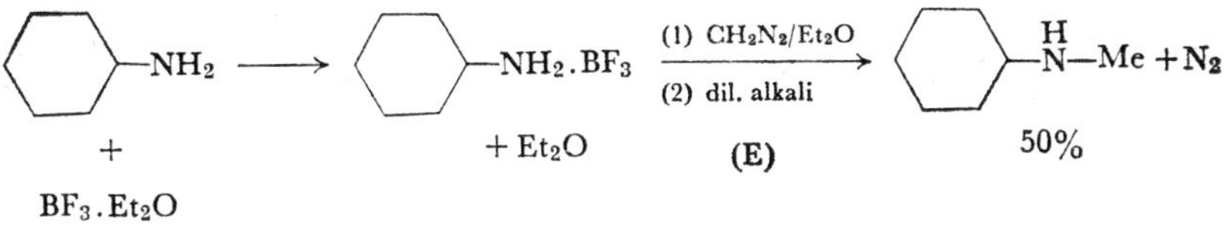

$$\text{(cyclohexyl)}-NH_2 \longrightarrow \text{(cyclohexyl)}-NH_2 \cdot BF_3 \xrightarrow[\text{(2) dil. alkali}]{\text{(1) } CH_2N_2/Et_2O} \text{(cyclohexyl)}-\overset{H}{\underset{}{N}}-Me + N_2$$

$$+ \qquad\qquad\qquad + Et_2O \qquad\qquad \textbf{(E)} \qquad\qquad\qquad 50\%$$

$$BF_3 \cdot Et_2O$$

Secondary amines formed in this way are usually contaminated by the tertiary dimethylamine formed by further methylation: dimethylcyclohexylamine was isolated in 25% yield from the above reaction (E). Polymethylene formed during these acid-catalysed reactions becomes the principal product if no alcohol or amine is present and Bawn has shown that these nucleophiles terminate the chain extension:

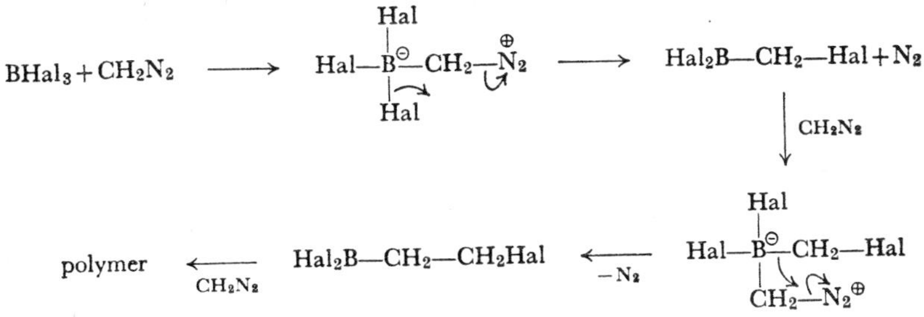

$$BHal_3 + CH_2N_2 \longrightarrow Hal-\overset{Hal}{\underset{Hal}{\overset{\mid}{B}}}{}^{\ominus}-CH_2-\overset{\oplus}{N_2} \longrightarrow Hal_2B-CH_2-Hal + N_2$$

$$\Big\downarrow CH_2N_2$$

$$\text{polymer} \xleftarrow[CH_2N_2]{} Hal_2B-CH_2-CH_2Hal \xleftarrow[-N_2]{} Hal-\overset{Hal}{\underset{CH_2-N_2^{\oplus}}{\overset{\mid}{B}}}{}^{\ominus}-CH_2-Hal$$

In the presence of alcohols or amines termination occurs with liberation of the -O- or -N-alkyl compound:

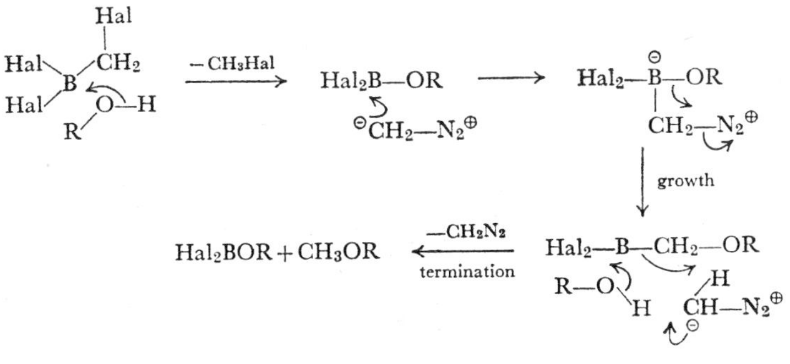

$$\overset{Hal}{\underset{Hal}{\overset{\mid}{\underset{}{B}}}}\overset{\overset{Hal}{\mid}}{\underset{\underset{R}{\mid}}{\overset{CH_2}{\underset{O-H}{}}}} \xrightarrow{-CH_3Hal} Hal_2B-OR \longrightarrow Hal_2-\overset{\ominus}{B}-OR$$

$$\qquad\qquad\qquad\qquad {}^{\ominus}CH_2-N_2^{\oplus} \qquad\qquad CH_2-N_2^{\oplus}$$

$$\Big\downarrow \text{growth}$$

$$Hal_2BOR + CH_3OR \xleftarrow[\text{termination}]{-CH_2N_2} Hal_2-\overset{}{B}-CH_2-OR$$

$$R-O\quad H \quad CH-N_2^{\oplus}$$

It follows that formation of methyl ethers and amines is favoured by addition of dilute diazomethane solutions to the substrate (cf. MeLi prep. p. 15).

Carbene Reactions. Diazomethane does not interact with solvents in the cold, but on heating or irradiating with ultraviolet light methylene is formed and it reacts rapidly and non-selectively with the solvent:

$$CH_2{-}N_2 \longrightarrow :CH_2 + N_2$$

$$CH_3{-}CH_2{-}O{-}CH_2{-}CH_3 \xrightarrow[:CH_2]{}$$

$$CH_3{-}\underset{CH_3}{\overset{H}{\underset{|}{\overset{|}{C}}}}{-}O{-}CH_2{-}CH_3 + CH_3{-}CH_2{-}CH_2{-}O{-}CH_2{-}CH_3$$

In solution methylene is probably in the singlet state having the structure

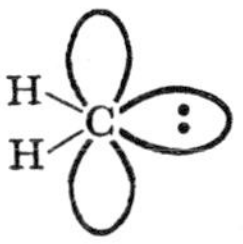
H
H
C

with an empty *p*-orbital and the unshared electron-pair in an orbital with *s*-character. In the gaseous phase collision with sister molecules results in conversion into the more stable triplet state with the structure

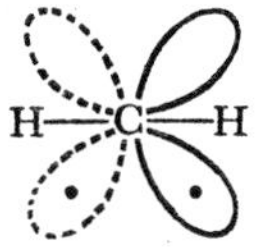
H
C
H

where the unshared electrons are split and occupy two different *p*-orbitals.

When a benzene solution of diazoacetic ester is heated in a glass-lined autoclave addition (F) occurs:

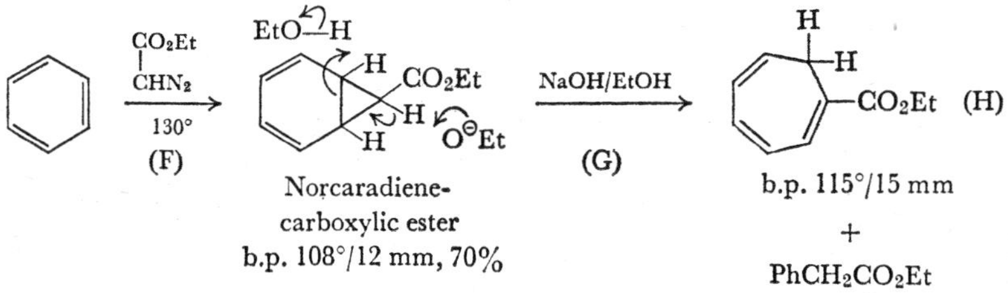
CO₂Et
CHN₂
130°
(F)
EtO
H
H
CO₂Et
H
H
O⊖Et
Norcaradiene-
carboxylic ester
b.p. 108°/12 mm, 70%
NaOH/EtOH
(G)
H
H
CO₂Et (H)
b.p. 115°/15 mm
+
PhCH₂CO₂Et

followed by the rearrangement (G) which affords isomers of (H) as principal products together with ethyl phenylacetate. Tropolone synthesis is illustrated by the formation of the ethyl ester of *O*-methylstipitatic acid (I):

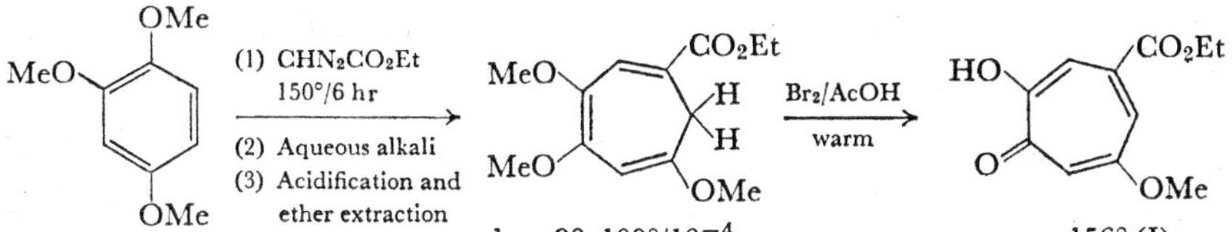

b.p. 80–100°/10⁻⁴mm → $80\text{–}100°/10^{-4}\text{mm}$
44%

m.p. 156° (I)
by sublimation

Ring expansions of this type are better effected by irradiation, which must be followed by careful fractionation because the product of methylene insertion in a C—H bond is also formed in substantial amounts:

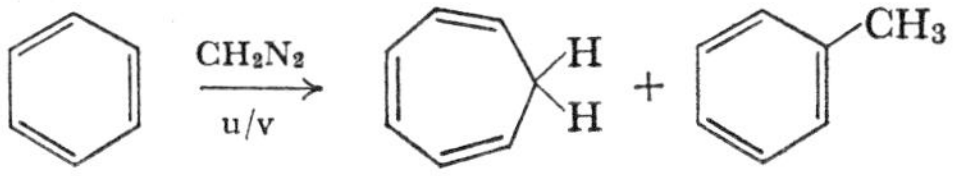

32%   9%

Reactions with Carbonyl Compounds. Diazoalkanes act here as a source of nucleophilic carbon:

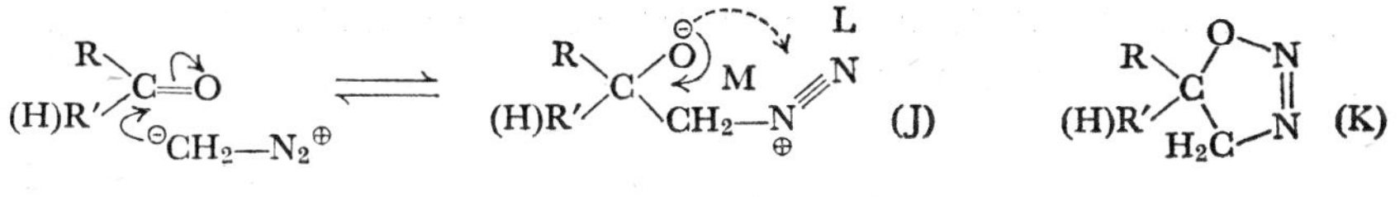

and the intermediate complex (J) can conceivably decompose in four ways. The formation of an oxadiazolidine (K via route L) is analogous to the 1,3-dipolar additions to carbon–carbon double bonds, but this is an unstable structure and the possible products are limited to three.

(*a*) an epoxide formed by route M;
(*b*) two different carbonyl compounds resulting from a 1,2-shift of the type:

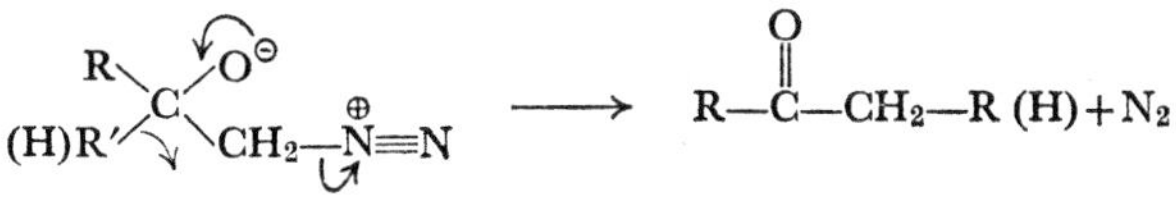

Note that these three types are all possible decomposition products of (K).

The ease of reaction follows the usual order for carbonyl compounds, aldehydes being more reactive than ketones and aromatic compounds

189

less reactive than aliphatic. In solvent ether the shift of a hydride ion is preferred and aldehydes afford methyl ketones:

$$CH_3—(CH_2)_5—CHO \xrightarrow[CH_2N_2]{} CH_3—(CH_2)_5—CO—CH_3$$
$$75\%$$

Unsymmetrical ketones give both possible homologues in substantial yield unless one residue can stabilize negative charge more effectively than the other, when the latter will shift:

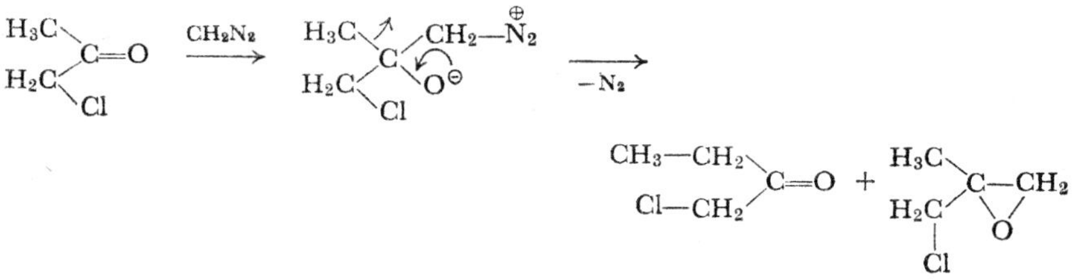

Epoxide formation is much reduced when homologues of diazomethane are used in conformity with lower rates of nucleophilic displacement at a secondary carbon atom (route M). On the other hand the yield of epoxide often rises when methanol is used as solvent.

Ring Enlargement. Cyclanones react with diazoalkanes to form the epoxide accompanied by products produced by ring expansion:

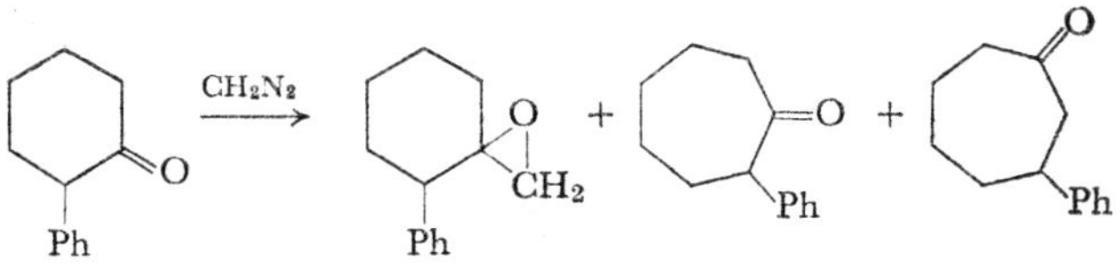

When, as above (N), the ring is 2-substituted the product ratio is partly determined by steric hindrance.

The relative rates of reaction of the cyclanones were found to be:

cyclopentanone	cyclohexanone	cycloheptanone	medium ring
1·0	2·5	1·25	slow

The method is most used for the synthesis of cycloheptanones because they themselves react more slowly than the cyclohexanone from which they are derived, although small amounts of the cyclooctanone and higher ketones will be formed by competitive capture of diazomethane. The high rate of the cyclohexanone reaction is in keeping with the work

190

of Brown who pointed out that ring strain in these ketones is relieved when a transition state with the normal tetrahedral angle is formed by nucleophilic attack;

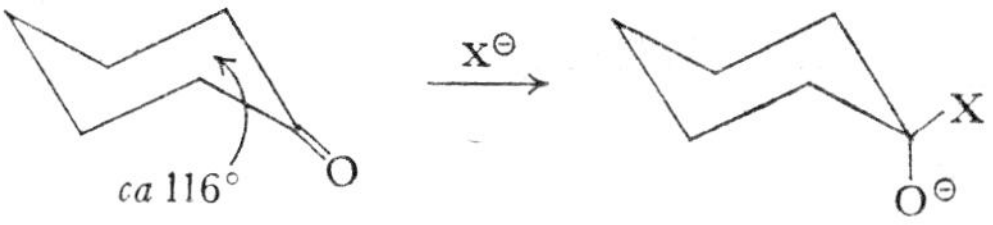
ca 116°
O
$X^\ominus$
X
$O^\ominus$

The reaction rate of medium ring ketones is accelerated by the addition of a Lewis acid, and Muller prepared α-methylcyclanones (C7→C14) in yields ranging from 57–82% by the addition of diazoethane/ether to the ketone and a catalytic amount of aluminium chloride in ether (cf. p. 187):

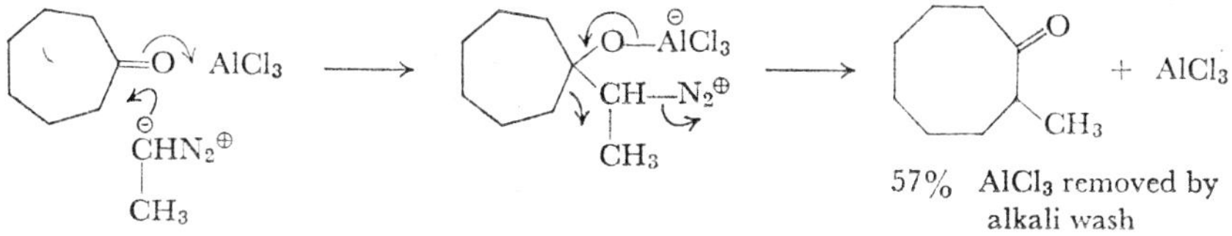
$AlCl_3$
$CHN_2^\oplus$
CH_3
$O—AlCl_3$
$CH—N_2^\oplus$
CH_3
O
$+ AlCl_3$
CH_3
57% $AlCl_3$ removed by alkali wash

There was no epoxide formation.

The ring expansion of *cis*-1-decalone (O) with retention of configuration shows that the reaction is stereospecific. The choice of *ex situ*

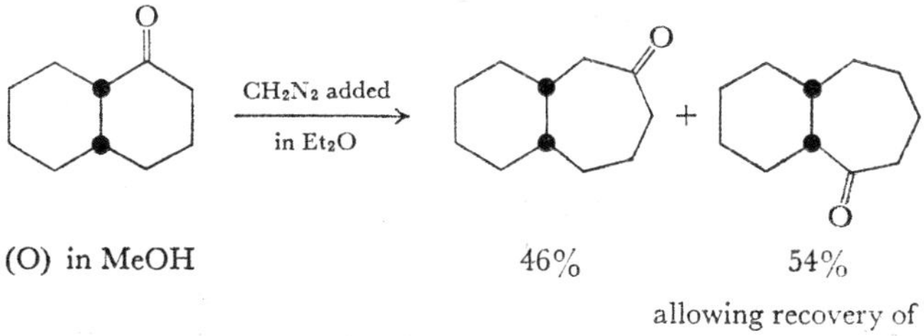
CH_2N_2 added
in Et_2O
(O) in MeOH
46%
54%
allowing recovery of (O)

conditions was necessary to avoid contact between the ketone and base.

Additions to Carbon–Carbon Multiple Bonds. Reaction occurs when the multiple bond is susceptible to nucleophilic attack. Thus in 1898 von Pechmann showed that pyrazole (P) was slowly formed from acetylene and diazomethane:

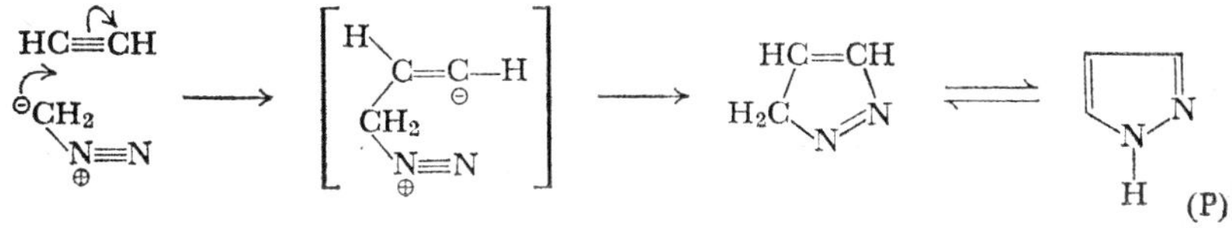
HC≡CH
$^\ominus CH_2$
N≡N
C=C—H
CH_2
HC=CH
H_2C
N
H
(P)

Diazocompounds

Attack by a carbanion is consistent with the increased rate of reaction with conjugated systems liable to Michael addition:

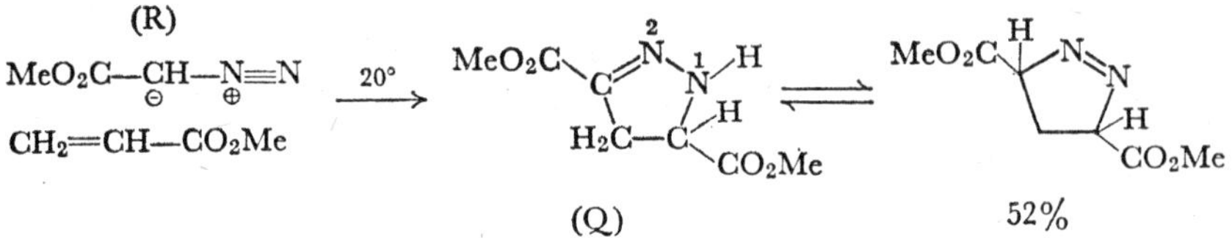

(R) MeO$_2$C—CH—N≡N / CH$_2$=CH—CO$_2$Me →(20°) (Q) ⇌ 52%

the conjugated Δ^2-pyrazolone (Q) is the form normally isolated. Since (R) is a mesomeric structure an alternative mode of addition via nucleophilic nitrogen MeO$_2$C—CH=N—N: could conceivably afford the product:

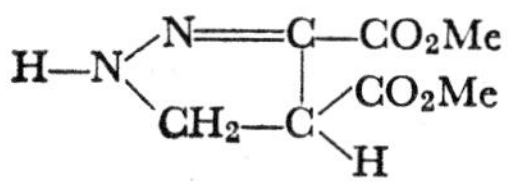

but this can be excluded because bromination–dehydrobromination affords dimethyl pyrazolone-3,5-dicarboxylate:

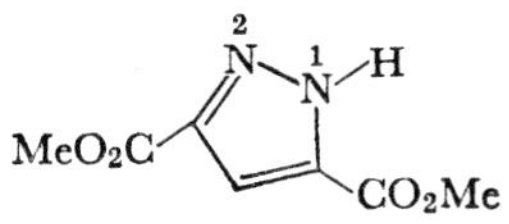

This reaction is a useful general route to these compounds. The two possible products were, however, isolated from the reaction:

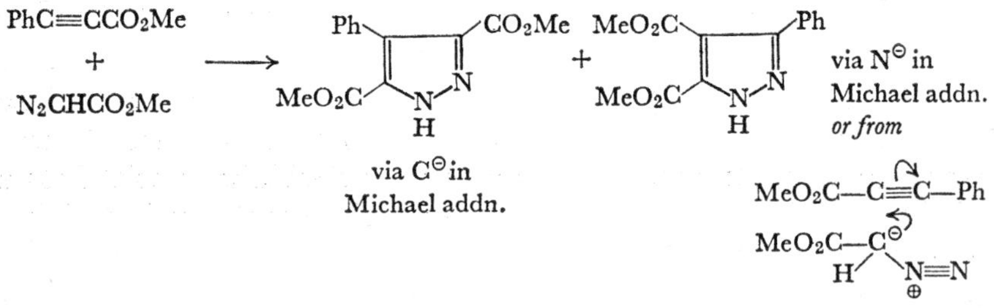

PhC≡CCO$_2$Me + N$_2$CHCO$_2$Me →

via C$^\ominus$ in Michael addn.

via N$^\ominus$ in Michael addn. or from

MeO$_2$C—C≡C—Ph / MeO$_2$C—C$^\ominus$—N≡N

The 'abnormal' course is also followed during additions to nitroalkenes.

Van Auken and Rinehart showed that additions of diazocompounds to conjugated double bonds were stereospecific:

192

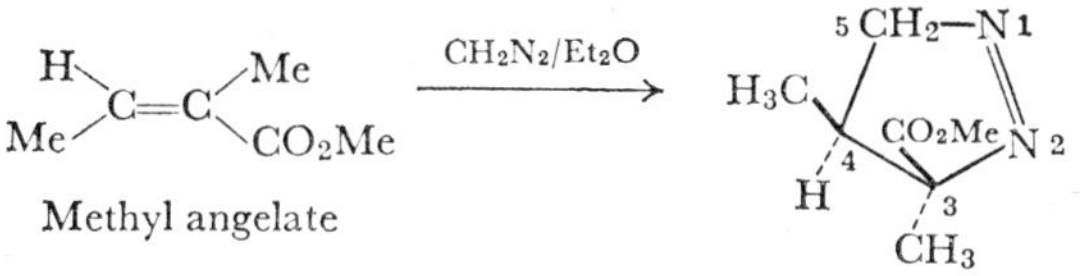

Methyl angelate

(S)

47%, b.p. 55°/0·5 mm

and also:

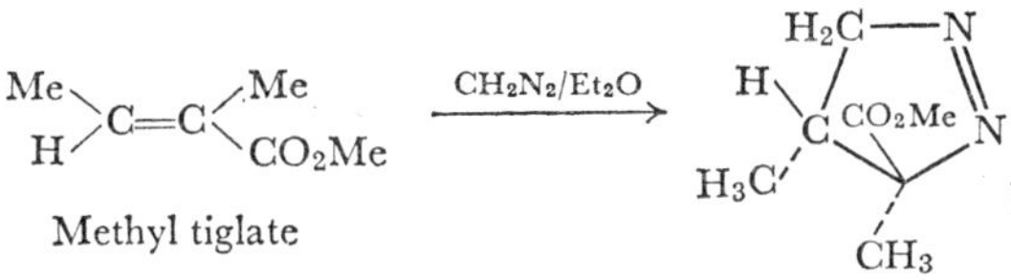

Methyl tiglate

(T)

b.p. 72°/1·5 mm, 62%

The infrared spectra of both products (S, T) lack N—H absorption excluding a Δ^1-pyrazoline structure and where in the N.M.R. spectrum of (T) the multiplet due to the hydrogen at C4 is at lower field (τ 7·85) than in that of (S, τ 8·28) because of deshielding by the adjacent *cis*-CO_2Me group. Hence *cis*-addition was the rule for both unsaturated esters. This result is incompatible with the two-step mechanism above (formation of P) because here a single bond free to rotate would be formed

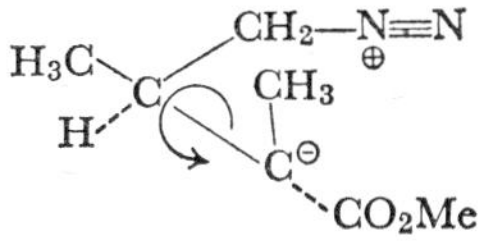

and the addition could not be stereospecific. It follows that the reaction type is that described by Huisgen as a concerted 1,3-dipolar-addition. Pyrazolines decompose on heating to give cyclopropanes:

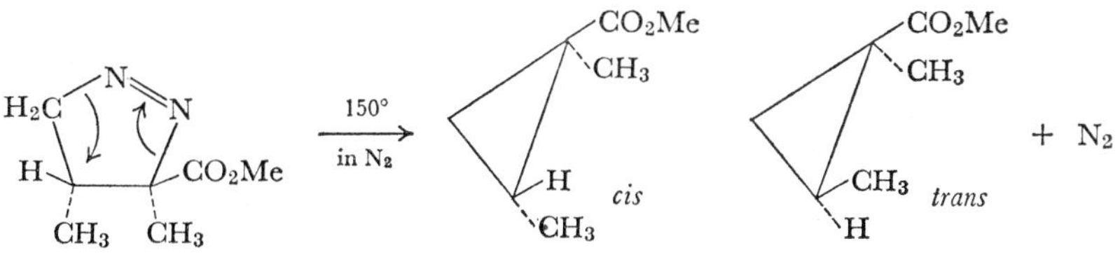

(T)

Total yield 83% *cis*:*trans* = 1·0:0·7

The Formation and Reactions of Diazoketones. The method most frequently used is the reaction between acid chlorides and diazoalkanes in ether or methylene chloride at 0°.

$$R-CO \cdot Cl \atop {}^{\ominus}CH_2-N_2^{\oplus} \longrightarrow R-C{\overset{O}{\underset{H}{\diagdown}}}{\overset{Cl^{\ominus}}{\underset{N_2^{\oplus}}{\diagup}} }C{\overset{H}{\diagup}} \longrightarrow R-CO-\overset{\ominus}{\underset{H}{C}}-N_2^{\oplus} + HCl$$

Unsaturated centres in the acid chloride do not interfere unless they themselves undergo the cyclo-addition already referred to ((S), (T), p. 193). The hydrogen chloride liberated must be taken up by base (triethylamine) or excess diazomethane which reacts as follows:

$$CH_2^{\ominus}\cdot\overset{\oplus}{N}\equiv N \overset{H^{\oplus}}{\longrightarrow} CH_2-\overset{\oplus}{N}\equiv N \longrightarrow CH_3-Cl+N_2 \quad (cf. p. 186)$$

The homologous diazoalkanes must not be used in excess in this way because they themselves react with diazoketones:

$$O=C{\overset{N{\overset{NO}{\diagdown}}Et}{\underset{CONH_2}{\diagdown}}} \overset{\text{to KOH}}{\underset{\text{in PrOH/Et}_2O}{\longrightarrow}} CH_3-\overset{\ominus}{CH_2}-N_2^{\oplus} \overset{Cl-C_6H_4-CO\cdot Cl}{\underset{-20°}{\longrightarrow}}$$

distilled out in Et$_2$O, 75%

above 0°

$$CH_3-\overset{\ominus}{CHN_2^{\oplus}}$$

$$Cl-\!\!\!\bigcirc\!\!\!-C{\overset{O}{\underset{}{\parallel}}}-\overset{CH_3}{\underset{\ominus}{C}}-N_2$$

79%
m.p. 57°
yellow (petrol)

$$\left[Cl-C_6H_4-CO-\overset{CH_3}{\underset{\ominus}{C}}-N=N-\overset{H}{\underset{CH_3}{C}}-\overset{\oplus}{N}\equiv N \right]$$

$$\downarrow$$

$$Cl-C_6H_4-CO-\overset{}{\underset{CH_3}{C}}=N-N=CH-CH_3$$

a ketazine

$$\downarrow \text{hot, dilute H}_2\text{SO}_4$$

$$Cl-C_6H_4-CO-CO-CH_3 + NH_2-NH_2 + CH_3-CHO$$

Diazoketones are not conveniently prepared from α-aminoketones by analogy with α-aminoesters (p. 185) because of the instability of the former, which may in fact be obtained from diazoketones by their hydrogenation:

$$Ph-CO-CHN_2 \overset{H_2/PdO/EtOAc}{\longrightarrow} [Ph-CO-CH_2-NH_2] \overset{\text{evaporation}}{\underset{\text{in air}}{\longrightarrow}} Ph-C{\overset{N}{\underset{}{\diagdown}}}{\overset{}{\underset{}{}}}CH \atop HC{\overset{}{\underset{N}{\diagup}}}C{\overset{}{\diagdown}}Ph$$

(U)

$$+ NH_3$$

2,5-diphenyl pyrazine
m.p. 197°, 70%

The pyrazine (U) results from an anil condensation between two molecules of the ketone, followed by autoxidation. Another route to aminoketones is that selected for the synthesis of δ-aminolaevulinic acid, the biogenetic precursor of the pyrrole ring of the porphyrins:

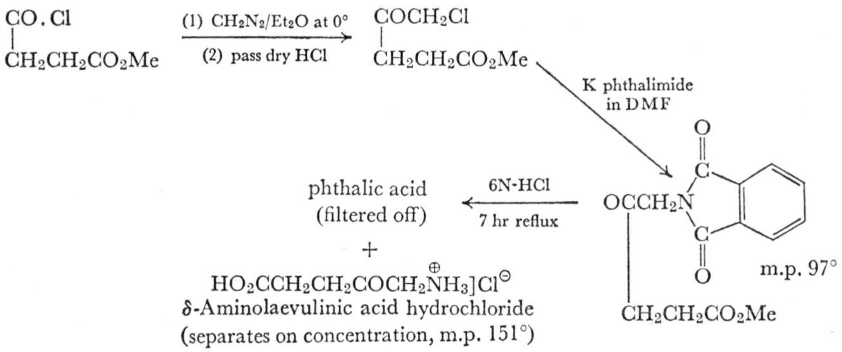

$CO.Cl$
$|$
$CH_2CH_2CO_2Me$

(1) CH_2N_2/Et_2O at 0°
⟶
(2) pass dry HCl

$COCH_2Cl$
$|$
$CH_2CH_2CO_2Me$

K phthalimide in DMF

phthalic acid (filtered off)

6N-HCl
⟵
7 hr reflux

$OCCH_2N$

$+$

$HO_2CCH_2CH_2COCH_2\overset{\oplus}{N}H_3]Cl^{\ominus}$
δ-Aminolaevulinic acid hydrochloride
(separates on concentration, m.p. 151°)

m.p. 97°

$CH_2CH_2CO_2Me$

Diazoketones can be obtained directly from ketones by a method due originally to Doering and developed by Regitz and Yates whereby the conjugate base of the ketone interacts with tosyl azide (V):

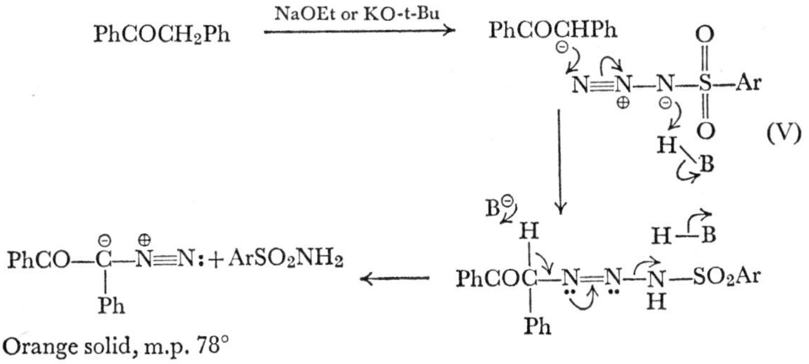

$PhCOCH_2Ph$

NaOEt or KO-t-Bu
⟶

$PhCO\overset{\ominus}{C}HPh$

$N{=}N{-}N{-}\overset{\parallel}{S}{-}Ar$

(V)

$B^{\ominus}$

$PhCO\overset{\ominus}{C}{-}N{=}N{-}\vec{N}{-}SO_2Ar$
$|$
Ph

$PhCO{-}\overset{\ominus}{C}{-}\overset{\oplus}{N}{\equiv}N{:}+ArSO_2NH_2$
$|$
Ph
Orange solid, m.p. 78°

Yields of 50–80% are obtained in syntheses of this type. Amines are satisfactory catalysts for the preparation of the diazo derivatives of highly stabilized conjugate bases of, for example, β-dicarbonyl compounds and the hydroxymethylene derivatives (p. 95) of simple ketones can be used (see structural formulae at top of p. 196).

Arndt–Eistert Homologation (1935). This widely applied procedure is dependent on the Wolff rearrangement of diazoketones which occurs

195

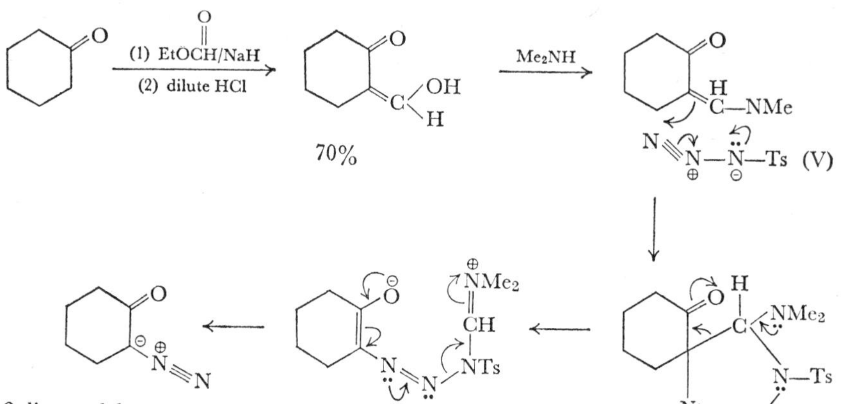

2-diazocyclohexanone

+

TsN=CH—NMe₂ ... $TsN{=}CH{-}NMe_2$

/H₂O ... H_2O

HNMe₂ + TsNHCHO ... $HNMe_2 + TsNHCHO$

After treatment with water the 2-diazocyclohexa-none was isolated in 83 % yield by ether extraction.

when they are heated alone or in solvents. The reaction is accelerated by silver salts and the mechanism is not fully determined, but the products are typically those of solvolysis of a ketene (W) formed by a rearrangement of the type:

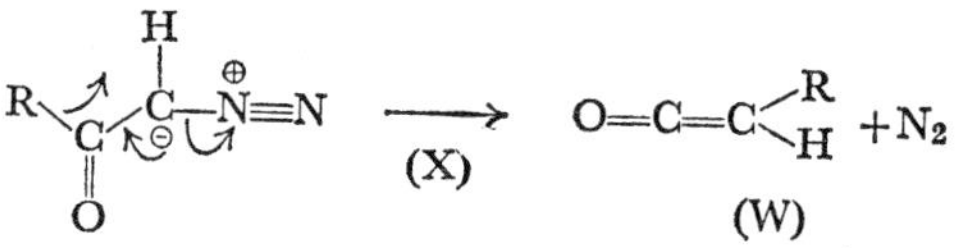

The diazo function provides a leaving group and the shift of the alkyl residue with its electrons stabilizes the α-carbon atom which would otherwise be left with a sextet of electrons:

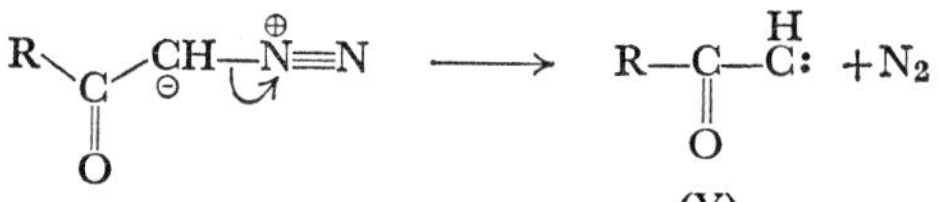

It is not clear whether a carbene (Y) is formed in this way or whether the reaction is concerted as written in (X).

Wiberg and Hutton showed that (−)-2-methylbutyric acid was converted into (−)-3-methylvaleric acid with complete retention of configuration during *rearrangement* in keeping with the above mechanism (X) where R— shifts with its bonding electrons:

196

$$CH_3-CH_2-\underset{\underset{CH_3}{|}}{\overset{\overset{H}{|}}{C}}-CO-CH_2N_2 \xrightarrow{\text{as X}} CH_3-CH_2-\underset{\underset{CH_3}{|}}{CH}-\underset{\underset{H-OH}{|}}{\overset{\overset{H}{|}}{C}}-\overset{\overset{(O-H)}{|}}{C}=O \longrightarrow$$

$$[\alpha]_D -3\cdot16°$$

$$\xleftarrow{\quad Ag^{\oplus}/H_2O/\text{dioxan}}$$

$$CH_3-CH_2-\underset{\underset{CH_3}{|}}{CH}-CH_2-CO_2H$$

$$[\alpha]_D -1\cdot32°$$
79% from diazoketone

although the acid chloride was formed with about 12% racemization in this sequence, probably due to enolization at the α-carbon atom:

$$\underset{Me}{\overset{H}{\underset{|}{Et-C}}}-\underset{OH}{\overset{O}{C}} \overset{H^{\oplus}}{\rightleftharpoons} \underset{Me}{\overset{Et}{}}C=C\underset{OH}{\overset{OH}{}}$$

The azulene synthesis of Plattner and Studer affords another example:

$$\underset{CH_2CO_2H}{\overset{CH_2CO_2H}{}} \xrightarrow[\text{(2) } CH_2N_2/Et_2O]{\text{(1) } SOCl_2} \underset{CH_2COCHN_2}{\overset{CH_2COCHN_2}{}} \xrightarrow[\text{AgNO}_3/60°]{\text{dioxan/H}_2O/NH_3} \underset{CH_2CH_2CONH_2}{\overset{CH_2CH_2CONH_2}{}}$$

10·0 g   11·5 g, m.p. 68° (Et$_2$O)   Diamide 8·6 g, m.p. 194°

(1) hydrolyse
(2) distil
Ce salt

6-Methylazulene blue-violet crystals, m.p. 83°

$$\xleftarrow[\text{(2) Pd/C/350°}]{\text{(1) dehydrate with } I_2}$$

$$\xleftarrow{MeMgI}$$

72% as semicarbazone ketone, b.p. 116°/13 mm via oxalic acid

There is a close analogy between the Wolff rearrangement and the formation of isocyanates from azides in the Curtius reaction, but even if the latter proceeds it cannot be assumed that an Arndt–Eistert synthesis will be successful; witness that triphenylacetyl azide readily yielded the isocyanate

$$Ph_3C-\overset{\overset{O}{\|}}{C}-\overset{\ominus}{N}-\overset{\oplus}{N}\equiv N \longrightarrow Ph_3C-N=C=O$$
m.p. 93°

but triphenylacetyldiazomethane gave abnormal products (problem 6).

197

A general procedure due to Wilds and Meader is to decompose the diazoketone by brief heating in a mixture of tertiary base (e.g. γ-collidine, b.p. 178°) and a high boiling alcohol (e.g. benzyl alcohol, b.p. 205°):

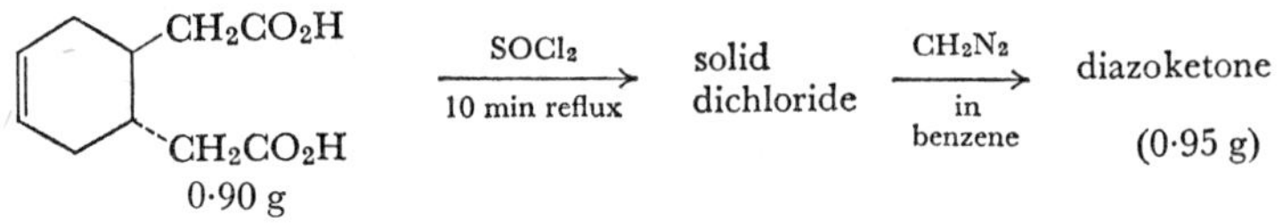

heated at 170° in the mixed solvent when nitrogen evolution was complete in 8 min, hydrolysis of the dibenzyl ester (3·0 g) afforded the acid:

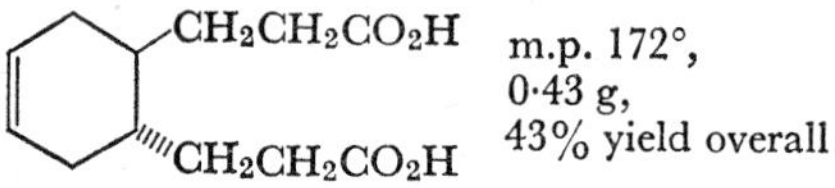

Newman and Beal's modification requires a solution of silver benzoate in triethylamine and an alcohol. The diazoketone must have an acidic hydrogen atom, base is essential, and radical trapping reagents must be excluded; the mechanism (Z) was suggested to account for these requirements:

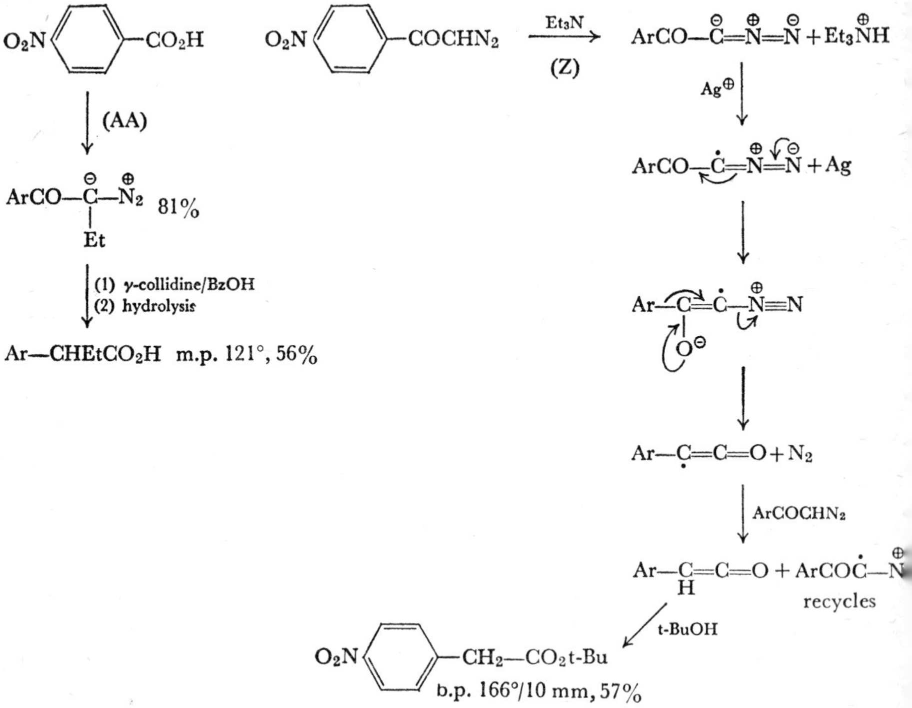

COMPARE THE SEQUENCES (Z) AND (AA)

Carbon–carbon double bonds can participate if a transition state for intramolecular reaction can be established:

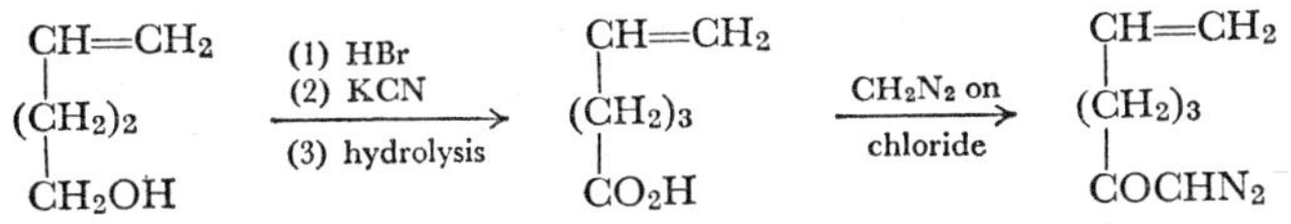

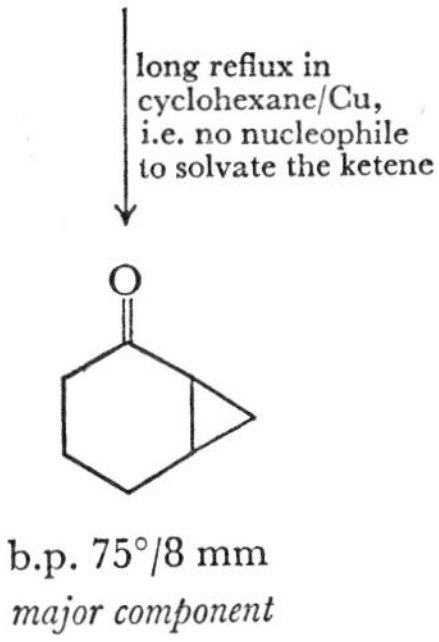

$$\underset{\substack{|\\ (CH_2)_2\\ |\\ CH_2OH}}{CH=CH_2} \xrightarrow[\text{(3) hydrolysis}]{\substack{\text{(1) HBr}\\ \text{(2) KCN}}} \underset{\substack{|\\ (CH_2)_3\\ |\\ CO_2H}}{CH=CH_2} \xrightarrow[\text{chloride}]{CH_2N_2 \text{ on}} \underset{\substack{|\\ (CH_2)_3\\ |\\ COCHN_2}}{CH=CH_2}$$

A possible mechanism is the addition of a carbene to the double bond in a bicyclic three-centre transition:

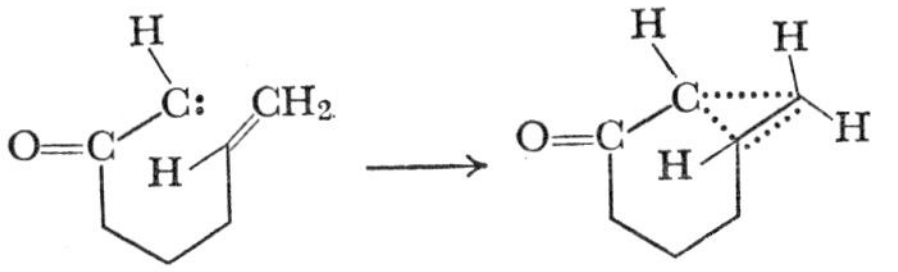

long reflux in cyclohexane/Cu, i.e. no nucleophile to solvate the ketene

b.p. 75°/8 mm

major component

Some Other Reactions. Diacylethylenes can be obtained by coupling diazoketones; a reaction of value in chain extension:

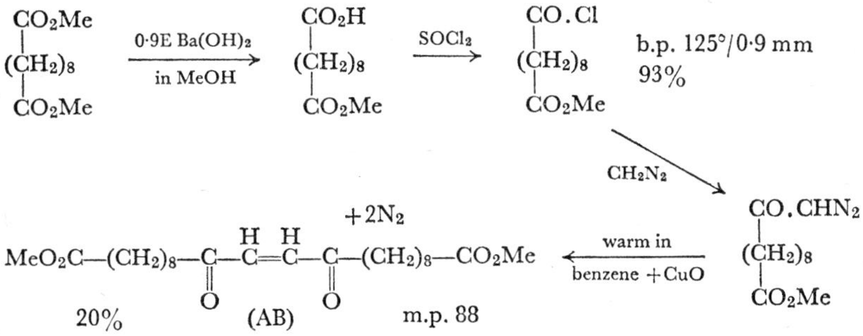

$$\underset{\substack{|\\ (CH_2)_8\\ |\\ CO_2Me}}{CO_2Me} \xrightarrow[\text{in MeOH}]{0\cdot9E\ Ba(OH)_2} \underset{\substack{|\\ (CH_2)_8\\ |\\ CO_2Me}}{CO_2H} \xrightarrow{SOCl_2} \underset{\substack{|\\ (CH_2)_8\\ |\\ CO_2Me}}{CO.Cl} \quad \begin{array}{l}\text{b.p. } 125°/0\cdot9\text{ mm}\\ 93\%\end{array}$$

CH₂N₂

$$\underset{20\%}{MeO_2C-(CH_2)_8-\overset{\overset{\displaystyle O}{\|}}{C}-\overset{H}{\underset{}{C}}=\overset{H}{\underset{}{C}}-\overset{\overset{\displaystyle O}{\|}}{C}-(CH_2)_8-CO_2Me} \xleftarrow[\text{benzene }+CuO]{\text{warm in}} \underset{\substack{|\\ (CH_2)_8\\ |\\ CO_2Me}}{CO.CHN_2}$$

+2N₂

(AB)   m.p. 88

The mechanism is probably one of carbene dimerization. Protection of the carbonyl groups of (AB) by ketalization and reduction of the olefin leads to the 1,4-diketone, one of a class of precursors for the synthesis of five-ring heterocycles.

β-Ketoesters are derived from the reaction between acid chlorides and diazoacetic ester:

199

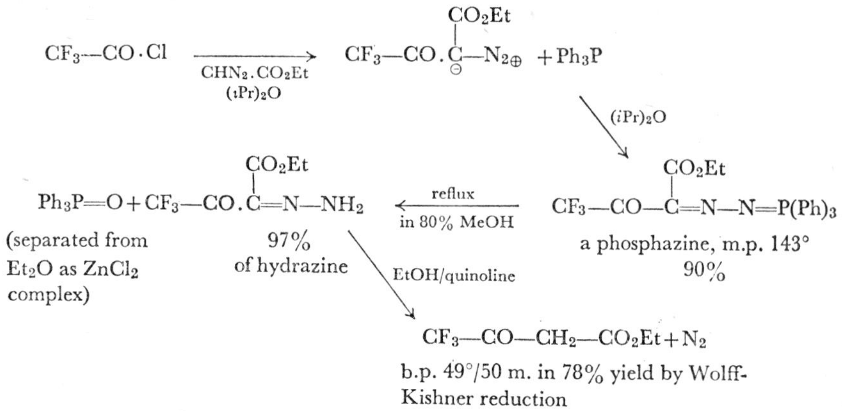

$$CF_3\text{---}CO\cdot Cl \xrightarrow[\substack{CHN_2.CO_2Et \\ (\iota Pr)_2O}]{} CF_3\text{---}CO.\underset{\ominus}{\overset{CO_2Et}{C}}\text{---}N_{2\oplus} + Ph_3P$$

$(iPr)_2O$

$$Ph_3P\text{=}O + CF_3\text{---}CO.\overset{CO_2Et}{C}\text{=}N\text{---}NH_2 \xleftarrow[\text{in }80\% \text{ MeOH}]{\text{reflux}} CF_3\text{---}CO\text{---}\overset{CO_2Et}{C}\text{=}N\text{---}N\text{=}P(Ph)_3$$

(separated from   97%   a phosphazine, m.p. 143°
Et_2O as $ZnCl_2$ of hydrazine   90%
complex)   EtOH/quinoline

$$CF_3\text{---}CO\text{---}CH_2\text{---}CO_2Et + N_2$$

b.p. 49°/50 m. in 78% yield by Wolff-
Kishner reduction

Cyclodiazoalkanes, the Diazirines. These interesting compounds were first prepared from ketones by Schmitz in 1959:

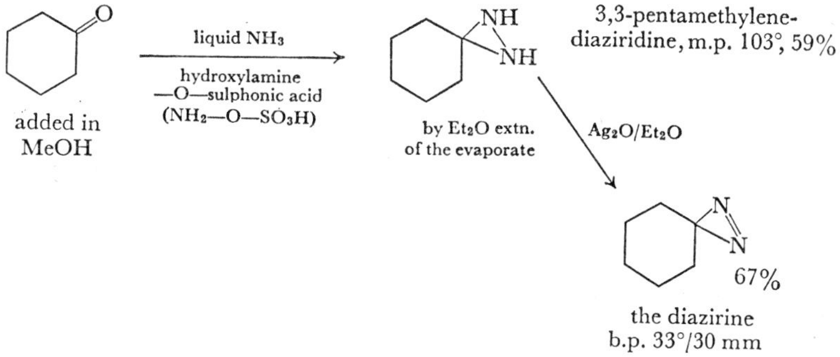

3,3-pentamethylene-
diaziridine, m.p. 103°, 59%

added in
MeOH

liquid NH_3

hydroxylamine
—O—sulphonic acid
$(NH_2\text{---}O\text{---}SO_3H)$

by Et_2O extn.
of the evaporate

Ag_2O/Et_2O

67%
the diazirine
b.p. 33°/30 mm

They differ however in their chemical properties from acyclic diazocompounds, for example:

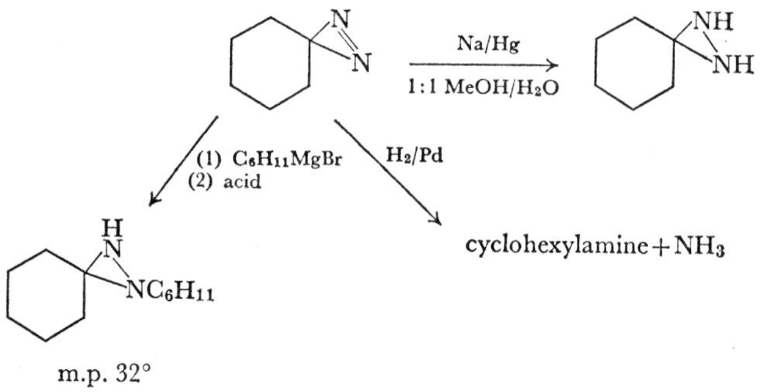

Na/Hg
1:1 MeOH/H_2O

(1) $C_6H_{11}MgBr$
(2) acid

H_2/Pd

cyclohexylamine + NH_3

m.p. 32°

200

Further Reading

GENERAL

R. HUISGEN, *Angew. Chem.*, 1955, **67**, 439.
F. WEYGAND and H. J. BESTMANN, *Newer Methods of Preparative Organic Chemistry*, Vol. 3. Interscience, New York, 1964.
H. ZOLLINGER, *Azo and Diazo Chemistry*. Interscience, New York, 1961.

TOPICS

W. E. BACHMANN and W. S. STRUVE, *Org. Reactions*, 1942, **1**, 38 (Arndt–Eistert).
P. A. S. SMITH in DE MAYO, *Molecular Rearrangements*, Vol. 1. Interscience, London, 1963.
W. VON DOERING and W. R. ROTH, *Angew. Chem.*, Intern. Edit., 1963, **2**, 115 (addition to strained rings).
R. GOMPER, *Adv. Hetero. Chem.*, 1963, **2**, 245 (reactions with CH_2N_2).

PROBLEMS

1. Work out syntheses of:

(a) Ph_2CN_2

H. H. Czmant and C. McGinnis, *J. Amer. Chem. Soc.*, 1950, **72**, 2890.

(b) $CCl_3COCH_2CO_2Et$ from chloral.

H. Schlotterbeck, *Ber.*, 1907, **40**, 3000.

(c)   from indane.

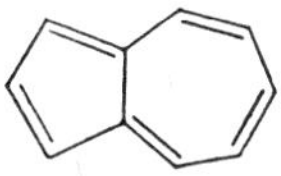

J. Mathieu and A. Allais, *Cahiers de Synthese Organique*, Vol. 6, p. 198. Masson et Cie, Paris, 1957.

(d)   fomindole.

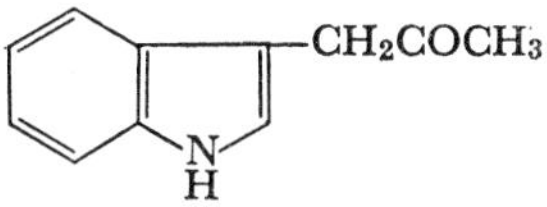

J. Novak *et al.*, *Coll. Czech. Chem. Comm.*, 1957, **22**, 1848.

(e)   from *o*-nitrobenzoic acid.

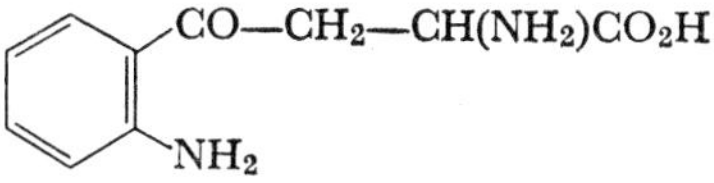

2. Account for:

(a)   The high yield of oxide in:

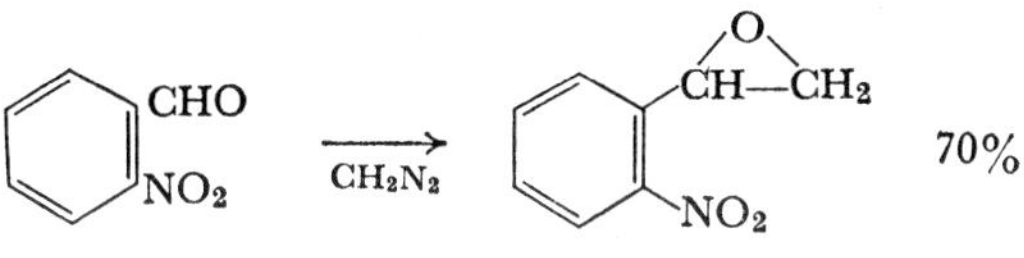

70%

Diazocompounds

and for the stability of $p\text{-}NO_2C_6H_4\overset{\underset{|}{CH_3}}{C}OCN_2$, m.p. 112°.

(b) $CCl_3CH_2OH \xrightarrow{CH_2N_2} CCl_3CH_2OMe$ without addition of acid in solvent heptane but not in ether.

(c) decomposes to give $\longrightarrow$

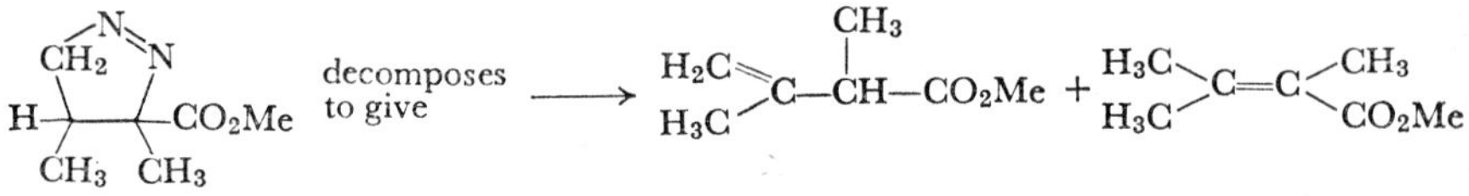

(d) $\xrightarrow[\text{or Et}_2\text{Nh}]{\text{PhLi}}$

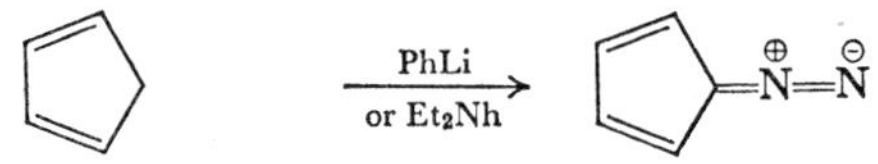

$CH_3\text{---}C_6H_4\text{---}SO_2N_3$

How would you expect the product to react with Ph_3P?

T. Weil and M. Cais, $J. Org. Chem.$, 1963, **28**, 2472.

3. Give mechanisms for:

(a) $\xrightarrow{\text{base}}$ $PhCH_2CO_2Et$

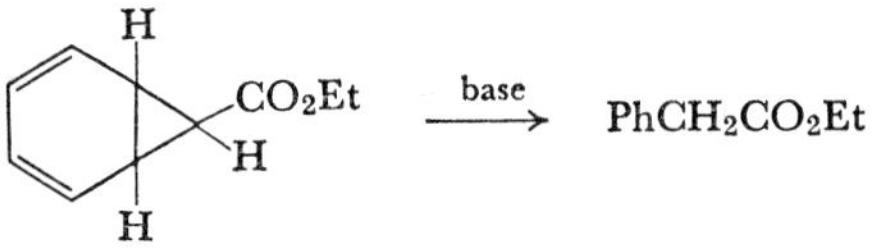

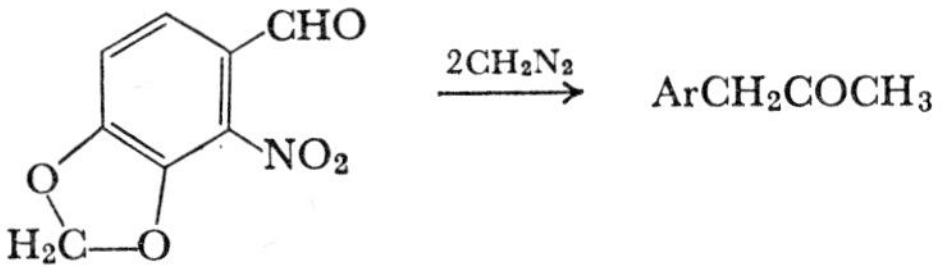

(b) $\xrightarrow{2CH_2N_2}$ $ArCH_2COCH_3$

(c) $H\text{---}C\equiv C\cdot CHO$ $\xrightarrow{CH_2N_2}$

(d) $2CH_3(CH_2)_5CHO + \overset{\underset{|}{CO_2Et}}{CHN_2}$ $\longrightarrow$

(e) $\xrightarrow[\text{(2) t-BuOH/PhCO}_2\text{Ag}]{\text{(1) CH}_2\text{N}_2}$

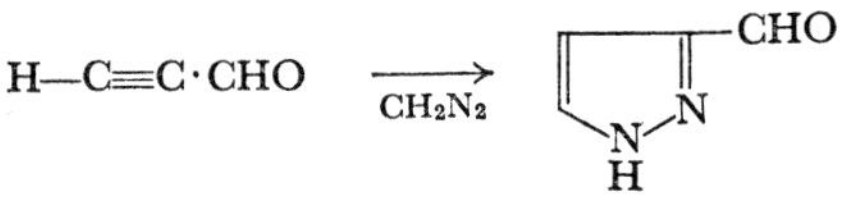

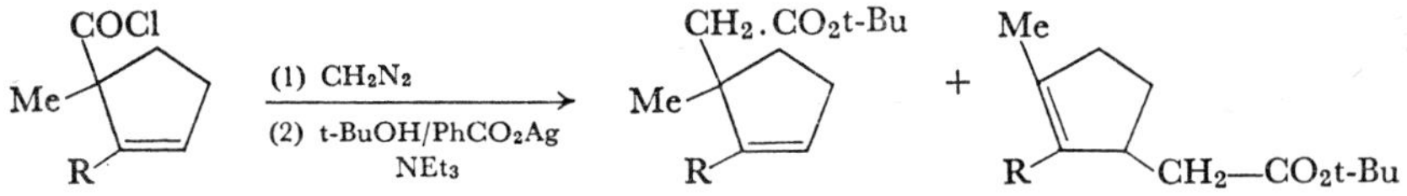

A. L. Wilds $et\ al.$, J. Amer. Chem. Soc., 1962, **84**, 1504.

4. Rationalize the synthesis of (A) from ethyl hydrogen pimelate by the following steps: (i) $SOCl_2/CH_2N_2$, (ii) potassium phthalimide, (iii) aqueous acid, and (iv) aqueous KCNO.

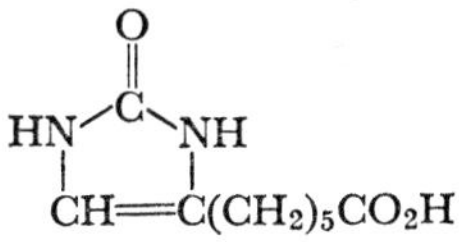

$$
\begin{array}{c}
O \\
\parallel \\
HN{-}C{-}NH \\
| \quad\quad | \\
CH{=}C(CH_2)_5CO_2H
\end{array}
$$

(A)

K. Dittmer, M. F. Ferze and V. du Vigneau, *J. Biol. Chem.*, 1946, **164**, 19.

5. How could you synthesize (B) from isobutyraldehyde following its base-catalysed

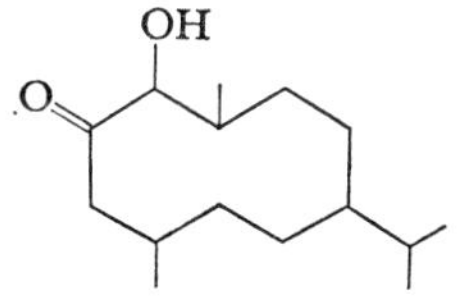

(B)

condensation with 2 mols of cyanoacetamide (Guareschi reaction) and subsequent steps including: hydrolysis, reduction, and chain extension with 2 mols of a malonic ester?

M. Suchy and F. Sorm, *Coll. Czech. Chem. Comm.*, 1958, **23**, 2175.

6. Write a mechanism for:

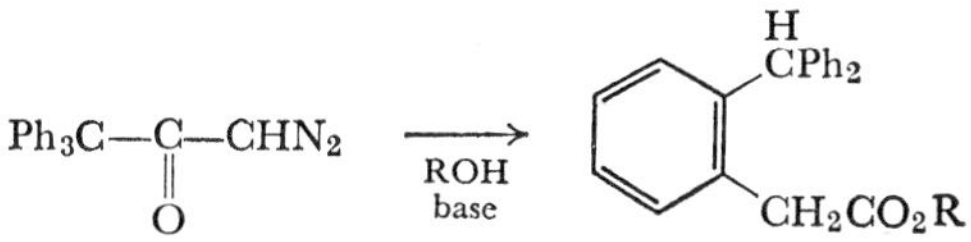

$$
\underset{O}{\overset{\displaystyle Ph_3C{-}\underset{\parallel}{C}{-}CHN_2}{}} \xrightarrow[\text{base}]{ROH}
$$

(benzene ring with substituents: $\overset{H}{\underset{}{}}CPh_2$ and CH_2CO_2R)

A. L. Wilds *et al.*, *J. Amer. Chem. Soc.*, 1962, **84**, 1503.

INDEX

Page numbers in **bold** type indicate principal references. A figure in parentheses refers to a problem on the given page.